MUSTELIDS IN A MODERN WORLD
Management and conservation aspects of
small carnivore: human interactions

Edited by Huw I. Griffiths

Backhuys Publishers, Leiden, 2000

Cover: Cover photograph: Wolverine – photo by Roy Anderson.
    Photos for paper by Kranz & Toman: All photos by A. Kranz.

ISBN 90-5782-066-8

Printed in The Netherlands

Mustelids in a modern world

CONTENTS

PREFACE

The mustelids – otters, badgers, martens, weasels and their allies – make up one of the most diverse families of modern-day carnivores. However, unlike many other carnivore families, mustelids have rarely attracted the attention, interest or sympathy of the public. Human attitudes to mustelids are fraught with contradictions. Almost every school child knows of the highly photogenic otters and, in parts of western Europe, badger conservation and welfare evokes emotions that often seem to verge on the fanatical. In contrast, many other people view mustelids rather more negatively. Gamekeepers and hunters may see them as killers of ground-nesting gamebirds and their chicks, farmers often perceive them as pests (menaces to crops or livestock), and public health officials worry about plague, rabies and bovine tuberculosis. To add to the confusion, many mustelids are economically significant as furbearers, so adding all the controversy associated with the fur industry.

Despite these diverse views, mustelids are the most common predatory mammals in many northern-hemisphere ecosystems. Furthermore, like all other predatory species, they exist under increasing pressure in a world where human population and infrastructure permeate even the wildernesses. So, even in a society with a growing conservation ethic, mustelids are often hunted or persecuted, and their habitats are being altered, fragmented and eroded (as are those of their prey species). Survival in the modern, human-dominated world seems a challenging prospect.

The present volume arose out of informal discussions held around the mustelid session of the Euro-American Mammal Congress in Santiago de Compostela (Spain) in July 1998. This gave workers from many countries and a broad range of disciplines the chance to come together, and to compare experiences and viewpoints. This was a relatively rare occasion as mustelid specialists tend align with one or other of the two relevant IUCN groups (Small Carnivores, Otters). As few technical or popular works deal with mustelids, it was felt that it was timely to take a wider view, and to examine themes relevant to the conservation of the group as a whole. The result is the present volume; a selection of invited thematic essays and research papers that aims to provide "snap shots" which explore some aspects of how these creatures live in human-dominated landscapes. We cannot, of course deal with every problem faced by every species, but I hope that the result does illustrate the major issues, and provides some insights as to how these magnificent animals can survive in the new millennium.

Many people have helped in the realisation of this project, most particularly the authors themselves. We would also like to thank Dr. Santiago Reig and the organisers of the Euro-American Congress, the European Mammal Society (SEM), Sociedad Española para la Conservacion y Estudio de los Mamiferos, the American Society of Mammalogists and the authorities of Xunta de Galicia and Universidade de Santiago de Compostela. I would also like to thank the many colleagues who took the time and trouble to critically review chapters for this book: Dan Harrison

(Orono, USA), Lorenz Hauser, David Watts and Graham Ferrier (Hull, England), Tim Roper (Brighton, England), Audrey Magoun (Fairbanks, Alaska), Derek Yalden (Manchester, England), Martyn Gorman (Aberdeen, Scotland), Andrew Kitchener (Edinburgh, Scotland), Don Jefferies (Peterborough, England), Vivian Banci (Maple Ridge, Canada), Hans Kruuk (Aboyne, Scotland), Yves Garant (Trois-Rivières, Canada), Paddy Sleeman (Cork, Irish Republic), Carolyn King (Waikato, New Zealand), Johnny Birks (Malvern, England), Boris Kry?tufek (Ljubljana, Slovenia), Angela Glatston (Rotterdam, the Netherlands), Piero Genovesi (Ozzana Emiliana, Italy), Danielle Schreve (London, England) and Alan Turner (Liverpool, England). Thanks also to Laura Hindle and the Hull *"Mammal Conservation"* students for their efforts on my behalf.

Especial thanks are due to Keith Scurr who made a stirling effort with the artwork, for which I (and the individual authors) am truly grateful, and to Jane Reed for cups of tea and for proof-reading beyond the call of duty!

A brief note on names

Throughout this volume formal names for mammal species follow those in Wilson & Reeder (1993). In the case of subspecies, authors have been left to their own discretion. Until very recently, the mustelids were thought to be composed of several subfamilies: otters (Lutrinae), badgers (Melinae), weasels and martens and their allies (Mustelinae) and skunks (Mephitinae). Recent molecular systematic work (Dragoo & Honeycutt, 1997) suggest that the skunks and the SE Asian ferret badgers are sufficiently distinct to merit a family of their own: Mephitidae, however, new palaeontological evidence presented by Wolsan (1999) seems to contradict this. The authors in the present volume have all continued to place the skunks and ferret badgers within the mustelids.

References

Dragoo, J.W. & Honeycutt, R.L. (1997). Systematics of mustelid-like carnivores. *Journal of Mammalogy*, **78:** 426-443.
Wilson, D.E. & Reeder, D.A. (1993). *Mammal species of the world: a taxonomic and geographic reference* (2nd ed.). Washington (DC); Smithsonian Institution Press.
Wolsan, M. (1999). Oldest mephitine cranium and its implications for the origins of skunks. *Acta Palaeontologica Polonica*, **44:** 223-230.

AUTHORS' ADDRESSES

Helen E. Abel: Department of Geography, University of Hull, Kingston-upon-Hull, GB-HU6 7RX, UK.

Luciano Bani: Department of Environmental Sciences, University of Milano, Via L. Emanueli 15, I-20126 Milano, Italy.

Lucy Barron: Wildlife Conservation Research Unit, Department of Zoology, University of Oxford, South Parks Road, Oxford, GB-OX1 3PS, UK.

Johnny D.S. Birks: The Vincent Wildlife Trust, 10 Lovat Lane, London, GB-EC3R 8DN, UK. Correspondence to: VWT, 119 Church Street, Great Malvern, Worcestershire, GB-WR14 2AJ, UK. E-mail: johnnybirks@compuserve.com

Ivan Bonfanti: Department of Environmental Sciences, University of Milano, Via L. Emanueli 15, I-20126 Milano, Italy.

Steven W. Buskirk: Department of Zoology and Physiology, Box 3166, University of Wyoming, Laramie, Wyoming 82071, USA. E-mail: marten@uwyo.edu

Ruth Charles: Department of Archaeology, University of Newcastle, Newcastle-upon-Tyne, GB-NE1 7RU, UK. E-mail: Ruth.Charles@newcastle.ac.uk

Chris L. Cheeseman: Central Science Laboratory, Sand Hutton, York, GB-YO4 1LW, UK.

Angus Davison: The Vincent Wildlife Trust, 10 Lovat Lane, London, GB-EC3R 8DN, UK. Correspondence to: Institute of Genetics, Queen's Medical Centre, University of Nottingham, Nottingham, GB-NG7 2UH, UK. E-mail: a.davison@hgmp.mrc.ac.uk

Elisabetta de Carli: Department of Environmental Sciences, University of Milano, Via L. Emanueli 15, I-20126 Milano, Italy.

Richard J. Delahay: Central Science Laboratory, Sand Hutton, York, GB-YO4 1LW, UK.

Don S. Eastman: Department of Biology, University of Victoria, PO Box 3020, Victoria, BC-V8W 3N5, Canada.

Lorenzo Fornasari: Department of Environmental Sciences, University of Milano, Via L. Emanueli 15, I-20126 Milano, Italy. E-mail: faunaw@staff.it

Peter Giere: Fachbereich Biologie, Philipps Universität Marburg, Karl von Frisch Straße, D-35032 Marburg, Germany. Correspondence to: Institut für Systematische Zoologie, Museum für Naturkunde, Invalidenstraße 43, D-10115 Berlin, Germany. E-mail: h0662dgx@rzhu-berlin.de

Paul Giller: Department of Zoology and Animal Ecology, University College Cork, Lee Maltings, Prospect Row, Cork, Irish Republic.

Pete Gober: USFWS Ecological Services, 420 S. Garfield Ave., Suite 400, Pierre, SD 57501-5408, USA.

Mary C. Gough: Centre for Land Use and Water Resources Research, Porter Building, St Thomas' Street, University of Newcastle, Newcastle-upon-Tyne, GB-NE1 7RU, UK. E-mail: M.C.Gough@newcastle.ac.uk

Huw I. Griffiths: Department of Geography, University of Hull, Kingston-upon-Hull, GB-HU6 7RX, UK. E-mail: H.I.Griffiths@geo.hull.ac.uk

Tim D. Hounsome: Central Science Laboratory, Sand Hutton, York, GB-YO4 1LW, UK.

Andreas Kranz: Department of Wildlife Biology & Game Management, Universität für Bodenkultur – BOKU Wien, Peter Jordanstraße 76, A-1190 Vienna, Austria. E-mail: Kranz@mail.dacice.cz

Boris Kryštufek: Slovenian Museum of Natural History, Prešernova 20, PO Box 290, SI-1001 Ljubljana, Slovenia. E-mail: bkrystufek@pms-lj.si

Arild Landa: Norwegian Institute for Nature Research, Tungasletta-2, N-7005 Trondheim, Norway. Correspondence to: Greenland Institute of Natural Resources, PO Box 570, DK-3900 Nuuk, Greenland. E-mail: arild@natur.gl

Mats Lindén: Department of Animal Ecology, Swedish University of Agricultural Sciences, S-90183 Umeå, Sweden.

Liang-Kong Lin: Laboratory of Wildlife Ecology, Department of Biology, Tunghai University, Taichung, Taiwan. E-mail: lklin@mail.thu.edu.tw

John D.C. Linnell: Norwegian Institute for Nature Research, Tungasletta-2, N-7005 Trondheim, Norway.

Mike Lockhart: USFWS National Black-Footed Ferret Conservation Centre, 410 E. Grand Avenue, Suite 315, Laramie, WY 82070, USA.

David W. Macdonald: Wildlife Conservation Research Unit, Department of Zoology, University of Oxford, South Parks Road, Oxford GB-OX1 3PS, UK.

Peter J. Mallinson: Central Science Laboratory, Sand Hutton, York, GB-YO4 1LZ, UK.

Tiit Maran: European Mink Conservation Centre, Tallinn Zoo, 1 Paldiski Road 145, Tallinn EE-0035, Estonia.

Paul Marinari: USFWS National Black-Footed Ferret Conservation Centre, 410 E. Grand Avenue, Suite 315, Laramie, WY 82070, USA.

Renato Massa: Department of Environmental Sciences, University of Milano, Via L. Emanueli 15, I-20126 Milano, Italy.

Robbie A. McDonald: Department of Biological Sciences, University of Waikato, Private Bag 3105, Hamilton, New Zealand.

John E. Messenger: The Vincent Wildlife Trust, 10 Lovat Lane, London, GB-EC3R 8DN, UK. Correspondence to: VWT, 1a Southlea, Craig Road, Llandrindod Wells, Powys, GB-LD1 5HS, UK. E-mail: johnmessenger@compuserve.com

Miroljub Milenković: Institute for Biological Research "Sini?a Stankovi?", 29. Novembra 1142, YU-11000 Beograd, Yugoslavia.

Arne Moksnes: Norwegian University of Science and Technology, Department of Zoology, N-7055 Dragvoll, Norway.

Elaine C. Murphy: Science & Research Unit, Department of Conservation, Private Bag 4715, Christchurch, New Zealand. E-mail: emurphy@doc.govt.nz

Paola Ottino: Department of Zoology and Animal Ecology, University College Cork, Lee Maltings, Prospect Row, Cork, Irish Republic. Correspondence to: Via del Casaletto 387, I-00151 Roma, Italy. E-mail: ottinop@tin.it

Milan Paunović: Natural History Museum, Njegoševa 51, YU-11000 Beograd, Yugoslavia. E-mail: paunmchi@Eunet.yu

Gilbert Proulx: Alpha Wildlife Research & Management Ltd., 229 Lilac Terrace, Sherwood Park, Alberta, T8H 1W3, Canada. E-mail: alphawild@telusplanet.net

Jean-François Robitaille: Department of Biology, Laurentian University, Sudbury, Ontario, P3E 2C6, Canada. E-mail: robitail@nickel.laurentian.ca

Lucy M. Rogers: Central Science Laboratory, Sand Hutton, York, GB-YO4 1LW, UK. E-mail: l.rogers@csl.gov.uk

Eivin Røskaft: Norwegian Institute for Nature Research, Tungasletta-2, N-7005 Trondheim, Norway.

Steve P. Rushton: Centre for Land Use and Water Resources Research, Porter Building, St Thomas' Street, University of Newcastle, Newcastle-upon-Tyne, GB-NE1 7RU, UK.

Vadim E. Sidorovich: Wildlife Conservation Research Unit, Department of Zoology, University of Oxford, South Parks Road, Oxford, GB-OX1 3PS, UK. Correspondence to: Institute of Zoology, National Academy of Sciences of Belarus, Skoriny str. 27, Minsk - 220072, Belarus. E-mail: mustbel@mustbel.belpak.minsk.by

Jon E. Swenson: Norwegian Institute for Nature Research, Tungasletta-2, N-7005 Trondheim, Norway.

Aleš Toman: Czech Agency of Nature and Landscape Conservation, Pavlov 54, CZ-58401 Ledec n. S., Czech Republic.

Frank A.M. Tuyttens: Wildlife Conservation Research Unit, Department of Zoology, University of Oxford, South Parks Road, Oxford, GB-OX1 3PS, UK. Correspondence to: Department of Mechanisation, Labour, Buildings, Animal Welfare & Environmental Protection, Van Gansberghelaan 115, B-9820 Merelbeke, Belgium. E-mail: rvl.cigr@pophost.eunet.be

Astrid Vargas: USFWS National Black-Footed Ferret Conservation Centre, 410 E. Grand Avenue, Suite 315, Laramie, WY 82070, USA. E-mail: astrid_vargas@mail.fws.gov
Present address: Carlota Alessandri 69, apt. 9-10, Torremolinos 29620, Malaga, Spain.

CHAPTER 1

Conservation of Scandinavian wolverines in ecological and political landscapes

Arild Landa[*] John D.C. Linnell, Mats Lindén, Jon E. Swenson, Eivin Røskaft & Arne Moksnes

Abstract

An intense eradication campaign in the late 19th and early 20th centuries resulted in fragmented and small populations of wolverine, *Gulo gulo*, in Scandinavia. Wolverines received protection in 1969 in Sweden, in 1972 in southern Norway and in 1983 in the rest of Norway. As a result wolverines have returned to parts of their former range. Ecological studies suggest that large areas exist where wolverines have the biological potential to re-establish themselves. However, after these predators received protection, conflicts have increased with livestock industries based on free-ranging sheep, *Ovis aries*, and semi-domestic reindeer, *Rangifer tarandus*. This is due both to increasing numbers of predators and, in many areas, increasing numbers of livestock. Norway has abundant, good quality wolverine habitat, one of the richest economies in the world, and a clear mandate from the public for the conservation of large predators. However, the political influence of segments of the livestock industry has resulted in a management system that jeopardises the future of wolverines in Norway. In contrast, in Sweden, where there are no free-ranging sheep in wolverine habitat and a different system of compensation for reindeer depredation exists, the future of wolverines appears more secure. Wolverine conservation is possible in Norway, but it requires reduced conflicts with both reindeer and sheep husbandry. This will require a clear centrally co-ordinated plan and the zoning of both wolverines and livestock; wolverines may need to be removed from some areas where they occur today and prevented from colonising other areas. Changes in livestock production methods also will be required.

Introduction

All over the world carnivores have been hunted by humans, either because of their valuable fur (Tapper & Reynolds, 1996) or because of direct competition or conflict with human activities (Boitani, 1995). Conflicts mainly have arisen because carnivores do not distinguish between wild prey and domestic livestock. This conflict between predator and herder has been one of the main factors directly responsible for reducing the number and distribution of medium-sized and large carnivores (Linnell *et al.*, 1996). Furthermore, by accelerating the rate and expanding the

---

[*] Corresponding author.

Mustelids in a modern world
Management and conservation aspects of small carnivore: human interactions
edited by Huw I. Griffiths, pp. 1–20
© 2000 Backhuys Publishers, Leiden, The Netherlands

scope of disturbance and habitat change, humans have undermined the resilience and viability of large carnivore populations, and caused widespread declines (Weaver *et al.*, 1996; Weber & Rabinowitz, 1996). Thus, in many countries large carnivores have been exterminated for a century or more. However, in several regions, including Europe, protection from hunting has allowed populations to increase again (Swenson *et al.*, 1995; Breitenmoser, 1998).

The conservation of large carnivores is among the most challenging tasks facing conservation biologists (Noss *et al.*, 1996) as fundamental aspects of large carnivore ecology make conservation difficult. Firstly, as predators they require a functioning prey base. Secondly, they have large area requirements, with individual home ranges being in the order of 10s, 100s or 1000s of square kilometres. Finally, carnivores occur at low densities (Becker, 1991) and usually have relatively low reproductive rates (Weaver *et al.*, 1996). Therefore, conservation requires large areas of good quality habitat, a very rare and expensive commodity in our modern, crowded world.

Large carnivore conservation is as much, if not more, a problem of sociology and politics as biology (Wemmer *et al.*, 1987; Koch, 1994; Breitenmoser, 1998). Social attitudes range from the extremely negative to the extremely positive. Because of depredation upon livestock and wild ungulates, many farmers and hunters perceive large carnivores as threats to their livelihoods or recreation, or even to personal safety, and thus often hold negative attitudes towards them (e.g. Oli *et al.*, 1994; Pate *et al.*, 1996; Sagør & Aasetre,1996). On the other hand, many people who experience no personal hardship from large carnivores often value them to the point of making practical management impossible (Mech, 1995). The use of the courts and public referenda to manage North American wildlife has become increasingly common (Koch, 1994; Mech, 1995). Although increased public awareness of management issues is desirable (Koch, 1994), debates over the management of large carnivores are rarely based on scientific knowledge and often result either in over-protection (Mech, 1995) or the obstruction of publicly-mandated conservation programs (Bangs & Fritts, 1996).

Against this background, the objective of this paper is to present the ecological and political aspects of wolverine, *Gulo gulo*, conservation in Norway, and to contrast this with the situation in neighbouring Sweden. We shall provide a brief summary of the historical development of wolverine populations and management strategies, and outline aspects of wolverine ecology, their depredations upon livestock, and some possible solutions to the conflicts. In particular, we wish to demonstrate that, despite having abundant habitat, abundant national wealth, and a clear mandate from the public to preserve large carnivore populations, the present politics of the conflict with the livestock industry are jeopardising the future of the wolverine in Norway.

Near extinction and the beginnings of recovery, 1846-1990

The history of wolverines in Scandinavia parallels that of all large carnivores throughout the World (Gunson, 1992; Boitani, 1995; Breitenmoser, 1998). Bounties paid by the state led to a very high harvest of wolverines. Between the introduction of state bounties in 1846 and wolverine protection in 1982 (Table 1) a total of 5,042 wolverine bounty payments were made in Norway and over 8,000 in Sweden (Kvam *et al.*, 1984, 1988; Landa & Skogland, 1995). The objective was clearly one of extermination, motivated by depredation on domestic sheep, *Ovis aries*, and semi-domestic reindeer, *Rangifer tarandus*, and by the ingrained ecological ethic of the times which required the "taming of nature" and the removal of animals which were not "useful" (Boitani, 1995). Although wolverine bounty statistics do not perfectly reflect population densities, up until the early 1980s they can be used as a rough indicator of population size (Kvam *et al.*, 1984; Landa & Skogland, 1995). Bounties paid (see Fig. 1) clearly show a strongly decreasing trend, with the population reaching its lowest levels in the 1970s.

Originally, wolverines were found throughout the boreal forest and mountain areas of Norway and Sweden (Johnsen, 1928; Lönnberg, 1936; Fig. 2a). The result of more than a century of state-subsidised control was that, by the 1970s, wolverines were functionally extinct; only stray individuals were left in southern Norway

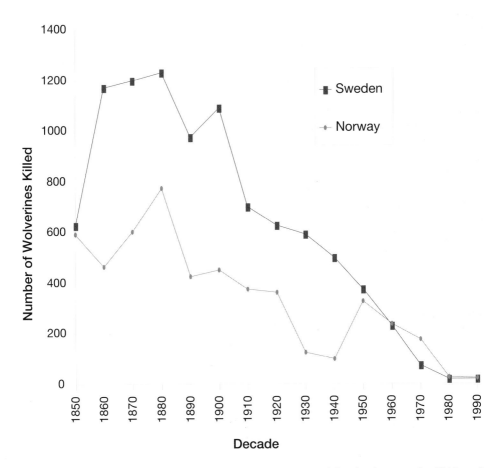

Fig. 1. Numbers of bounties paid for wolverines in Norway and Sweden between the 1840s and 1980s (from Landa & Skogland, 1995).

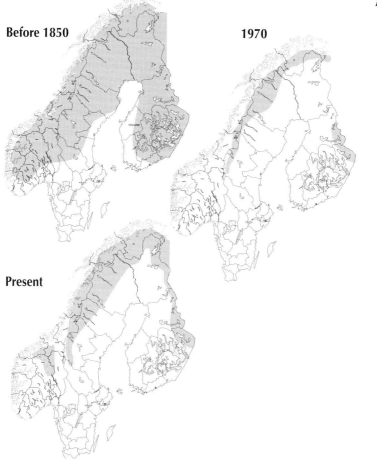

Fig. 2. Distribution of wolverines: (a) historical changes in the distribution of wolverines in Fennoscandia during the 20th century, (b) breeding dens recorded in Norway and Sweden in 1995-97.

following the killing of seven adults in the Jotunheimen area in the 1960s (Myrberget & Grotnes, 1969). Furthermore, populations were greatly reduced throughout northern parts of Scandinavia. The last refuge of wolverines was in the mountains along the border between Norway and Sweden (Haglund, 1966; Myrberget & Sørumgård, 1975; Ahlén, 1977; Heggberget & Myrberget, 1980).

Following protection (Table 1), wolverine populations began to recover (Heggberget & Myrberget, 1980). In 1979 reproduction was documented again on the Snøhetta Plateau in south-central Norway (Kvam *et al.*, 1984), probably as a result of immigration from Sweden. In northern Norway the population stabilised and began to increase. Based on a combination of scattered observations and surveys, there were an estimated 120-180 wolverines in Norway in the period 1978-83 (Kvam *et al.*, 1984). However, this estimate needs to be treated with caution, as similar methods

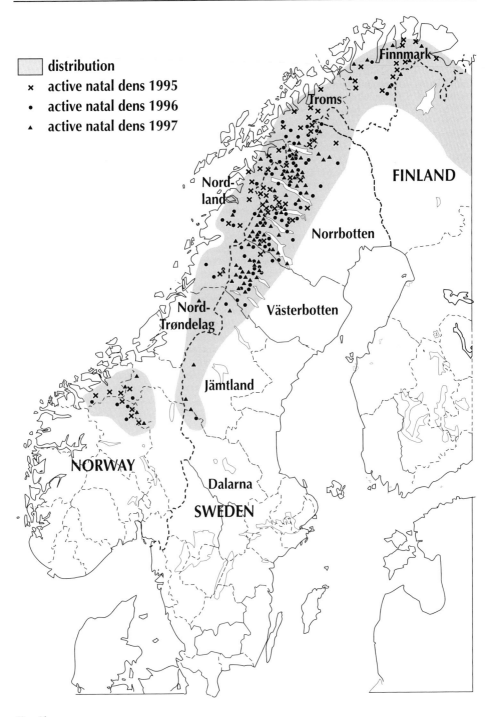

Fig. 2b.

Table 1. Dates relevant to the management of wolverines in Scandinavia 1846-1998.

Date	Legislation/Event
1846	Introduction of state bounties on large carnivores
1967	Exterminated in south Norway
1969	Protected in Sweden
1972	Hunting from snow-scooters banned
1973	Protected in south Norway
1973	Legislation to ensure compensation for livestock killed by protected carnivores is introduced
1976	Protected in north Norway from March-May
1976	Norway signs Washington Convention (CITES)
1978 -83	Beginning of nationwide survey of wolverine status
1979	Wolverines recolonise south Norway
1980	Norway signs European Convention for the Protection of Animals Kept for Farming Purposes
1982	Protected in all Norway
1982	Protected in Finland 1986 Norway signs Berne Convention
1988 -95	Beginning of wolverine research project on Snøhetta plateau
1992	Beginning of wolverine research project in northern Sweden
1992	White paper on carnivore management (St.mnd. nr. 27)
1993	Opens for licensed hunting of wolverines in north Norway
1993	Norway signs Rio Biodiversity Convention
1996	Beginning of wolverine research project in Troms county
1996	Opens for licensed control of wolverines in Sweden
1997	White paper on carnivore management (St.mnd. nr. 35)
1998	Opens for licensed hunting of wolverines in south Norway
1998	Draft wolverine Action Plan for Norway, Sweden and Finland prepared under the auspices of WWF

dramatically overestimated the size of the population of brown bear, *Ursus arctos* (Kolstad *et al.*, 1986; Elgmork, 1988; Swenson *et al.*, 1995). On the basis of these surveys, and the interests of the livestock industry and conservation organisations, a series of attempts were made to formulate a government policy and management plan for wolverine (Vaag, 1987). These culminated in a government policy paper (Miljøverndepartement, 1991-92). Following changing public opinion in favour of large-carnivore conservation (Dahle, 1990) this policy paper confirmed government commitment to the maintenance of viable carnivore populations. The main thrust of the conservation strategy was to create three large Core Conservation Areas (CCAs), one in south-central Norway and two along the Norwegian/Swedish border in Nordland and Troms counties, in which wolverines would be given the greatest protection from harvest. Outside of these areas wolverines would be less strictly protected. These core areas contain large areas of private land, although they also contain some small national parks. The only difference in administration between their inside and outside is the ease with which control permits for wolverines are issued. The same policy paper also pointed out the lack of knowledge about wolverine ecology and population densities in Norway, and in Scandinavia as a whole.

The ecological landscape – research results 1985–1996

Early research on wolverines in Scandinavia consisted largely of snow-tracking studies (Haglund 1966), the monitoring of dens and numbers (Kvam *et al.*, 1984), and preliminary attempts to capture and radio-collar wolverines (Kvam & Røskaft, 1987;
Bjärvall *et al.*, 1996). However, these early studies did not provide enough data for
management purposes. In response to this lack of knowledge, a research program was
begun on the Snøhetta Plateau in south-central Norway in 1989. Data collection
included monitoring the population's development and reproduction, radio-collaring
wolverines, diet analysis, genetic studies, and studies of wolverine-sheep conflicts.
Most of the data presently available on wolverine ecology in Norway have come from
this study site. However, in 1996 began a second telemetry-based study in Troms
county, northern Norway, which will continue to run until 2000, and a parallel project
began in the Sarek area of northern Sweden in 1992 (Lindén *et al.*, 1994, 1995).

Diet and prey availability

Throughout their range, the wolverine's main food source is meat from large ungulates (Haglund, 1966; Hornocker & Hash, 1981; Magoun, 1987; Pulliainen, 1988;
Banci, 1994). Although wolverines have been reported to kill ungulates as large as
elk, *Alces alces*, under certain snow conditions (Haglund, 1966) they are generally
regarded as being very ineffective predators of wild ungulates (Pulliainen, 1988). In
most areas they are regarded as scavengers, obtaining their food from the carcasses
of prey killed by other, more efficient predators such as wolves, *Canis lupus*.
However, wolverines are very effective predators of domestic ungulates like sheep
and semi-domestic reindeer (Bjärvall *et al.*, 1990; Gudvangen *et al.*, 1998).

Snøhetta represents an unusual situation for wolverines in that there are no larger predators in the region (wolves were exterminated in the early 1900s), and
wolverines are probably inefficient predators of the wild reindeer on the plateau
(Skogland, 1989). Despite this, reindeer were the most frequently occurring dietary
component in wolverine scats found during the spring denning season (Landa *et al.*,
1997), most likely derived from animals that had died during the winter, or from
slaughter remains left over from the autumn hunt. Small rodents and hares were the
next most frequently occurring prey remains in scats (Landa *et al.*, 1997).

Reproduction

Wolverines have low reproductive rates because of small litters (one to three cubs)
and a variable number of subadult breeders (Rausch & Pearson, 1972; Myrberget &
Sørumgård, 1979; Banci & Harestad, 1988; Landa *et al.*, 1997). A variable proportion of adult females do not breed, possibly to the extent that individuals only breed
every second year in northern Sweden (M. Lindén, unpubl.). This relatively low
reproductive rate probably contributes to the observed low resilience of many
wolverine populations (Weaver *et al.*, 1996). A surprising feature of wolverine
reproductive ecology in Snøhetta was the importance of the abundance of small
rodents. The occurrence of small rodents in the wolverine's diet was related to
cycles in rodent abundances, and explained much of the variation in cub production

(Landa *et al.*, 1997). This has led to a pulsed reproductive pattern on the Snøhetta Plateau.

Habitat and home range

Wolverines demonstrate broad habitat use, using alpine habitats, the birch forest zone, and even the upper part of the deciduous forest in Snøhetta (Landa *et al.*, 1998a). During winter, lower altitudes were used more than in summer (Landa *et al.*, 1998a), a finding consistent with other studies (Hornocker & Hash, 1981; Whitman *et al.*, 1986). Home ranges in Snøhetta were among the largest reported for the species. Adult males used an average of 663 km^2 and adult females used 335 km^2. It is not clear if this large home range use is due to poor carrying capacity or unsaturated habitat, although approximately similar home range sizes have been found in northern Sweden (Lindén *et al.*, 1994, 1995; Bjärvall *et al.*, 1996). Radio-collared wolverines have demonstrated their ability to cross the valleys containing transportation corridors that separate the various plateaux around Snøhetta. In addition, denning females have reappeared in mountain ranges surrounding Snøhetta. This indicator of good dispersal ability will be crucial for wolverine survival in the naturally fragmented alpine habitats of south Norway, and to ensure genetic exchange with the larger and more continuous populations farther north in Norway and Sweden (Duffy *et al.*, submitted).

Habitat suitability

In Norway none of the areas large enough to support wolverines can be classified as true wilderness, so that wolverines will always have to coexist with some human activity. It is this pattern of human use of wildlands that most differentiates Scandinavian conservation strategy (the "multi-use landscape") from that in North America where much wilderness remains still (Weaver *et al.*, 1996). Although the Norwegian mountains are becoming increasingly developed with roads, power lines, tourist trails, cabins and hydroelectric power developments, the degree of development is low compared to other European countries. Therefore, the Norwegian mountains still represent good quality habitat for wolverines, especially as the radio tracking of wolverines has revealed that they are able to travel through the developed areas and transport corridors which occur within their home ranges (Landa *et al.*,1998a). Reindeer, either wild or semi-domestic, are found in all alpine areas (Skogland, 1994; Mysterud & Mysterud, 1995) and small game are relatively abundant. Based on our understanding of wolverine habitat requirements, most of the mountain and forest areas offer the potential for wolverine recovery.

The situation in Sweden is somewhat similar, although there are probably fewer people living in the vicinity of wolverine habitat than in Norway. Some large, road-less areas in the north are more similar to true wilderness than anything in Norway. On the other hand, snow-scooter regulations are much more liberal in Sweden, allowing easy access to wolverine habitat to people that do live close to the mountains. Snow-scooter driving is very tightly regulated in Norway, and in effect is not allowed for recreational purposes. Wolves are absent from all areas where wolverines occur today in both Norway and Sweden, and are not likely to be permitted to re-colonise these areas in the future because of the potential for conflicts with live-stock. However, lynx, *Lynx lynx*, populations have become re-established in most areas of Scandinavia. Lynx are a very effective predator of reindeer (both wild and domestic) and their presence may provide more carrion for wolverines. However, the importance of this intra-guild interaction is unknown (Landa *et al.*, 1998c).

Distribution and numbers

Since the recolonisation of the Snøhetta Plateau was detected first (in 1979), the wolverine population has been relatively stable at between 11 and 17 individuals, at a density of 0.28-0.38 inds./100 km^2. Extrapolating to the whole of the south-central core conservation area, between 36 and 50 wolverines may be supported with-in its 13,500 km^2 area (Landa *et al.*, 1998a). Data are insufficient for a formal pop-ulation viability analysis; however, it appears obvious that the long-term demographic and genetic viability of this isolated population will be greatly enhanced if contact with the larger populations to the north can be maintained.

Landa *et al.* (1998b) estimate the minimum population density of wolverines in Norway and Sweden using all known breeding dens from 1994-1996 (Fig. 2b). The distribution pattern of dens revealed an isolated population centred on Snøhetta in south-central Norway, and a more or less continuous population along the Swedish/northern Norwegian border (Fig. 2b). Assuming a normal age and sex structure, there were an estimated minimum of 147 ± 25 and 265 ± 55 wolverines in Norway and Sweden, respectively (Landa *et al.*, 1998b). Using non-comparable methods, Finland estimated a minimum of 110 individuals in 1995 (Anon., 1996). These recent estimates are more likely to be accurate than any of the previous esti-mates (e.g. Kvam *et al.*, 1984).

Depredation upon sheep and semi-domestic reindeer

One of the main barriers to large carnivore conservation is depredation on domes-tic livestock (Quigley & Crawshaw, 1992; Oli *et al.*, 1994; Kaczensky, 1996; Meriggi & Lovari, 1996; Aanes *et al.*, 1996; Breitenmoser, 1998). Wolverines are rarely associated with such depredation in North America, largely because their fine-scaled distribution does not overlap that of domestic sheep (Banci, 1994). However, wolverine depredation on livestock has been one of the main reasons for their control, and subsequent decline, in Scandinavia (Myrberget & Grotnes, 1969).

The husbandry systems

Two species of livestock dominate the conflict between wolverine conservation and livestock husbandry: domestic sheep and semi-domestic reindeer. Sheep farming is widespread throughout Norway (about 2.5 million sheep are released each summer) although it is especially intensive in the south-west (Mysterud & Mysterud, 1995; Fig. 3a). Sheep are grazed on mountain and forest pastures only during the summer (June to August), because winter conditions are too harsh (Mysterud & Mysterud, 1995). Although shepherds were commonly used to protect sheep in former times, the dramatic reduction in large carnivore populations during this century allowed the development of a herding system whereby sheep largely are left unattended during the summer grazing season (Mysterud *et al.*, 1996). Supervision consists, at best, of infrequent checks on the flock. Because there are few fences to restrict sheep movements, flocks can spread out over 10s or 100s of square kilometres. Therefore this supervision is a way of documenting losses rather than preventing them (Linnell *et al.*, 1996). This form of extensive sheep husbandry is absent in Sweden.

Fig. 3a.

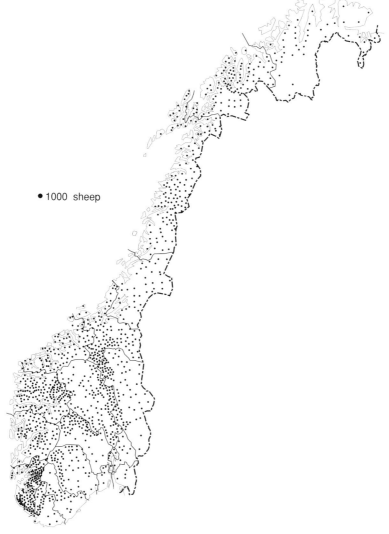

● 1000 sheep

Fig. 3. Distribution of domestic animals with which wolverine comes into conflict: (a) domestic sheep in Norway, (b) semi-domestic reindeer in Fennoscandia (data from Miljøverndepartentet, 1991-1992; Mysterud & Mysterud, 1995).

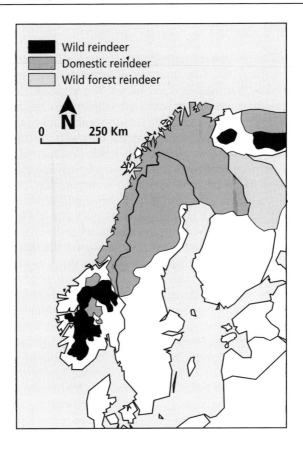

Fig. 3b.

There are presently an estimated 210,000 semi-domestic reindeer grazing in Norway and 300,000 in Sweden (Fig. 2b). As semi-domestic reindeer herding is intrinsically tied to the Saami culture of central and northern Scandinavia, the herding of reindeer needs to be considered as both an economic activity and a part of the identity of an ethnic minority. Although the age of the tradition is debated, evidence suggests that it goes back hundreds and maybe thousands of years (Paine, 1994). The development of motorised vehicles (snow-scooters, helicopters and trucks) has led to changes in the method of husbandry during recent decades (Muller-Wille & Pelto, 1971). However, the central principles of the herding system are based around large herds of reindeer moving over vast areas of mountain pasture, often in a distinct, seasonal pattern (Bjärvall *et al.*, 1990). The degree of herding and supervision varies greatly, but herds often are left unattended for long periods. The main difference with respect to sheep husbandry is that reindeer are free-ranging for the entire year and are therefore vulnerable to predation for a longer period than sheep (Mysterud & Mysterud, 1995; Bjärvall *et al.*, 1990).

Losses to carnivores

Since herding began, herders have known that carnivores kill many sheep and reindeer. However, because of the low intensity of supervision in modern husbandry systems, many animals that die are never found. There has, therefore, been much debate about the extent to which carnivores are responsible for the recorded losses (Mysterud & Mysterud, 1995). A series of studies using radio-mortality collars during the 1980s and 1990s documented that predation was a major cause of mortality (Bjärvall *et al.*, 1990; Mysterud & Warren, 1992; Kvam *et al.*, 1995; Mysterud & Mysterud, 1995). For example, studies in areas where sheep losses are high have revealed that, in some extreme cases, predation is responsible for up to 64% of all mortality of lambs grazing on summer pasture (Mysterud & Mysterud, 1995).

Among free-ranging sheep, a loss of *c.* 2% of ewes and *c.* 5% of lambs widely is regarded as a "normal loss" (Mysterud & Mysterud, 1995). In Norway, compensation is usually paid for everything above this level provided that a herder can document that at least some predation has occurred in his flock. Such background loss figures for semi-domestic reindeer are not available (Kvam *et al.*, 1995), leading to much debate over how much compensation should be paid. Since this system was first introduced the numbers of sheep and reindeer for which compensation has been paid have increased dramatically (Fig. 4). Although an increasing number of wolverines in some areas may have lead to an increase in depredation, in other areas the number of sheep has increased. For example, the number of sheep recorded in the official organised grazing on the Snøhetta Plateau has increased from 3,000 ewes and 4,500 lambs in 1979 to 12,000 ewes and 19,000 lambs in 1994. It is likely that some stocks were not affiliated within organised grazing at the beginning of this period. However, the wolverine population has been relatively stable during this period, and the claimed losses of ewes have increased from 50 to 300 and of lambs from 400 to 1,900. No other large carnivores occur in the region, so it is likely that wolverines are responsible for most of the mortality (Gudvangen *et al.*, 1998; Mysterud *et al.*, 1994).

In Sweden a new compensation scheme for losses of semi-domesticated reindeer to carnivores was introduced in 1996. Compensation is paid according to the number of carnivore reproductions documented in the grazing areas, and is based on active wolverine natal dens and family groups of lynx recorded. This system is especially important because the new compensation scheme makes it economically profitable to verify as many active wolverine dens as possible within the area of reindeer husbandry, to reduce predation through improved husbandry, and to stop poaching. Nearly 100,000 Swedish crowns (about $US 13,000) was paid for each active den in 1996 and 1997. However, a fixed amount of money is put aside each year, so increases in the numbers of active natal dens mean lower compensation rates per den.

Methods to reduce predation

As losses of livestock in Scandinavia are several orders of magnitude higher than those reported from North America and other regions in Europe where carnivore-livestock conflicts occur (Fritts *et al.*, 1992; Breitenmoser, 1998) wolverine conservation will depend on finding ways to reduce the conflict with the livestock industry. Even

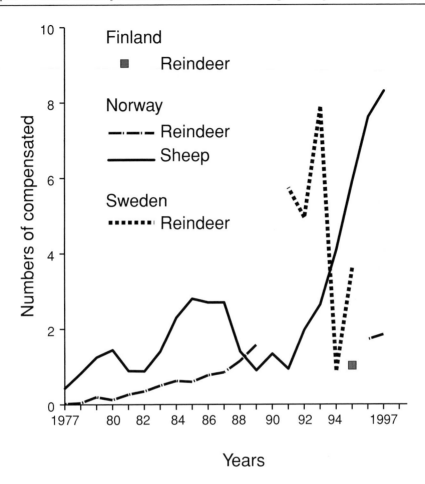

Fig. 4. Development of the numbers of sheep and semi-domestic reindeer for which compensation has been paid since 1974. Note that the low numbers during the first years in Norway may reflect a time lag for the herders to take advantage of the system. As compensation is also paid for many individuals for which an exact cause of death is not known, some of the variation in numbers compensated for is due to changes in the compensation system, as well as changes in the numbers killed.

after protection in south Norway in 1973, permits have been issued by the management authorities for the control of wolverines in areas associated with high rates of depredation. In addition, a number of wolverines have been killed illegally (Bevanger, 1992). Between 1979 and 1995, a minimum of 15 wolverines were killed (both legally and illegally) within the limited area of the Snøhetta Plateau. The only significant reduction in sheep losses was found for lambs in the same grazing season that the wolverines were killed. As no longer-term benefits could be detected (Gudvangen *et al.*, 1998) the removal of individual wolverines was not a suitable means of reducing depredation. Further reduction in depredation would require the killing of more wolverines, a process not compatible with the objective of maintaining a wolverine population within the plateau. The translocation of depredating wolverines has only been attempted in Finland (Anon., 1998) and, as the animals were not followed up, it was impossible to evaluate the success of these translocations. However, because international experience with the translocation of problem animals has been far from successful, this cannot be regarded as a real option (Linnell *et al.*, 1996, 1997).

It was hoped that a system of aversive conditioning and repellents could provide a relatively easy and cheap solution. Many studies in North America have attempted to reduce carnivore predation on sheep using similar methods (Gustavson, 1982; Hatfield & Walker, 1994). Experiments were made with a series of volatile chemicals and captive wolverines in an attempt to find a suitable predator repellent (Landa & Tømmerås, 1996). These compounds were then contained inside a dispenser and tested in the field. Small-scale tests in 1993 and 1994 gave encouraging results (Landa & Tømmerås, 1997); wolverines did not kill as many of the dispenser-equipped lambs as expected. However, a large-scale test in 1995, in which wolverines did not have access to lambs without dispensers, led to no reduction in depredation rates (Landa *et al.*, 1998d). It appears that the wolverines were able to habituate to the chemicals, or learned to change their bite-site to avoid the dispenser.

As has been found in many other studies, it appears that the only way to protect sheep from large carnivores effectively is through the use of traditional herding methods which incorporate shepherds and livestock-guarding dogs (Linnell *et al.*, 1996, Mysterud *et al.*, 1996). However, these methods are labour intensive and expensive, and require a complete restructuring of the herding system. Instead of allowing the sheep to spread out and wander at will through the mountains it would be necessary to herd the flocks constantly to keep them together. Although potentially possible, there is likely to be little acceptance of methods such as these amongst farmers, and the economic barriers are likely to be enormous. Changing sheep breeds may bring some benefits and needs to be further investigated (Gudvangen *et al.*, 1998). The only other option is that of the increased zoning of land use (Linnell *et al.*, 1996; Sagør *et al.*, 1997) which is outlined in the final section here.

Semi-domestic reindeer present a far greater problem. As well as being exposed to predation year-round, the animals cannot be herded or managed as intensively as sheep because of their greater susceptibility to stress and the fragility of their grazing resources. The only strategies that might help to reduce predation would include improving the body condition of the herds and maintaining a constant human presence close to them.

The political landscape in the 1990s

In response to the ever-increasing losses of sheep and semi-domestic reindeer to large carnivores (Fig. 4), a number of management actions have occurred during the six years since the first government white paper in 1992, that have weakened the protection of wolverines in Norway (see below). It is too early to determine how the changes in compensation practice will affect the conflict in Sweden.

Licensed hunting

In 1993 the licensed hunting of wolverines was introduced as a form of population control in northern Norway (Nordland and Troms counties). In the four hunting seasons since then, a total of 30 wolverines from a quota of 51 have been shot. In addition, 15 have been shot under depredation permits (Table 2). The responsibility for issuing these permits and quotas rests with the environmental protection offices of the various counties. In winter 1997-98 a controversial season was also opened for licensed hunting in south Norway. A politically appointed regional wolverine management committee (consisting almost entirely of representatives of the livestock industry) was responsible for setting a quota of 13 individuals. Hunting was not allowed inside the core conservation area, but could occur right up to its border (during mid-winter there is a risk that wolverines will make excursions outside their normal home ranges, thus there will always be a risk of draining individuals from the core area; Landa *et al.*, 1998a). Sweden reintroduced licensed hunting in 1996 to reduce predation on reindeer. Subsequently, seven wolverines were killed in 1997.

In the light of the results from Snøhetta, where limited control had no long-term effect on sheep losses, the logic of this licensed hunting as a method of reducing depredation has to be questioned. In addition, there appears to have been a decline in the wolverine population in Troms County because the quotas were based on over-estimates. For example, in 1996-97 a total of 10 licenses were issued, and in the spring two cubs were removed from a den and sent to a zoo. Reanalysis of population estimates led to an estimate of 41 ± 11 animals (Landa *et al.*, 1998b). In other words, permits had been issued for the removal of >25% of the population. There also are no data on the effect of this control on the population's social structure and reproduction. Recent studies on brown bear in Sweden have revealed that the killing of adult males results in high rates of infanticide (Swenson *et al.*, 1997). The population-level effect of killing male wolverines has not yet been evaluated; however, there is cause for concern because infanticide is suspected in this species (Lineitsev *et al.*, 1987; Bjärvall *et al.*, 1996; M. Lindén, unpubl.). In our opinion there needs to be much greater regulation of the permit issuing process, and a

Table 2. Wolverines killed in Norway under licensed hunting or predation control permits since protection was first introduced. Additional wolverines were killed in the course of normal hunting in north Norway prior to 1982. The numbers in brackets represent the quota or number of permits issued.

| Period | Licensed hunting | | Depredation control | | Total |
	North	South	North	South	
1972-81	–	–	6	6	
1982-92	–	–	34	11	45
1993-94	4 (11)	–	2	–	6
1994-95	8 (13)	–	6	–	14
1995-96	7 (13)	–	6	–	13
1996-97	11 (14)	–	3	–	14
1997-98	7 (19)	2 (13)	–	–	9

complete re-evaluation of the process behind the setting of quotas with respect to population estimates. Fortunately a new national monitoring plan for all large carnivores (including wolverines) is being developed which should improve the scientific basis for this process (Linnell *et al.*, 1998).

Core areas

In Norway a second government white paper on large carnivore management was presented in 1997 (Miljøverndepartementet, 1996-97). In this document the two core areas in north Norway were removed. The logic justifying this action was that because the wolverine population had increased in northern Norway there was no longer any need for CCAs. However, without the core areas there will be no security against over-harvest from licensed hunting or depredation control in the future. The southern CCA was maintained, however, there has been no attempt to reduce conflicts within the CCA by removing sheep from the area, resulting in continual conflicts within and around its borders.

Status

Norway has the weakest protection status for wolverines in Fennoscandia, the management authority recently having downgraded the species from "vulnerable" to "rare". Finland classifies wolverines as "endangered", while Sweden classifies them as "vulnerable" (Anon., 1996; Bergström *et al.*, 1996; Landa *et al.*, 1998b). Because these classifications do not agree with the relative population estimates, there is clearly a need to standardise the classification procedure.

Bio-political lessons

As with brown bear (Swenson *et al.*, 1995), the different social and political systems in Norway and Sweden have led to very different situations for wolverine management. The future of wolverines appears to be relatively secure in Sweden because management policy consistently treats wolverine conservation seriously, and managers are prepared to carry out necessary actions. The situation in Norway is much less secure, but provides some important lessons for large carnivore conservation in general.

The main lesson from wolverine management in Norway is that large carnivore conservation is not easy. Ecology is only a small part of the process. Though Norway has abundant, good quality habitat, one of the richest economies in the world, and a clear mandate from the Norwegian population as a whole for the conservation of large carnivores, the political influence of a small minority (mainly sheep farmers and reindeer herders) is able to jeopardise the future of wolverines in Norway (Bevanger, 1992). Enormous subsidy and compensation payments have done nothing to ease the conflicts. It appears that the planning process should be evaluated, rather than expecting conservation biologists to solve this problem. All stakeholders should be brought to the "bargaining table" before government draws up its management policy. A stakeholder group should be balanced and not dominated by any particular interest group. It is case studies like these, where biology takes second place to politics, that make the conservation of large carnivores a case-by-case activity, and in many ways emphasises why conservation biology as a science often has poor predictive power (Caughley, 1994; Landa, 1997).

Another lesson is that government policy documents often have been interpreted at both central and regional levels in a manner which does not adhere to their stated objectives or to international obligations (Table 1). Management practices often are incompatible with the stated objectives of preserving viable populations. In Norway the environmental movement is very weak, and has no tradition of litigation. The result is that there is little check upon poor management practices.

Recommendations

Wolverine conservation is possible in Norway, but it requires a reduction in the conflict with reindeer and sheep. This will require a centrally co-ordinated plan and zoning of both wolverines and livestock; wolverines may need to be removed from some areas where today they occur and be prevented from colonising other areas. Changes in livestock production will also be required, for example: (1) removing sheep from some high conflict areas, (2) converting sheep farming operations to cattle operations, and (3) introducing new husbandry methods (Linnell *et al.*, 1996). These are very difficult management decisions and may be politically unpalatable to many groups within society. However, if the will of the majority of people (*i.e.* that wolverines should be conserved) is to be brought about, these management decisions need to be implemented. Half measures will not serve either the wolverines or the livestock herders. An action plan for the conservation of wolverines in Europe has recently been prepared under the auspices of WWF International (Landa *et al.*, 1998c). Although this is not legally binding upon any national government, the adoption of the points mentioned in the plan would help to reduce conflicts and to conserve wolverines. We therefore hope that it may serve as a framework for wolverine management in the future.

Acknowledgements

The work on which this paper is based has been supported by the Norwegian Research Council, the Norwegian Directorate for Nature Management, the Swedish Environmental Protection Agency, the World-Wide Fund for Nature (Sweden), the World-Wide Fund (Norway), the Council of Europe and the Norwegian Institute for Nature Research. Audrey Magoun and Vivian Bianci have provided valuable comments on an earlier draft of this manuscript. We thank them all.

References

Aanes, R., Swenson, J.E. & Linnell, J.D.C. (1996). Rovvilt og sauenæring i Norge. I. Tap av sau til rovvilt: en presentasjon av tapets omfang basert på brukeropplysninger. *NINA Oppdragsmelding*, **434**: 1-37 (in Norwegian).
Ahlén, I. (1977). *Om bevarande av hotade djurarter i Sverige*. Stockholm; Skogshögskolan – Faunavård, Naturvårdsverket (in Swedish).

Anon. (1996). *Management of bear, wolf, wolverine and lynx in Finland (Publication 6a/1996).* Helsinki; Ministry of Agriculture and Forestry.

Anon. (1998). *Förslag till åtgärdsprogram - Järv. Naturvårdsverket (Unpubl. Report).* Stockholm; Swedish Nature Protection Agency (in Swedish).

Banci, V. (1994). Wolverine. In: L.F. Ruggiero, K.B. Aubry, S.W. Buskirk, L.J. Lyon & W.J. Zielinski (eds.), *The scientific basis for conserving forest carnivores, American marten, fisher, lynx and wolverine (US Department of Agriculture Forest Service General Technical Report RM-254)*: 99-123.

Banci. V. & Harestad, A.S. (1988). Reproduction and natality of wolverine. *Annales Zoologici Fennici*, **25**: 265-270.

Bangs, E.E. & Fritts, S.H. (1996). Reintroducing the gray wolf to central Idaho and Yellowstone National Park. *Wildlife Society Bulletin*, **24**: 402-413.

Becker, E.F. (1991). A terrestrial furbearer estimator based on probability sampling. *Journal of Wildlife Management*, **55**: 730-737.

Bergstrøm, M.R., Franzén, T.B.R., Henriksen, G., Nieminen, M., Overrein, Ø. & Stensli, O.M. (1996). Store rovdyr. Samordning av forvaltningstiltak på Nordkalotten. *Nordkalottkommitéens Rapportserie*, **42**: 1-45 (in Swedish).

Bevanger, K. (1992).Report on the Norwegian wolverine (*Gulo gulo* L.). *Small Carnivore Conservation*, **6**: 8-10.

Bjärvall, A., Franzèn, R., Nordkvist, M.& Åhlman, G. (1990). *Renar och rovdjur: rovdjurens effekter på rennäringen.* Solna; Naturvårdsverket förlag (in Swedish).

Bjärvall, A., Danielsson, S., Franzén, R. & Segerström, P. (1996). Experiences with the first radio-collared wolverines in Sweden. *Journal of Wildlife Research*, **1**: 3-6.

Boitani, L. (1995). Ecological and cultural diversities in the evolution of wolf human relationships. In: L.N. Carbyn, S.H. Fritts & D.R. Seip (eds.), *Ecology and conservation of wolves in a changing world*: 3-12. Edmonton (Alberta); Canadian Circumpolar Institute.

Breitenmoser, U. (1998). Large predators in the Alps: the fall and rise of man's competitors. *Biological Conservation*, **83**: 279-289.

Caughley, G. (1994). Directions in conservation biology. *Journal of Animal Ecology*, **63**: 215-244.

Dahle, L., Solberg, B. & Sødahl, D.P. (1990). En intervjuundersøkelse om befolkningens holdninger til og betalingsvillighet for å bevare bjørn, jerv, og ulv i Norge. *Fauna (Oslo)*, **43**: 187-188 (in Norwegian).

Elgmork, K. (1988). Reappraisal of the brown bear status in Norway. *Biological Conservation*, **46**: 163-168.

Flook, D.R., & Rimmer, J. (1965). Cannibalism in starving wolverines and sex identification from skulls. *Canadian Field Naturalist*, **79**: 171-173.

Fritts, S.H., Paul, W.J., Mech, L.D. & Scott, D P. (1992). Trends and management of wolf-livestock conflicts in Minnesota. *US Fish & Wildlife Service Resource Publication*, **181**: 1-27.

Gudvangen, K., Landa, A., Swenson, J.E. & Røskaft, E. (1998). Jerv og sau i Snøhettaområdet. In: T. Kvam & B. Jonson (eds.), *Store rovdyrs økologi I Norge: Sluttrapport. NINA Temahefte*, **8**: 26-33 (in Norwegian).

Gunson, J.R. (1992). Historical and present management of wolves in Alberta. *Wildlife Society Bulletin*, **20**: 330-339.

Gustavson, C.R. (1982). An evaluation of taste aversion control of wolf (*Canis lupus*) predation in northern Minnesota. *Applied Animal Ethology*, **9**: 63-71.

Haglund, B. (1966). De stora rovdjurens vintervanor. *Viltrevy*, **4**: 1-311 (in Swedish).

Hatfield, P.G. & Walker, J.W. (1994). An evaluation of pred-x eartag in protection of lambs from coyote predation (Sheep Research Report no. 3). *US Department of Agriculture – Agriculture Research Service*, **1994** (4): 1-193.

Heggberget, T. M. & Myrberget, S. (1980). Bestanden av jerv Norge i 1970-åra. *Fauna (Oslo)*, **33**: 52-55 (in Norwegian).

Hornocker, M.G. & Hash, H.S. (1981). Ecology of the wolverine in northwestern Montana. *Canadian Journal of Zoology*, **59**: 1286-1301.

Johnsen, S. (1929). *Rovdyr og rovfuglstatistikken i Norge (Årbok Naturvidenskabelig 2).* Bergen; Bergen Museum (in Norwegian).

Kaczensky, P. (1996). *Livestock-carnivore conflicts in Europe.* Munich; Munich Wildlife Society.

Koch, D.B. (1994). Biopolitical management of mountain lions, tule elk, and black bears in California. *International Conference on Bear Research and Management*, **9**: 561-566.

Kolstad, M., Mysterud, I., Kvam, T., Sørensen, O.J. & Wikan, S. (1986). Status of the brown bear in Norway: distribution and population 1978-1982. *Biological Conservation*, **38**: 79-99.

Kvam, T. & Røskaft, E. (1987). Project Jerv 1986. *Økoforsk notat*, **1987**: 1-236 (in Norwegian).

Kvam, T., Overskaug, K. & Sørensen, O.J. (1984). Jerven (*Gulo gulo* L.) i Norge: utbredelse og bestand 1978-1983. *Directorate for Nature Management, Viltrapport*, **32**: 1-76 (in Norwegian).

Kvam, T., Overskaug, K. & Sørensen, O. J. (1988). The wolverine *Gulo gulo* in Norway. *Lutra*, **31**: 7-20.

Kvam, T., Nybakk, K., Overskaug, K., Sørensen, O.J. & Brøndbo, K. (1995). Gaupa tar mye mer rein enn antatt. *Reindriftsnytt*, **1995**: 40-43 (in Norwegian).

Landa, A. (1997). The relevance of life history theory to harvest and conservation. *Fauna Norvegica (Series A)*, **18**: 43-55.

Landa, A. & Skogland, T. (1995). The relationship between population density and body size of wolverines *Gulo gulo* in Scandinavia. *Wildlife Biology*, **1**: 165-175.

Landa, A. & Tømmerås, B.Å. (1996). Do volatile repellents reduce wolverine *Gulo gulo* predation on sheep? *Wildlife Biology*, **2**: 119-126.

Landa. A. & Tømmerås, B.Å. (1997). A test of aversive agents on wolverines. *Journal of Wildlife Management*, **61**: 510-516.

Landa, A., Strand, O., Swenson, J.E. & Skogland, T. (1997). Wolverines and their prey in southern Norway. *Canadian Journal of Zoology*, **75**: 1292-1299.

Landa, A., Strand, O., Linnell, J.D.C. & Skogland, T. (1998a). Home range sizes and altitude selection for arctic foxes and wolverines in an alpine environment. *Canadian Journal of Zoology*, **76**: 448-457.

Landa, A., Franzén, R., Tufto, T.B.J., Lindén, M. & Swenson, J.E. (1998b). Wolverines in Scandinavia: population size and distribution in 1996. *Wildlife Biology*, **4**: 159-168.

Landa, A., Lindén, M. & Kojola, I. (1998c). *Draft action plan for conservation of the wolverine in Europe*. Berne; WWF-Europe.

Landa, A., Krogstad, S., Tømmerås, B.Å. & Tufto, J. (1998d). Do volatile repellents reduce wolverine *Gulo gulo* predation on sheep ? - results of a large scale experiment. *Wildlife Biology*, **4**: 111-118.

Lindén, M., Sandell, M., Segerström, P. & Läntha, J.E. (1994). *Det svenska Järvprojektet – ekologi och bevarande (Årsrapport 1994)*. Umeå; Swedish University of Agricultural Science (in Swedish).

Lindén, M., Franzén, R., Segerström, P. & Stuge, J. (1995). *Det svenska Järvprojektet - ekologi och bevarande (Årsrapport 1995)*. Umeå; Swedish University of Agricultural Science (in Swedish).

Lineitsev, N.S., Shapkin, A.M. & Krashevsky, U.R. (1987). [The wolverine of the Enisei North.] *Nauchno-Tekhnichensky Biulleten, VASKhNL (Novosibirsk)*, **5**: 11-16 (in Russian).

Linnell, J.D.C., Smith, M.E., Odden, J., Kaczensky, P. & Swenson, J.E. (1996). Strategies for the reduction of carnivore - livestock conflicts: a review. *NINA Oppdragsmelding*, **443**: 1-118.

Linnell, J.D.C., Aanes, R., Swenson, J.E., Odden, J. & Smith, M.E. (1997). Translocation of carnivores as a method for managing problem animals: a review. *Biodiversity and Conservation*, **6**: 1245-1257.

Lönnberg, E. (1936). Bidrag til järvens historia i Sverige. *Kungliga Svenska Vetenskapsakademiens Skrifter i Naturskyddsärenden*, **32**: 1-38 (in Swedish).

Magoun, A.J. (1987). Summer and winter diets of wolverines, *Gulo gulo*, in arctic Alaska. *Canadian Field Naturalist*, **191**: 392-397.

Mech, L.D. (1995). The challenge and opportunity of recovering wolf populations. *Conservation Biology*, **9**: 270-278.

Meriggi, A. & Lovari, S. (1996). A review of wolf predation in southern Europe: does the wolf prefer wild prey to livestock? *Journal of Applied Ecology*, **33**: 1561-1571.

Miljøverndepartementet (1991-92). *Om forvaltning av bjørn, jerv, ulv og gaupe (Rovvitmeldingen)* (*Stortings Melding 27*). Oslo; Ministry of the Environment (in Norwegian).

Miljøverndepartementet (1996-97). Om rovviltforvalting (*Stortings Melding 35*). Oslo; Ministry of the Environment (in Norwegian).

Muller-Wille, L. & Pelto, J. (1971). Technological change and its impact in arctic regions: Lapps introduce snowmobiles into reindeer herding. *Polarforschung*, **1/2**: 142-148.

Myrberget, S. & Grotnes, P. (1969). Sau og jerv i Jotunheimen. *Norsk Natur*, **5**: 75-84 (in Norwegian).

Myrberget, S. & Sørumgård, R. (1975). Jervens og gaupas status i Norge. *Naturen*, **4**: 170-174 (in Norwegian).

Myrberget, S. & Sørumgård, R. (1979). Fødselstidspunkt og kullstørrelse hos jerv. *Fauna (Oslo)*, **32:** 9-13 (in Norwegian).

Mysterud, I. & Mysterud, I. (1995). *Perspektiver på rovdyr, ressurser og utmarksnæringer i dagens- og framtidens Norge: en konsekvensutredning av rovviltforvaltningens betydning for småfenæring, reindrift og viltinteresser. Sluttrapport, KUR-prosjektet.* Oslo; Norsk sau og geitalslag (in Norwegian).

Mysterud, I. & Warren, J.T. (1992). Tap av sau i utmark: dødsvarsler systemet som hjelpemiddel. *Statens fagtjeneste for landbruket (SFFL)*, **2-92:** 1-17 (in Norwegian).

Mysterud, I., Warren, J.T. & Lynnebakken, T. (1994). Tap av sau i Målselv 1993. *Sau og Geit*, **1994:** 66-70 (in Norwegian).

Mysterud, I., Gautestad, A.O. & Mysterud, I. (1996). *Rovvilt og sauenæring i Norge VI: Kommentarer til gjeting som forebyggende tiltak.* Unpubl. Report. Oslo; University of Oslo, Department of Biology (in Norwegian).

Noss, R.F., Quigley, H.B., Hornocker, M.G., Merrill, T. & Paquet, P.C. (1996). Conservation biology and carnivore conservation in the Rocky Mountains. *Conservation Biology*, **10:** 949-963.

Oli, M.K., Taylor, I.R. & Rogers, M.E. (1994). Snow leopard *Panthera uncia* predation of livestock: an assessment of local perceptions in the Annapurna conservation area, Nepal. *Biological Conservation*, **68:** 63-68.

Paine, R. (1994). *Herds of the tundra: a portrait of Saami reindeer pastoralism.* Washington (DC); Smithsonian Institution Press.

Pate, J., Manfredo, M.J., Bright, A.D. & Tischbein, G. (1996). Coloradans' attitudes toward reintroducing the gray wolf into Colorado. *Wildlife Society Bulletin*, **24:** 421-428.

Pulliainen, E. (1988). Ecology, status and management of the Finnish wolverine *Gulo gulo* populations. *Lutra*, **31:** 21-28.

Quigley, H.B. & Crawshaw, P.G. (1992). A conservation plan for the jaguar *Panthera onca* in the Pantanal region of Brazil. *Biological Conservation*, **61:** 149-157.

Rausch, R.L. & Pearson, A.M. (1972). Notes on the wolverine in Alaska and the Yukon Territory. *Journal of Wildlife Management*, **36:** 249-268.

Sagør, J.T. & Aasetre, J. (1996). Forvaltere og bønder: kan de enes om bjørneforvaltningen? *Norwegian University of Science and Technology, Centre for Environment and Development SSMU-Rapport*, **1/96:** 1-94 (in Norwegian).

Sagør, J.T., Swenson, J.E. & Røskaft, E. (1997). Compatibility of brown bear *Ursus arctos* and free-ranging sheep in Norway. *Biological Conservation*, **81:** 91-95.

Skogland, T. (1989). Comparative social organization of wild reindeer in relation to food, mates and predator avoidance. *Advances in Ethology*, **29:** 1-74.

Skogland, T. (1994). *Villrein: fra urinnvåner til miljøbarometer.* Olso; Teknologisk Forlag (in Norwegian).

Swenson, J.E., Wabakken, P., Sandegren, F., Bjärvall, A., Franzén, R. & Söderberg, A. (1995). The near extinction and recovery of brown bears in Scandinavia in relation to the bear management policies of Norway and Sweden. *Wildlife Biology*, **1:** 11-25.

Swenson, J.E., Sandegren, F., Söderberg, A., Bjärvall, A., Franzén, R. &. Wabakken, P. (1997). Infanticide caused by hunting of male bears. *Nature (London)*, **386:** 450-451.

Vaag, A.B. (1987). Landsplan for forvaltning av bjørn, jerv og ulv. *Directorate for naturforvaltning rapport*, **6:** 1-35 (in Norwegian).

Weaver, J.L., Paquet, P.C. & Ruggiero, L.F. (1996). Resilience and conservation of large carnivore conservation in North America. *Conservation Biology*, **10:** 964-976.

Weber, W. & Rabinowitz, A. (1996). A global perspective on large carnivore conservation. *Conservation Biology*, **10:** 1046-1054.

Wemmer, C., Smith, J.L.D. & Mishra, H.R. (1987). Tigers in the wild: the biopolitical challenges. In: R.L. Tilson & U.S. Seal (eds.), *Tigers of the world: the biology, biopolitics, management, and conservation of an endangered species*: 396-405. Park Ridge (NJ); Noyes Publications.

Whitman, J.S., Ballard, W.B. & Gardner, C.L. (1986). Home range and habitat use by wolverines in southcentral Alaska. *Journal of Wildlife Management*, **50:** 460-463.

CHAPTER 2

A comparison of the management of stoats and weasels in Great Britain and New Zealand

Robbie A. McDonald & Elaine C. Murphy

Abstract

In Great Britain, stoats and weasels are native predators of game birds, some of which are intro-duced. By contrast, in New Zealand stoats and weasels are introduced predators that prey on native birds and other wildlife. In Britain, there has been some concern that both species may be in decline. Solutions to these practical problems have stimulated a substantial volume of research on stoat and weasel management, and in this chapter we compare and contrast the findings of research in these two countries. Both species have historically been considered to be vermin, despite their reputed beneficial role in controlling rodent populations. Stoat and weasel populations are particularly hard to monitor, but tracking tunnels and kill trapping records, when adjusted for effort, are useful indices of abundance. Stoats in particular present a serious threat to many species of birds in New Zealand and can have a significant impact on game birds and waders in Britain. This impact is increased when stoat populations exhibit a numerical response to increased rodent populations. Lethal control methods, such as trapping and shooting in Britain and trapping and poisoning in New Zealand, can reduce stoat and weasel populations, but only locally and temporarily. Effective and efficient control of predation by mustelids depends not only on improving control technologies but also on the development of a better understanding of their population biology and spatial behaviour.

Introduction

Stoats, *Mustela erminea*, and weasels, *Mustela nivalis*, are the smallest members of Family Mustelidae. They have a widespread distribution in the northern Holarctic but have also been introduced into New Zealand. Stoats and weasels are native to Great Britain but they come into conflict with humans because they are predators of both native and introduced game birds. In New Zealand conflict arises because they are introduced predators of native wildlife, particularly birds. In some parts of their range' concern has been expressed for their conservation status and in certain countries they receive statutory protection while in others they are considered to be pests. They therefore present a range of conservation and management problems, depending on their location, and have complex interactions with humans belonging to different interest groups.

Both stoats and weasels are opportunist predators. They are good climbers and they eat whatever is found in abundance. In Britain the diet of the stoat consists prin-cipally of lagomorphs, mainly rabbits, *Oryctolagus cuniculus*, and small rodents and

Mustelids in a modern world
Management and conservation aspects of small carnivore: human interactions
edited by Huw I. Griffiths, pp. 21–40
© 2000 Backhuys Publishers, Leiden, The Netherlands

birds (including game birds) (Day, 1968; McDonald *et al.*, in press). In New Zealand stoats prey mainly on birds, rats, *Rattus* spp., feral house mice, *Mus musculus*, rabbits and invertebrates, but their diet varies greatly according to the habitat they occupy (King, 1990). In Britain field voles, *Microtus agrestis*, are an important component of the diet of the weasel and the importance of other rodents, rabbits and song birds varies according to their abundance (Day, 1968; Tapper, 1979; King, 1980a; McDonald *et al.*, in press). In New Zealand the weasel's diet consists mainly of house mice, birds, lizards and invertebrates (King, 1990; King *et al.*, 1996; Murphy *et al.*, 1998a).

Both species are commonly trapped by British gamekeepers as part of predator control programs intended to promote stocks of game birds (Tapper, 1992). In New Zealand stoats in particular present a serious threat to the future existence of several endemic bird species (McLennan *et al.*, 1996; O'Donnell *et al.*, 1996; Wilson *et al.*, 1998). In arctic regions stoats and weasels have limited commercial significance as furbearers, but their value has declined significantly in recent years as the result of low prices for small pelts (McDonald & Harris, 1998). Despite their abundance and importance in certain systems, stoats and weasels have been comparatively little-studied and exchanges between researchers working on management and those working on conservation have been limited. In this review we aim to bring together themes of research on stoats and weasels in two countries where much recent work on the conservation and management of small mustelids has been conducted: Great Britain and New Zealand.

The history of stoat and weasel management

Great Britain

Even prior to the development of the game estate, stoats and weasels were commonly regarded as vermin, worthy of destruction and occasional bounties. However, attempts at control were opportunistic and not systematic or widespread. Indeed, some early accounts acknowledged the potentially useful role of weasels in the control of other pests. Tame weasels could be run on leads in the garden to discourage moles or used to get pigeons out of dovecotes, while, less favourably for the weasel, spreading the ashes of a burnt weasel in the garden or sprinkling the brain and hair of a weasel on cheese were both reputed to keep mice away (Dannenfeldt, 1982). In Britain, stoats and weasels eventually became firmly classified as pests in their own right. Dannenfeldt (1982) reports that, in the reign of Henry VIII (1509–1547), a bounty scheme was enacted whereby churchwardens ensured that every community held and maintained nets, traps and "engines" for the destruction of vermin, including a range of mustelid species. In the case of weasels and stoats the bounty was one penny (1 d) a head. However, vermin could not be destroyed by any means where it might disturb the breeding of hawks, doves, deer and rabbits, in order to protect these favoured species from what would today be called non-target effects.

With the development of the sporting estate in Great Britain during the 18th and 19th centuries, stoats and weasels became targets for much more systematic control efforts. Shooting became a highly fashionable pastime towards the end of the 19th century and the desire for large bags of birds meant that extensive predator control regimes became a vital part of enhancing the stocks of game for shooting (Middleton, 1967; Tapper, 1992). The main strategy was the elimination of all potential predators of eggs, chicks and adult birds. All carnivorous birds and mammals, including stoats and weasels, were targeted using a range of methods, including traps, poisons, snares and shooting. Tapper (1992) reported that at the peak of the fashion for shooting, over 23,000 gamekeepers were employed in the control of predators. The effect of their combined efforts was more marked for some species than others. Wild cats, *Felis silvestris*, polecats, *Mustela putorius*, and pine martens, *Martes martes*, were all reduced to the point of near extinction in Britain (Langley & Yalden, 1977). However, despite continually large bags of both species, stoats and weasels appeared to be able to resist the effects of this intensive control (King, 1980b; Tapper *et al.*, 1982) and they are still the most common native carnivores in Britain (Harris *et al.*, 1995). Their tolerance of control efforts has largely been ascribed to their high reproductive rates and ability to recolonise areas where local extinctions had taken place (King & Moors, 1979; King, 1980b).

New Zealand

The endemic fauna of New Zealand evolved in the absence of mammalian predators and has proved particularly vulnerable to some of the mammals introduced since human settlement (King, 1984). A number of alien species, notably rats, were introduced with early colonists. However, the widespread belief that mustelids could reduce or vanquish populations of their prey and a misplaced faith in this form of pest biocontrol led to the decision deliberately to introduce three mustelid species in an attempt to control rabbits. Originally caught and transported from Britain, ferrets, *Mustela furo*, were released into New Zealand in large numbers from 1882 (Lavers & Clapperton, 1990) and stoats and weasels from 1884 (King, 1990).

At the time some conservationists expressed concern that mustelids would have a devastating effect on native birds, but their warnings were ignored (King, 1984; Hill & Hill, 1987). Indeed, all introduced mustelids were protected by law for many years as the natural enemy of the rabbit. However, by the late 1880s it became obvious that native ground birds were being decimated. In the 1890s Richard Henry took a first step towards controlling the risks presented by alien predators by trying to establish kiwi, *Apteryx* spp., and kakapo, *Strigops habroptilus* (a large, nocturnal, flightless parrot) on mustelid-free islands (Hill & Hill, 1987). Despite these early concerns, it was not until 1936 that legal protection for mustelids was lifted. Between 1944 and 1948, 50,957 stoat skins were bought by J.K. Mooney, Ltd. and this represented about 90% of stoat skins offered on the New Zealand fur market (Wodzicki, 1950). Bounty payments were also paid by acclimatisation societies from 1932 for mustelid tails, but these payments ended in 1950, bounty hunters merely having cropped rather than controlled populations (Wodzicki, 1950; King, 1984).

Stoats are now the most widespread of the three mustelids in New Zealand. They are found in a variety of habitats from sea level to well above the tree line, in both the North and South Island, and are one of the commonest predators in forests (King, 1990). However, in open country where ferrets and feral cats, *Felis catus*, are abundant, stoats are not so common. Weasels are widely but sparsely distributed and are the least common mustelid. They are found in grassland, scrub and forest (King, 1990).

Since their introduction, mammalian predators have been responsible for many extinctions and declines in New Zealand's native fauna (King, 1984; Clout & Saunders, 1995). Birds have been particularly affected with over 40% of the pre-human land bird fauna being lost, and the proportion of the surviving avifauna classed as threatened is higher than in any other country (Clout, 1997). Although mustelids were comparatively late arrivals in New Zealand, about thirteen species or subspecies of birds either suddenly declined or vanished shortly after their introduction (King, 1984). Until recently nature conservation in New Zealand has mostly involved the legal protection of native wildlife and the establishment of national parks and reserves, based on the northern hemisphere experience of conservation on continental areas (Clout & Saunders, 1995). However, it is becoming obvious that passive protection is not good enough for a number of vulnerable species and the continuing impact of introduced pests is viewed as the most significant threat remaining to New Zealand's biodiversity (Clout & Saunders, 1995; Clout, 1997). The need for widespread control of stoats using existing technologies is currently viewed as an intractable problem, and the need to develop novel and effective techniques for the effective control of stoat predation has been highlighted in the recently released draft strategy for New Zealand's biodiversity (Department of Conservation, 1998a).

Management problems

Monitoring stoat and weasel populations

One of the key management difficulties presented by stoats and weasels is that it is exceptionally hard to survey or to monitor their populations (King & Edgar, 1977; Macdonald et al., 1999). Data on population status are important for prioritising conservation actions, as in Britain's Biodiversity Action Plan (Anon., 1994), and for planning a management response to increased predation risk when a predator population is higher than expected (e.g. O'Donnell & Phillipson, 1996).

Mustelids generally live at low densities and are very wide ranging relative to their small body size (King, 1989). Furthermore, population size and social structure are highly flexible and are subject to extensive changes between both seasons and years (Lockie, 1966; King, 1989; Erlinge & Sandell, 1986). Therefore, both direct and indirect sampling techniques for stoat and weasel populations are highly problematic. In colder climates, tracks in snow can be counted and used as an index of activity (Nyholm, 1959; King, 1989). Macdonald et al. (1998) listed field signs, road kills, hair tubes and tracking tunnels as potentially useful survey methods, but recommended using camera traps calibrated by live-trapping and gamekeepers' records. The use of sightings data, tracking tunnels and capture-mark-recapture have so far proved unfruitful in trials in Britain (Morris & Birks, 1997). Two mainstream methods are commonly used in both Britain and New Zealand - kill trapping and tracking tunnels.

In their most systematic form, as employed in New Zealand, kill-traps, usually Mark IV or VI steel Fenn traps (A. Fenn & Co., Hoopers Lane, Astwood Bank,

Redditch, UK) are set in sampling lines with a given spacing, and the number of captures/100 trap nights is recorded. In Britain, game estates commonly record the number of stoats and weasels trapped by gamekeepers each year. These data are then contributed to the National Game Bag Census administered by The Game Conservancy Trust (Tapper, 1992). This is the largest ongoing census scheme for stoats and weasels that we are aware of, and gamekeepers' records have been described in a number of publications (e.g. Middleton, 1934; King, 1980b; Tapper, 1982, 1992). However, game estates do not as a rule record the amount of effort they make in order to catch stoats and weasels. Therefore, it is not possible to calibrate the numbers caught/trap night as is done in New Zealand. This has proven particularly problematic for interpreting trends in British stoat and weasel populations (Tapper, 1992; McDonald & Harris, 1999).

Kill trapping is subject to a number of biases, especially when conducted in the same area on a permanent basis. For example, after older, resident animals are removed, juveniles may move in to replace them and a locally-biased age sample may result. Kill-trapping may also reduce population density and change age distributions. In a study of 63 stoats collected between 1983–87 from New Zealand's Pureora Forest, King *et al.* (1996) found that both the capture rate of stoats and the proportion of adults caught declined after the first year of regular kill trapping, and that it remained lower than in the first year for the rest of the study. The importance of these biases is likely to increase as populations become more isolated and levels of immigration are lower. Despite these biases, kill trapping does provide unequivocal distributional information, as well as providing otherwise unobtainable samples which may be used to obtain information on demography and diet. McDonald & Harris (1999) concluded that the use of trapping records is likely to be the only reliable, large-scale method of monitoring stoat and weasel populations in Britain. However, they also recommended that British monitoring schemes are improved by instituting a simultaneous survey of the trapping effort made by gamekeepers.

Footprint tracking tunnels periodically have been used in the study of mustelid populations (King & Edgar, 1977) and, while they have been tested recently in Britain without much success (Morris & Birks, 1997), they are becoming the standard method for monitoring mustelids in New Zealand (Murphy *et al.*, 1999). The proportion of meat-baited tracking tunnels containing mustelid footprints is used as an index of mustelid abundance. As there is a degree of overlap in their sizes, ferret, stoat and weasel prints cannot always be distinguished reliably.

The impact of stoats and weasels on game birds in Great Britain

Scientific data evaluating the impact of predation on game birds specifically by stoats and weasels are comparatively sparse. While there is clear potential for experimental studies in this area, there has been no specific study on this subject in Britain. However, evidence of the role of predation by stoats and weasels is available from scientific studies of predation on game birds by a suite of predators (e.g. Potts, 1986; Hudson, 1992; Tapper *et al.*, 1996) and of predation on non-game birds (Dunn, 1977; Tapper, 1979; King, 1980a; Robson, 1998). Several studies have recorded the diet of weasels and stoats in Britain (e.g. Day, 1968; Potts & Vickerman, 1974; Tapper, 1979; King, 1980b; McDonald *et al.*, in press) and have found that the importance of game birds is usually small relative to other prey items. However, it is a fallacy to interpret this as evidence of little or no impact on game birds since these are usually much scarcer than other prey items, e.g. rabbits and voles (Tapper *et al.*, 1982).

Summarising the fate of almost 14,000 nests of grey partridge, *Perdix perdix*, and red-legged partridge, *Alectoris rufa*, monitored on game estates where intensive predator control took place, Middleton (1967) attributed 145 out of 1,993 (7.2%) cases of predation to stoats. One (0.1%) nest was thought to have been destroyed by a weasel while 711 (35.6%) nests were lost to foxes, *Vulpes vulpes* (Middleton, 1967). Similar figures were recorded for pheasants, *Phasianus colchicus*, by the Game Conservancy's Pheasant Nest Record Scheme which found that stoats accounted for approximately 11% of the nests that were destroyed by predators (Anon., 1981). Hudson (1992) reported that in a sample of 1,383 corpses of full-grown red grouse, *Lagopus lagopus scoticus*, collected on game estates, stoats were responsible for the death of 1.4% and 10.5% in Scotland and England, respectively. The difference was explained by the relative importance of predation by foxes in Scotland where foxes were more abundant. Tapper *et al.* (1982) described a case where 15 out of 61 partridge nests on part of a Norfolk game estate were reported to have been destroyed by a single stoat, and King (1989) has also reviewed a number of anecdotal cases describing predation by stoats on game bird chicks and eggs.

In a three-year study of curlew, *Numenius arquata*, living on a grouse moor in northern England, Robson (1998) recorded that 45% of nests were destroyed and 54% of radio-tagged chicks were killed by stoats, even though year-round trapping was taking place on his study site. Using a model of curlew demography he concluded that predation by stoats was a major limiting factor for the curlew populations on his study site, and that productivity was insufficient to sustain the curlew population in the long term. Dunn (1977) and King (1980b) describe the substantial impact of predation by weasels on tits, *Parus* spp., nesting in boxes in Wytham Wood, near Oxford. The effects were especially pronounced during periods of particularly low rodent abundance or particularly high abundance of nesting tits. Tapper (1979) also concluded that when field vole populations were low, birds (mainly passerines) were weasels' main alternate prey.

Reviewing the results of a number of studies, Potts (1986) compared grey partridge nesting success in areas with and without intensive control of a range of predators, including stoats and weasels. He concluded that nesting density was consistently higher in areas with active gamekeepers and that predation was by far the most important cause of nest loss. Subsequently, in a six year experiment, Tapper *et al.* (1996) removed stoats and weasels as well as foxes, corvids, rats, *Rattus norvegicus*, and feral cats from a treatment area while leaving the predator community untouched on a control site. Both autumn and subsequent spring breeding densities of partridge were increased on the treatment site but not on the control area. When treatment and control protocols were swapped, the same pattern was observed and the authors concluded that predation played a key role in limiting the production and subsequent breeding density of partridges (Tapper *et al.*, 1996). Unfortunately, neither of these two important studies discerned the relative importance of predation by stoats and weasels from that of foxes, corvids and other predators.

Tapper (1976) calculated from a dietary study that an individual weasel could account for four game bird chicks a summer while a stoat could account for eleven. He concluded that predation by weasels and stoats could be an important factor in limiting partridge abundance when both predators and prey occurred at normal densities. In summarising the impact of mammalian predators on partridge, Tapper *et al.* (1982) concluded that predation was an important factor in limiting populations, especially during the summer nesting period, and that the control of predators, including stoats and weasels, was warranted as a method of enhancing game populations. Predator control has been found to be particularly effective when conducted alongside a programme of habitat improvement, and game management authorities consider the two activities to be inseparable tools in the protection of wild game birds (Potts, 1980, 1986).

The impact of stoats and weasels on endangered species in New Zealand

Although stoats were implicated in the decline of some native bird species soon after their introduction to New Zealand (Moors, 1983; King, 1990), the extent to which they are still contributing to the decline of native birds is only now beginning to be understood. Their impact on threatened and endangered species is of particular concern.

Kiwis are endemic to New Zealand and the smallest of the ratites, an ancient group of flightless birds. There are four species and all have declined significantly since human settlement (McLennan *et al.*, 1996). Predation of young kiwis, chiefly by stoats, is currently the most important factor contributing to the continuing decline of mainland kiwi populations (McLennan *et al.*, 1996). Stoat abundance can be extremely low and yet can still make a substantial difference to kiwi survival and often current trapping regimes do not reduce densities sufficiently to protect young kiwis (Peters, 1997; Pierce, 1997).

Forests of southern beech, *Nothofagus* spp., synchronously produce huge crops of seed (mast) at intervals of three to 11 years (Wardle, 1984). Stoat density fluctuates widely between years, but is particularly high in the year following a seedfall - the result of major increases in bird, invertebrate and mouse abundances, all of which are prey for stoats (King, 1983; Murphy & Dowding, 1995; Fitzgerald *et al.*, 1996). This increase in stoat abundance has been shown to have a detrimental impact on a number of bird species, particularly hole-nesters such as kaka, *Nestor meridionalis*, an endemic forest parrot (Wilson *et al.*, 1998), yellowhead (O'Donnell *et al.*, 1996) and the yellow-crowned parakeet, *Cyanoramphus auriceps* (Elliott *et al.*, 1996).

Predation by stoats upon nestling and adult female kaka is causing an overall decline, and in many instances the local extinction, of the species (Wilson *et al.*, 1998). In one study in beech forest, in over 11 years and 20 breeding attempts, only four kaka fledglings survived to independence and nine young kaka and four adult females were killed on the nest (Wilson *et al.*, 1998). Wilson *et al.* (1998) predict that stoat predation will cause kaka to become extinct on mainland New Zealand unless stoats and/or kaka are actively managed. A research plan for kaka has been published recently (Moorhouse & Greene, 1998) and the impact of stoats and other predators on kaka will be determined in different forest habitats.

The yellowhead is a small, insectivorous, endemic forest passerine which, in the 19th century, was among the most abundant forest birds on South Island. They have now all but disappeared from 75% of their former range and are considered endangered (O'Donnell, 1993). Research has shown that stoat predation causes periodic yellowhead population crashes in the years following heavy beech seeding, but that this impact can be mitigated by intensive trapping focused on high stoat density years (O'Donnell *et al.*, 1996).

Productivity and mortality of the yellow-crowned parakeet is also closely related to cycles of beech seeding. Yellow-crowned parakeet numbers in Fiordland increased dramatically after a beech seedfall but declined one year later (Elliott *et al.*, 1996). Parakeets appear to be very vulnerable to stoat predation. Trapping which reduced stoat numbers enough to make a significant difference to yellowhead survival was of no benefit to parakeets, as stoats remained in sufficient numbers and preyed on all accessible parakeet nests (Elliott *et al.*, 1996).

Stoats also have been implicated in the decline of the endangered New Zealand dotterel, *Charadrius obscurus*. They are believed to have been the major cause of the decline of the southern subspecies *C. o. obscurus* (Dowding, 1999) and have been shown to have a dramatic local impact on the northern subspecies, *C. o. aquilonius*; one female stoat killing 1% of the breeding adults within two months (Dowding & Murphy, 1996). Predation by stoats, ferrets and feral cats is also the principal cause of chick mortality in yellow-eyed penguin, *Megadyptes antipodes*, on the New Zealand mainland (Darby & Seddon, 1990; Moller *et al.*, 1995). Most mainland breeding sites are on land which has been cleared for farming, and current habitat management around breeding sites aims to exclude livestock (which trample nests) and restore coastal scrub and forest. It was thought that this re-vegetation might help exclude predators by acting as a barrier, but studies show that stoats, ferrets and cats readily use these vegetation buffer zones (Alterio *et al.*, 1998).

Very little is known about the impact of weasels in New Zealand. As they eat lizards, birds and invertebrates, they could be a problem for certain endemic species; the remains of a Whitaker's skink, *Cyclodina whitakeri* (a threatened reptile), were found recently in a trapped weasel (Miskelly, 1997). Weasels and stoats are now both targeted in a localised control programme to protect the lizards, but as yet the efficacy of these measures has not been investigated.

Management objectives and activities

Game protection

In Britain game shooting has declined from its heyday in the early part of the 20th century (Tapper, 1992). However, it is still a major participant sport and contributes several million pounds to the rural economy. Shooting takes place in a range of settings, from large wealthy estates employing teams of gamekeepers devoted to promoting wild game, to small private syndicates that lease shooting rights and employ a part-time keeper to manage smaller stocks of hand-reared birds. More than 2,500 individuals are still employed either full or part time as gamekeepers in Great Britain (Tapper, 1992; Reynolds & Tapper, 1996) and principal amongst their duties is the control of predators. The principal objective of predator control is to enhance populations of game, ideally such that spring breeding stocks are increased as well as autumn shooting stocks.

Stoats and weasels may be controlled legally in Britain by two main methods - shooting and trapping. The deliberate use of chemical control agents to control carnivores is now illegal. Non-lethal methods of controlling predation by stoats and weasels upon British game birds have not been described formally and there have been no scientific studies of suitable techniques. Possible non-lethal methods might include exclosures, taste aversion and supplementary feeding. Predation by weasels on the tits of Wytham Wood was effectively eliminated by replacing trunk-mounted wooden nest boxes with free-hanging concrete boxes that were, essentially, weasel proof (McCleery & Perrins, 1991; McCleery *et al.*, 1996). However, it is hard to imagine a similar technique for protecting ground nesting game birds, given the size difference between large game birds and these small predators. Pens for releasing hand-reared game birds are designed to exclude foxes, and they are particularly effective when electric fencing is used around the perimeter of the pens (Anon., 1991). Balharry & Macdonald (1999) have designed an effective electric fencing system that protects game birds held in pens from predation by pine martens. However, these systems are not likely to be successful in eliminating predation by much smaller stoats and weasels. Similarly, in American trials, electric fencing was found not to prevent access by small mustelids to nesting ducks (Greenwood & Arnold, 1990; Lokemoen & Woodward, 1993). Rusiniak *et al.* (1976) found evidence of conditioned taste aversion in laboratory ferrets, but to our knowledge this has not been tested in stoats or weasels. Reynolds & Tapper (1996) have considered the relative merits of a range of non-lethal approaches to the control of mammalian predation, though these were mainly with a view to reducing predation by canids.

Stoats and weasels are shot opportunistically. Stoats, being the larger species, are more conspicuous and a larger target and so they are shot much more frequently than weasels (Tapper, 1992; McDonald, 1998). Shooting may be a particularly effective tool for controlling stoat populations since, unlike trapping, it shows no bias towards males and the sex ratio of shot samples is not significantly different from 1:1 (McDonald, 1998). Removing female stoats in the months of April and May is likely to have a disproportionate effect on stoat populations, since dependent young will probably die if their mothers are shot in this early period of their development. Weasels are shot comparatively rarely and the smaller females particularly so (McDonald, 1998). The effect of shooting on weasel populations is not, therefore, likely to be substantial.

The majority of stoats and weasels taken by gamekeepers are trapped. Formerly, the main type of trap used to take stoats and weasels was a steel trap with a four inch jaw and a flat spring, known as a gin (Bateman, 1971, 1979). This and similar steel traps could be set in tunnels to kill small predators, such as stoats and weasels, in the open as a leg hold trap for larger animals, and on poles to catch birds of prey (Bateman, 1971). However, the use of gin traps is no longer permitted in Britain. Their most common replacement is the steel Fenn mark IV or mark VI which has a coiled steel spring, though several other types of spring trap and live trap are also approved for use (Bateman, 1971, 1979). Other than live traps, all approved traps are designed to kill the animal by breaking its back and the Fenn has been shown to be markedly more humane than the gin (King, 1981). All types of trap must be checked every day and must be set in tunnels to prevent larger animals being caught. Other than this, there are no limitations on the season, density or location in which traps may be set. Trapping is particularly intensive in March, April and May (McDonald & Harris, 1999). However, some gamekeepers run traps all year round.

Changes in the stoat and weasel management practices adopted by gamekeepers have accelerated since the 1960s. In many areas of Britain, habitat degradation and intensive agriculture has led to greatly depleted populations of wild game birds (Potts, 1986; Tapper, 1992). Hand-rearing and releasing non-native game birds, mainly pheasants but also red-legged partridge, is now the principal method of maintaining sufficient stocks to sustain most shoots. Many gamekeepers perceive stoats and weasels as less of a threat to reared game birds than to wild birds, and as less of a threat in either situation than other mammalian predators, principally red foxes (McDonald & Harris, 1999). Therefore, over the last 30 years, high labour costs and the increasing prevalence of hand-reared game have led to a decline in the effort being put into controlling stoat and weasel populations (Tapper, 1992).

In 1997 gamekeepers that relied on reared birds ran approximately half the number of traps for half as many months as keepers that relied on maintaining stocks of wild game (McDonald & Harris, 1999). In effect, this is the result of an assessment of the costs and benefits of controlling stoat and weasel populations in modern day game management. The costs of the time and effort put into running a large-scale, year round trapping programme on an estate where most birds are hand-reared do not appear to be outweighed by the benefits in terms of increased wild bird populations. Stoats, in particular, prey to some extent on reared birds, particularly shortly after birds are released into outdoor holding pens. However, gamekeepers commonly protect newly released poults by running a small number of traps around the pen perimeter during this critical period. In a 1997 survey of 148 gamekeepers who relied on reared birds, 31 (21%) only ran traps in the immediate vicinity of their release pens (McDonald, unpubl. data).

Currently, approximately 20% of gamekeepers (McDonald & Harris, 1999), usually those working on larger or wealthier estates, still attach significant prestige to the prevalence of wild game birds. In these areas, predator control is generally more intensive and trapping stoats and weasels is still a large part of the game-keeper's job. This is particularly true of estates promoting red grouse and grey partridge, both native game species that are not readily hand-reared (Tapper, 1992). Recently, the formation of groups for the promotion of wild pheasant stocks, such as the East Anglian Wild Pheasant Group (Anon., 1998), has led also to locally intensive trapping, specifically to enhance wild-breeding pheasant numbers.

Endangered species protection

A number of the New Zealand Department of Conservation's recovery plans for threatened bird species have identified predation by stoats as a major factor in their decline and stoat control has been identified as a required management action. Species threatened by stoat predation live in a broad range of habitat types, reflecting the wide distribution of stoats in New Zealand. Recovery plans are now in place for several species including: takahe, *Porphyrio mantelli* (Crouchley, 1994a) (a flightless gallinule now restricted to sub-alpine grassland), the forest-dwelling yellowhead (O'Donnell, 1993), kiwis (Butler & McLennan, 1991), and the New Zealand dotterel (Dowding, 1993) (a shorebird of sandy beaches).

Conservation efforts for some species have been focused on the maintenance of predator-free islands, on which native species and those translocated from the mainland can be more easily protected. Richard Henry's early attempts at establishing kiwis and kakapo on predator-free islands failed (Hill & Hill, 1987) because stoats are good swimmers and islands as far as 1,200 m offshore are subject to regular immigration by stoats, with a possible record crossing of 1,650 m (Taylor & Tilley, 1984; McKinlay, 1997). Recently, Maud Island has illustrated the limitations of concentrating on predator-free islands for species conservation. This 309 ha island is 900 m from the mainland and is of particular conservation value as it is rodent-free and, until 1982, was mustelid-free. Some rare endemic species have survived on the island and others, such as the kakapo, have been introduced. In 1982 numbers of saddlebacks, *Philesturnus carunculatus* (an endemic forest species), which recently had been introduced, declined dramatically. When taped saddleback calls were used to try and attract the birds, a stoat appeared. Although Fenn trapping began immediately, using a wide variety of baits and lures, it was seven months before the first stoats were caught (Crouchley, 1994b). It is now thought that the first stoat seen was a female and it had a litter of young before being caught. The last stoat caught on the island was in 1993, and regular stoat trapping both on the island and nearby mainland is now undertaken to keep Maud Island stoat-free. Early detection of stoat sign is very important. Sandy beaches have been useful in revealing stoat footprints and sand pits have been placed on all main tracks on the island.

A recent initiative undertaken by the New Zealand Department of Conservation is the establishment and intensive management of 'Mainland Islands' (Department of Conservation, 1998b). Although many species recovery plans continue to be focused on predator-free offshore islands, some of the techniques developed for island restoration are being used to restore damaged ecosystems on the mainland. Currently the Department of Conservation manages six Mainland Island projects, covering 9,400 ha and costing over $NZ 1 million during the 1997/98 financial year (Saunders, 1999). An integral part of the Mainland Islands initiative is the control of stoats (e.g. Butler, 1997; Beaven, 1998).

As part of this and other initiatives, developing methods for improving the effectiveness of stoat control has been given high priority in New Zealand. Currently, control relies largely on labour-intensive trapping using Fenn traps in tunnels, conducted in a similar manner to that employed by gamekeepers. However, novel baits and tunnel design for traps are continually being investigated (e.g. Dilks *et al.*, 1996; Maxwell *et al.*, 1997). Hen eggs and rabbit meat are currently the most commonly used baits. Synthetic scent lures based on two compounds identified in stoat anal sac secretions have been trialed, but these lures were not as successful as eggs for catching stoats in Fenn traps (Clapperton *et al.*, 1994).

Preliminary work using anal sac secretions as a lure shows promise, but further work is needed (K. Clapperton & J. McLennan, unpubl.). The smell of dead mice, dead day-old chickens, raw meat and raw hen eggs were highly attractive to stoats, but artificial odours used by fur trappers in North America and flavours used in the food industry were not (Spurr, 1998).

Two ultrasonic devices, Transonic™ ESP and Yard Gard™ (Weitech Inc., USA) have been trialed to see if they repelled captive stoats from a food source. Both these devices are claimed by the manufacturer to repel animals such as rats and ferrets. Although most of the stoats tested were initially repelled, this effect was short-lived and all eventually fed near the ultrasonic devices (Spurr, 1997).

The use of poisoned eggs in bait stations to control stoats has been developed recently (Spurr & Hough, 1997). Field trials using hen eggs poisoned with sodium monofluoroacetate (1080) and diphacinone resulted in large reductions in stoat populations (Spurr, 1998), and this method is a potentially cost effective way of controlling stoats over large areas.

Australian brushtail possums, *Trichosurus vulpecula*, were introduced in the 19th century to establish a fur trade in New Zealand but have since become a major problem for conservation and animal health; their browsing severely damages native forest and they are reservoirs of the bacterium causing bovine tuberculosis, *Mycobacterium tuberculosis* (Cowan, 1990). Large-scale poisoning by aerial application of bait or use of ground bait stations is routinely carried out to control possums. The two main agents used are sodium monofluoroacetate (1080) and brodifacoum (Eason *et al.*, 1993; Henderson *et al.*, 1994). When it was realised that these poisoning operations were also controlling another introduced pest, the ship rat, *Rattus rattus* (Murphy & Bradfield, 1992; Innes *et al.*, 1995), many subsequent control operations undertaken for conservation purposes were designed to take advantage of this (e.g. Bradfield & Flux, 1996; Speed & Bancroft, 1997; Pierce, 1997). It has recently been discovered that these operations have also been inadvertently killing stoats through secondary poisoning, mostly from their eating poisoned rat and possum carcasses (Gillies & Pierce, 1999; Murphy *et al.*, 1999). Although there is an initial high kill of resident stoats, once reinvasion by stoats occurs the secondary poisoning effect is lost until rat 'vector' numbers build up again (Murphy *et al.*, 1998a; Gillies & Pierce, 1999). Also, with brodifacoum poison operations, after the initial lethal secondary poisoning effect, animals still can be exposed to sub-lethal doses. In one recent study, 78% of 40 stoats and 71% of 14 weasels trapped following a rat poisoning operation contained brodifacoum residues (Murphy *et al.*, 1998b).

The potential of using brodifacoum to poison stoats and other predators secondarily as a control method has been investigated recently (Alterio, 1996; Alterio *et al.*, 1997; Brown *et al.*, 1998). Although it is an effective method for killing resident stoats, human health concerns and non-target effects may preclude its use. In areas where it has been used for possum and rat control, brodifacoum residues have been detected in pigs, *Sus scrofa* (Murphy *et al.*, 1998b; Eason *et al.*, 1999), red deer, *Cervus elaphus scoticus* (G. Wright, pers. comm.), kiwis, and in a native owl, the morepork, *Ninox novaeseelandiae* (Murphy *et al.*, 1998b; Robertson *et al.*, 1999). A toxin that is less persistent may be a more acceptable method of secondarily poisoning predators.

More importantly from a conservation perspective, rat poisoning operations have recently been reported to induce changes in stoat diet. Exhibiting a functional response to changes in prey availability, stoats were found to switch to eating birds when rat abundance was reduced. Thus successful rat-poisoning operations resulted in higher rates of bird consumption by stoats than unsuccessful ones (Murphy & Bradfield, 1992; Murphy *et al.*, 1998b). Furthermore, mice appeared to increase in abundance after rat poisoning operations in the North Island (Innes *et al.*, 1995; Clout *et al.*, 1995). As mice are a major prey of weasels (King 1990; King *et al.*, 1996) this might be expected to affect weasels also. In one study, weasel numbers increased dramatically after a brodifacoum operation targeting rats. However, mice remained the principal constituent of weasel diets (Murphy *et al.*, 1998a). More research is needed into these unexpected effects of large scale poisoning campaigns before secondary poisoning is adopted as a national predator control strategy.

Conservation of stoats and weasels

Carnivores are often targeted as flagship, keystone or umbrella species for conservation, either because a 'trickle-down' effect is believed to conserve ecosystems or because they arouse public interest in conservation work. In Britain, there has been considerable effort made to conserve some native mustelids, notably otters, *Lutra lutra*, badgers, *Meles meles*, pine martens and polecats (e.g. Morris, 1993; Mitchell-Jones, 1996), all of which are strictly protected under nature conservation legislation. Stoats and weasels are currently the only native mustelids that have no conservation status in British law. Since they are alien pests and because of their impact on native wildlife, stoats and weasels are highly unlikely ever to receive any conservation protection in New Zealand, even though weasels are amongst the country's rarest mammals (King, 1990).

Britain is a signatory to the Bern Convention on the Conservation of European Wildlife and Natural Habitats. This agreement extends limited protection to stoats and weasels under Appendix III, which states that consideration for the status and exploitation of the listed species should be made by the appropriate statutory bodies. Britain's commitment to the Bern Convention was realised principally under the Wildlife and Countryside Act (1981) and its subsequent amendments. This Act regulates the methods applicable to the control of pests in general, but stoats and weasels do not receive particular protection under the species protection sections (Sections V and VI) of this Act and there are no plans to extend the level of protection to these species. Indeed, by giving stoats and weasels protection from trapping and shooting, when the conservation benefits of such protection are not clear, conservationists would lose the principal means of monitoring populations and thereby detecting other potential conservation problems.

Gamekeepers' trapping records have been cited as evidence for declines in stoat and weasel populations in Britain (Harris *et al.*, 1995; Macdonald *et al.*, 1998) and among the potential reasons for such a decline are: scarcity of prey, control by humans, intraguild predation by foxes, and secondary poisoning (Harris *et al.*, 1995). To these suggestions must also be added the possibility that the decline in trapping records is an artefact of reduced trapping effort by gamekeepers (Tapper, 1992; McDonald & Harris, 1999).

McDonald (1998) considered a number of these possibilities by studying stoats and weasels from game estates throughout Great Britain. In the areas sampled, there was no evidence from dietary data for food shortage for either species (McDonald *et al.*, in press). Rabbit abundance is increasing throughout Britain following recovery from myxomatosis (Trout *et al.*, 1986; Tapper, 1992) and stoats appear to be benefiting from this increase in prey availability (McDonald *et al.*, in press). Rabbits are a less important component of weasel diets, but weasels also appear to benefit from the increased availability of rabbits, especially in early spring when the abundance of small rodents is low (McDonald *et al.*, in press). Using a computer population projection model, gamekeeper control efforts were found not to cause a long-term decline in closed weasel populations (McDonald, 1998). Using a similar model, McDonald (1998) found that trapping and shooting had a marginal effect on closed stoat populations, but these effects were not thought to be significant in populations with normal levels of immigration and emigration, agreeing with the earlier conclusions of King & Moors (1979) and Tapper *et al.* (1982). Red foxes appear to be increasing in abundance in Britain (Tapper, 1992; Harris *et al.*, 1995) and there is some evidence that red fox and grey fox, *Urocyon cinereoargenteus*, abundance is inversely related to stoat and weasel abundance in Pennsylvania (Latham, 1952). Mulder (1990) also found that stoats declined dramatically in an area of sand dunes in the Netherlands following the arrival of foxes. Interactions between stoats and weasels and foxes have not been studied in Great Britain, but it seems plausible that increasing fox numbers may have an adverse effect on stoat and weasel populations, either by competition or direct predation.

Secondary exposure of stoats and weasels to anticoagulant rodenticides has recently been found to be commonplace on game estates in eastern and central England (McDonald *et al.*, 1998). In contrast to New Zealand, where the exposure of predators to rodenticides is thought to be the result of eating target species, *i.e.* rats and possums, McDonald *et al.* (1998) believe that non-target species (mainly mice, voles and rabbits) were the principal source of exposure in Britain. The impact of exposure to rodenticides on stoat and weasel populations in Britain is not yet known. If rodenticides affect adult survival then the impact may be limited, but if exposure affects productivity, then the potential impact of widespread rodenticide use may be substantial. Some form of rodenticide was used on 78% of arable farms in Britain in 1996 (De'Ath *et al.*, 1999) and on 91% of game estates in England in 1997 (McDonald & Harris, 2000). Large scale rodenticide applications are known to have an impact on stoat populations in New Zealand (see above). However, there are no confirmed records of fatalities of stoats or weasels caused by rodenticides in Britain, although this may be due to their small size and an inability to locate the carcasses of poisoned animals (McDonald *et al.*, 1998). Further studies are needed in this area to assess the ecological impact of rodenticide usage on non-target species and the conservation implications of any such impact.

The largest component of the decline in the numbers of stoats and weasels taken by gamekeepers since the 1960s is probably changes in the control practices adopted by the gamekeepers themselves. McDonald & Harris (1999) found that numbers of stoats and weasels trapped were closely related to trapping effort. Trapping effort has declined substantially over the last 30 years for the reasons discussed above and this led McDonald & Harris (1999) to conclude that the decline in game-bags is equally consistent with a decline in sampling effort as it is with declining stoat and weasel populations. If this is the case, and this can only be tested through continued sampling of gamekeepers where both game-bags and effort are monitored in detail, then there may be little cause for concern for the conservation status of either species at a national level. McDonald & Harris (1999) did find that weasel bags were particularly low in the south-west of Britain, even when variation in effort was taken into account, and this pattern warrants further investigation.

Conclusion: the future of stoat and weasel management in Great Britain and New Zealand

Policies and practices for the management of stoats and weasels in Britain and New Zealand appear to be developing in quite different directions. The effort being put into controlling stoat and weasel populations in Britain is in general decline and this seems likely to continue. In contrast, the need for the control of stoat predation in New Zealand is becoming increasingly acute and statutory involvement in developing and enacting control measures is set to continue for the foreseeable future.

Even though some British estates maintain an interest in wild game birds, it is highly unlikely that gamekeepers will ever be as numerous as they were at the beginning of the 20th century. In a few cases, gamekeepers themselves are undergoing a change in their traditional role towards that of a more general "wildlife officer". This may be the result of moves by the British government to support agri-environment schemes, by moving grant aid from agricultural production towards conservation. The combined incentives provided by game shooting and such schemes, and the resulting need to retain "in-house personnel" with wildlife expertise, means that for some estates, this new role for gamekeepers may be expanded in the new millennium.

Current levels of trapping and shooting of stoats and weasels in Britain do not appear to present a threat to the conservation of these species. However, the combined effects of control efforts and other potentially limiting factors such as secondary exposure to rodenticides, habitat loss and increasing fox populations require further investigation. Future research on stoat and weasel populations in Great Britain should also look towards optimising control practices so that the maximum reduction of predation is realised for minimum effort and minimum long-term impact on native predators. This aim is clearly desirable on economic, conservation and animal welfare grounds.

This objective is also held in New Zealand, where the government is attempting to conserve endangered species in a cost-effective way. Currently, stoat control in New Zealand relies largely on labour-intensive trapping and high priorities for conservationists in New Zealand are to refine trapping, poisoning and non-lethal techniques. In both Britain and New Zealand a better understanding of the population biology and spatial behaviour of mustelids, and of stoats in particular, would also be highly valuable. This knowledge will facilitate modelling exercises that can help determine when and how often control is needed to protect the relevant species.

Acknowledgements

Robbie McDonald is grateful to The Wingate Foundation and The Dulverton Trust for financial support, to the National Gamekeepers' Organisation for supporting a survey of their members and to Stephen Harris for supervising his PhD research, from which much of the material for this paper was derived. We are grateful to Jonathan Reynolds for providing key references on non-lethal predation control methods, to Lynette Clelland, Rod Hay and two anonymous referees for comments on the manuscript, and to Kay Clapperton, John McLennan, Glen Robson and Geoff Wright for access to unpublished information.

References

Alterio, N. (1996). Secondary poisoning of stoats (*Mustela erminea*), feral ferrets (*Mustela furo*), and feral house cats (*Felis catus*) by the anticoagulant poison brodifacoum. *New Zealand Journal of Zoology*, **23:** 331–338.

Alterio, N., Brown, K. & Moller, H. (1997). Secondary poisoning of mustelids in a New Zealand *Nothofagus* forest. *Journal of Zoology*, **243:** 863–869.

Alterio, N., Moller, H. & Ratz, H. (1998). Movements and habitat use of feral house cats *Felis catus*, stoats *Mustela erminea* and ferrets *Mustela furo*, in grassland surrounding yellow-eyed penguin *Megadyptes antipodes* breeding areas in spring. *Biological Conservation*, **83:** 187–194.

Anon. (1981). *Predator and squirrel control*. Fordingbridge; The Game Conservancy Ltd..

Anon. (1991). *Game bird releasing*. Fordingbridge; The Game Conservancy Ltd.

Anon. (1994). *Biodiversity: the UK Action Plan*. London; Department of the Environment.

Anon. (1998). Pheasant Research. *The Game Conservancy Review*, **29,** 75.

Balharry, E.A. & Macdonald, D.W. (1999). Cost-effective electric fencing for protecting gamebirds against pine marten *Martes martes* predation. *Mammal Review*, **29:** 67–72.

Bateman, J.A. (1971). *Animal traps and trapping*. Newton Abbot; David & Charles.

Bateman, J.A. (1979). *Trapping: a practical guide*. Newton Abbot; David & Charles.

Beaven, B.M. (1998). *Northern Te Urewera Ecosystem Restoration Project*. Gisborne (NZ); Department of Conservation.

Bradfield, P. & Flux, I. (1996). *The Mapara Kokako Project, 1989–1996, a summary report*. Hamilton (NZ); Department of Conservation, Waikato Conservancy.

Brown, K.P., Alterio, N. & Moller, H. (1998). Secondary poisoning of stoats (*Mustela erminea*) at low mouse (*Mus musculus*) abundance in a New Zealand *Nothofagus* forest. *Wildlife Research*, **25:** 419–426.

Butler, D. & McLennan, J. (1991). *Kiwi Recovery Plan* (*Threatened Species Recovery Plan Series No. 2*). Wellington (NZ); Department of Conservation.

Butler, D. (1997). Introduction to the Rotoiti nature recovery project St Arnaud's 'Mainland Island'. In: J. Sim & A. Saunders (eds.), *Predator Workshop, 1997* (*Proceedings of a workshop held 21–24 April, 1997, St. Arnaud, Nelson Lakes*): 7–9. Wellington (NZ); Department of Conservation.

Clapperton, B.K., Phillipson, S.M. & Woolhouse, A.D. (1994). Field trials of slow-release synthetic lures for stoats (*Mustela erminea*) and ferrets (*M. furo*). *New Zealand Journal of Zoology*, **21:** 279–284.

Clout, M. (1997). Predator management in New Zealand: an overview. In: J. Sim & A. Saunders (eds.), *Predator Workshop, 1997* (*Proceedings of a workshop held 21–24 April, 1997, St. Arnaud, Nelson Lakes*): 3–5. Wellington (NZ); Department of Conservation.

Clout, M.N. & Saunders, A.J. (1995). Conservation and ecological restoration in New Zealand. *Pacific Conservation Biology*, **2:** 91–98.

Clout, M.N., Denyer, K., James, R.E. & McFadden, I.G. (1995). Breeding success of New Zealand pigeons (*Hemiphaga novaeseelandiae*) in relation to control of introduced mammals. *New Zealand Journal of Ecology*, **19:** 209–212.

Cowan, P. (1990). Brushtail possum. In: C.M. King (ed.), *The handbook of New Zealand mammals*: 68–98. Auckland (NZ); Oxford University Press.

Crouchley, D. (1994a). *Takahe Recovery Plan* (*Threatened Species Recovery Plan Series No. 12*). Wellington (NZ); Department of Conservation.

Crouchley, D. (1994b). *Stoat control on Maud Island* (*Ecological Management 2*). Wellington (NZ); Department of Conservation, Threatened Species Unit.

Dannenfeldt, K.H. (1982). The control of vertebrate pests in Renaissance agriculture. *Agricultural History*, **56:** 542–559.

Darby, J.T. & Seddon, P.J. (1990). Breeding biology of yellow-eyed penguins (*Megadyptes antipodes*). In: L.S. Davis & J.T. Darby (eds.), *Penguin biology*: 45–62. San Diego (California); Academic Press.

Day, M.G. (1968). Food habits of British stoats (*Mustela erminea*) and weasels (*Mustela nivalis*). *Journal of Zoology*, **155**: 485–497.

De'Ath, A., Garthwaite, D.G. & Thomas, M.R. (1999). *Rodenticide usage on farms in Great Britain growing arable crops 1996 (Pesticide Usage Survey Report 144)*. London; MAFF Publications.

Department of Conservation (1998a). *New Zealand's Biodiversity Strategy: our chance to turn the tide. A draft strategy for public consultation*. Wellington (NZ); Department of Conservation.

Department of Conservation (1998b). *Restoring the dawn chorus. Department of Conservation Strategic Business Plan, 1998–2002*. Wellington (NZ); Department of Conservation.

Dilks, P.J., O'Donnell, C.F.J., Elliott, G.P. & Phillipson, S.M. (1996). The effect of bait type, tunnel design, and trap position on stoat control operations for conservation management. *New Zealand Journal of Zoology*, **23**: 295–306.

Dowding, J.E. & Murphy, E.C. (1996). Predation of northern New Zealand dotterels (*Charadrius obscurus aquilonius*) by stoats. *Notornis*, **43**: 144–46.

Dowding, J.E. (1993). *New Zealand Dotterel Recovery Plan (Threatened Species Recovery Plan Series No. 10)*. Wellington (NZ); Department of Conservation.

Dowding, J.E. (1999). Past distribution and decline of the New Zealand dotterel (*Charadrius obscurus*) in the South Island of New Zealand. *Notornis*, **46**: 167–180.

Dunn, E. (1977). Predation by weasels (*Mustela nivalis*) on breeding tits (*Parus* spp.) in relation to density of tits and rodents. *Journal of Animal Ecology*, **46**: 633–651.

Eason, C.T., Milne, L., Potts, M., Morriss, G., Wright, G.R.G. & Sutherland, O.R.W. (1999). Secondary and tertiary poisoning risks associated with brodifacoum. *New Zealand Journal of Ecology*, **23**: (in press).

Eason, C.T., Frampton, C.M., Henderson, R., Thomas, M.D. & Morgan, D. (1993). Sodium monofluoroacetate and alternative toxins for possum control. *New Zealand Journal of Zoology*, **20**: 329–334.

Elliott, G.P., Dilks, P.J. & O'Donnell, C.F.J. (1996). The ecology of yellow-crowned parakeets (*Cyanoramphus auriceps*) in Nothofagus forest in Fiordland, New Zealand. *New Zealand Journal of Zoology*, **23**: 249–265.

Erlinge, S. & Sandell, M. (1986). Seasonal changes in the social organisation of male stoats *Mustela erminea*: an effect of shifts between two decisive resources. *Oikos*, **47**: 57–62.

Fitzgerald, B.M., Daniel, M.J., Fitzgerald, A.E., Karl, B.J., Meads, M.J. & Notman, P.R. (1996). Factors affecting the numbers of house mice (*Mus musculus*) in hard beech (*Nothofagus truncata*) forest. *Journal of the Royal Society of New Zealand*, **26**: 237–249.

Gillies, C.A. & Pierce, R.J. (1999). Secondary poisoning of mammalian predators during possum and rodent control operations at Trounson Kauri Park, Northland, New Zealand. *New Zealand Journal of Ecology*, **23**: 183–192.

Greenwood R.J. & Arnold P.M. (1990). Protecting duck nests from mammalian predators with fences, traps, and a toxicant. *Wildlife Society Bulletin*, **18**: 75–82.

Harris, S., Morris, P., Wray, S. & Yalden, D. (1995). *A Review of British mammals: population estimates and conservation status of British mammals other than cetaceans*. Peterborough; Joint Nature Conservation Committee.

Henderson, R.J., Frampton, C.M., Thomas, C.D. & Eason, C.T. (1994). Field evaluation of cholecalciferol, gliftor, and brodifacoum for the control of brushtail possums (*Trichosurus vulpecula*). *Proceedings of the 47th New Zealand Plant Protection Conference*: 112–117.

Hill, S. & Hill, J. (1987). *Richard Henry of Resolution Island*. Dunedin (NZ); John McIndoe Ltd.

Hudson, P.J. (1992). *Grouse in space and time*. Fordingbridge; The Game Conservancy Ltd.

Innes, J., Warburton, B., Williams, D., Speed, H., & Bradfield, P. (1995). Large-scale poisoning of ship rats (*Rattus rattus*) in indigenous forests of the North Island, New Zealand. *New Zealand Journal of Ecology*, **19**, 5–17.

King, C.M. (1980a). The weasel (*Mustela nivalis*) and its prey in an English woodland. *Journal of Animal Ecology*, **49**: 127–159.

King, C.M. (1980b). Population biology of the weasel *Mustela nivalis* on British game estates. *Holarctic Ecology*, **3**: 160–168.

King, C.M. (1981). The effects of 2 types of steel traps upon captured stoats (*Mustela erminea*). *Journal of Zoology*, **195**: 553–554.

King, C.M. (1983). The relationships between beech (*Nothofagus* sp.) seedfall and populations of mice (*Mus musculus*) and the demographic and dietary responses of stoats (*Mustela erminea*), in three New Zealand forests. *Journal of Animal Ecology*, **52**: 141–166.

King, C. (1984). *Immigrant killers*. Auckland (NZ); Oxford University Press.

King, C. (1989). *The natural history of weasels and stoats*. London; Christopher Helm.

King, C.M. (Ed.) (1990). *The handbook of New Zealand mammals*. Auckland (NZ); Oxford University Press.

King, C.M. & Edgar, R.L. (1977). Techniques for trapping and tracking stoats (*Mustela erminea*): a review and a new system. *New Zealand Journal of Zoology*, **4**: 193–212.

King, C.M. & Moors, P.J. (1979). The life history tactics of mustelids, and their significance for predator control and conservation in New Zealand. *New Zealand Journal of Zoology*, **6**: 619–622.

King, C.M., Flux, M., Innes, J.G. & Fitzgerald, B.M. (1996). Population biology of small mammals in Pureora Forest Park: 1. Carnivores (*Mustela erminea, M. furo, M. nivalis*, and *Felis catus*). *New Zealand Journal of Ecology*, **20**: 241–251.

Langley, P.J.W. & Yalden, D.W. (1977). The decline of the rarer carnivores in Great Britain during the nineteenth century. *Mammal Review*, **7**: 95–116.

Latham, R.M. (1952). The fox as a factor in the control of weasel populations. *Journal of Wildlife Management*, **16**: 516–517.

Lavers, R.B. & Clapperton, B.K. (1990). Ferret. In: C.M. King (ed.), *The handbook of New Zealand mammals*: 320–330. Auckland (NZ); Oxford University Press.

Lockie, J.D. (1966). Territory in small carnivores. *Symposia of the Zoological Society of London*, **18**: 143–165.

Lokemoen, J.T. & Woodward, R.O. (1993). An assessment of predator barriers and predator control to enhance duck nest success on peninsulas. *Wildlife Society Bulletin*, **21**: 275–282.

Macdonald, D.W., Mace, G. & Rushton, S. (1999). *Proposals for future monitoring of British mammals*. London; Department of the Environment, Transport and the Regions.

Maxwell, J., Torr, S., Leary, H., Coates, G. & Forbes, V. (1997). Predator research in Fiordland trialing stoat control tunnels. In: J. Sim & A. Saunders (eds.), *Predator Workshop, 1997* (*Proceedings of a workshop held 21–24 April, 1997, St. Arnaud, Nelson Lakes*): 69–72. Wellington (NZ); Department of Conservation.

McCleery, R.H. & Perrins, C.M. (1991). Effects on predation on the numbers of Great Tits *Parus Major* In: C.M. Perrins, J.D. Lebreton & G.J.M. Hirons (eds.), *Bird population studies: relevance in conservation and management*: 129–147. Oxford; Oxford University Press.

McCleery, R.H., Clobert, J., Julliard, R. & Perrins, C.M. (1996). Nest predation and delayed cost of reproduction in the great tit. *Journal of Animal Ecology*, **65**: 96–104

McDonald, R.A (1998). The effects of wildlife management on stoats *Mustela erminea* and weasels *Mustela nivalis* in Great Britain. PhD thesis. Bristol; University of Bristol.

McDonald, R. & Harris, S. (1998). *Stoats and weasels*. London; The Mammal Society.

McDonald, R.A & Harris, S. (1999). The use of trapping records to monitor populations of stoats *Mustela erminea* and weasels *M. nivalis*: the importance of trapping effort. *Journal of Applied Ecology*, **36**: 679–688.

McDonald, R.A & Harris, S. (2000). The use of fumigants and anticoagulant rodenticides on game estates in Great Britain. *Mammal Review*, **30**: 57–64.

McDonald, R.A., Harris, S., Turnbull, G., Brown, P. & Fletcher, M. (1998). Anticoagulant rodenticides in stoats (*Mustela erminea*) and weasels (*Mustela nivalis*) in England. *Environmental Pollution*, **103**: 17–23.

McDonald, R.A., Webbon, C. & Harris, S. (in press). The diet of stoats (*Mustela erminea*) and weasels (*Mustela nivalis*) in Great Britain. *Journal of Zoology*.

McKinlay, B. (1997). The likelihood of arrival of stoats on islands. In: J. Sim & A. Saunders (eds.), *Predator Workshop, 1997* (*Proceedings of a workshop held 21–24 April, 1997, St. Arnaud, Nelson Lakes*): 51–53. Wellington (NZ); Department of Conservation.

McLennan, J.A., Potter, M.A., Robertson, H.A., Wake, G.C., Colbourne, R., Dew, L., Joyce, L., McCann, A.J., Miles, J., Miller, P.J. & Reid, J. (1996). Role of predation in the decline of kiwi, *Apteryx* spp., in New Zealand. *New Zealand Journal of Ecology*, **20**: 27–35.

Middleton, A.D. (1934). Periodic fluctuations in British game populations. *Journal of Animal Ecology*, **3**: 231–249.

Middleton, A.D. (1967). Predatory mammals and the conservation of game in Great Britain. *Annual Report of the Game Research Association*, **6**: 14–21.

Miskelly, C.M. (1997). Whitaker's skink *Cyclodina whitakeri* eaten by a weasel *Mustela nivalis* (Conservation Advisory Science Notes: 146). Wellington (NZ); Department of Conservation.

Mitchell-Jones, A.J. (1996). *Mammals in England. A conservation action priority list (English Nature Science No. 26)*. Peterborough; English Nature.

Moller, H., Ratz, H. & Alterio, N. (1995). *Protection of yellow-eyed penguins from predators (Wildlife Management Report No. 65)*. Dunedin (NZ); University of Otago.

Moorhouse, R.J. & Greene, T.C. (1998). *Research Plan for Kaka (Nestor meridionalis), 1996–2002*. Wellington (NZ); Department of Conservation.

Moors, P.J. (1983). Predation by mustelids and rodents on the eggs and chicks of native and introduced birds in Kowhai Bush, New Zealand. *Ibis*, **125**: 137–154.

Morris, C.J. & Birks, J.D.S. (1997). Preliminary monitoring work on stoats and weasels. In: *The Vincent Wildlife Trust Review of 1996*: 39–41. London; The Vincent Wildlife Trust.

Morris, P.A. (1993). *A Red Data Book for British mammals*. London; The Mammal Society.

Mulder, J.L. (1990). The stoat *Mustela erminea* in the Dutch dune region its local extinction and a possible cause: the arrival of the fox *Vulpes vulpes*. *Lutra*, **33**: 1–21.

Murphy, E. & Bradfield, P. (1992). Changes in diet of stoats following poisoning of rats in a New Zealand forest. *New Zealand Journal of Ecology*, **16**: 137–140.

Murphy, E.C. & Dowding, J.E. (1995). Ecology of the stoat in *Nothofagus* forest: Home range, habitat use and diet at different stages of the beech mast cycle. *New Zealand Journal of Ecology*, **19**: 97–109.

Murphy, E.C., Clapperton, B.K., Bradfield, P.M.F. & Speed, H.J. (1998a). Effects of rat-poisoning operations on abundance and diet of mustelids in New Zealand forests. *New Zealand Journal of Zoology*, **25**: 315–328.

Murphy, E.C., Clapperton, B.K., Bradfield, P.M.F. & Speed, H.J. (1998b). Brodifacoum residues in target and non-target animals following large-scale poison operations in New Zealand podocarp-hardwood forests. *New Zealand Journal of Zoology*, **25**: 307–314.

Murphy, E.C., Robbins, L., Young, J.B. & Dowding, J.E. (1999). Secondary poisoning of stoats after an aerial 1080 poison operation in Pureora Forest, New Zealand. *New Zealand Journal of Ecology*, **23**: 175–182.

Nyholm, E.S. (1959). Stoats and weasels and their winter habitats. In: C.M. King (ed.), *Biology of mustelids: some Soviet research* (English ed. 1975): 118–131. Boston Spa; British Library.

O'Donnell, C.F.J. & Phillipson, S.M. (1996). Predicting the incidence of mohua predation from the seedfall, mouse and predator fluctuations in beech forests. *New Zealand Journal of Zoology*, **23**: 287–293.

O'Donnell, C.F.J. (1993). *Mohua (yellowhead) Recovery Plan (Threatened Species Recovery Plan Series No. 6)*. Wellington (NZ); Department of Conservation.

O'Donnell, C.F.J., Dilks, P.J. & Elliott, G.P. (1996). Control of a stoat (*Mustela erminea*) population irruption to enhance mohua (yellowhead) (*Mohoua ochrocephala*) breeding success in New Zealand. *New Zealand Journal of Zoology*, **23**: 279–286.

Peters, D. (1997). Kiwi research at Waikaremoana. In: J. Sim & A. Saunders (eds.), *Predator Workshop, 1997 (Proceedings of a workshop held 21–24 April, 1997 St. Arnaud, Nelson, Lakes)*: 15–17. Wellington (NZ); Department of Conservation.

Pierce, R. (1997). Kiwi research by management in Northland. In: J. Sim & A. Saunders (eds.), *Predator Workshop, 1997 (Proceedings of a workshop held 21–24 April, 1997 St. Arnaud, Nelson, Lakes)*: 11–14. Wellington (NZ); Department of Conservation.

Potts, G.R. & Vickerman, G.P. (1974). Studies on the cereal ecosystem. *Advances in Ecological Research*, **8**: 107–197.

Potts, G.R. (1980). The effects of modern agriculture, nest predation and game management on the population ecology of partridges *Perdix perdix* and *Alectoris rufa*. *Advances in Ecological Research*, **11**: 2–79.

Potts, G.R. (1986). *The partridge, pesticides, predation and conservation*. London; Collins Professional & Technical Books.

Reynolds, J.C. & Tapper, S.C. (1996). Control of mammalian predators in game management and conservation. *Mammal Review*, **26**: 127–156.

Robertson, H.A., Colbourne, R.M., Graham, P.J., Miller, P.J. & Pierce, R.J. (1999). Survival of brown kiwi (*Apteryx mantelli*) exposed to brodifacoum poison in Northland, New Zealand. *New Zealand Journal of Ecology*, **23**: 225–231

Robson, G. (1998). The breeding ecology of curlew *Numenius arquata* on north Pennine moorland. PhD thesis. Sunderland; University of Sunderland.

Rusiniak, K.W., Gustavson, C.R., Hankins, W.G. & Garcia, J. (1976). Prey-lithium aversions II: laboratory rats and ferrets. *Behavioural Biology*, **17:** 73–85.

Saunders, A. (1999). *Mainland islands – a review*. Wellington (NZ); Department of Conservation.

Speed, H.J. & Bancroft, F.J. (1997). *Waipapa Restoration Project October 1995–May 1996*. Hamilton (NZ); Department of Conservation, Waikato Conservancy.

Spurr, E.B. (1997). *Assessment of the effectiveness of Transonic™ ESP and Yard Guard™ ultrasonic devices for repelling stoats* (*Mustela erminea*) (*Conservation Advisory Science Notes: 151*). Wellington (NZ); Department of Conservation.

Spurr, E.B. & Hough, S.J. (1997). *Instructions for using poisoned hen eggs for control of stoats* (*Mustela erminea*) (*Conservation Advisory Science Notes: 156*). Wellington (NZ); Department of Conservation.

Spurr, E.B. (1998). *The development of a long-life toxic bait and lures for mustelids* (*Landcare Research Contract Report: LC9899/26*). Wellington (NZ); Department of Conservation.

Tapper, S.C. (1976). The diet of weasels, *Mustela nivalis* and stoats, *Mustela erminea* during early summer, in relation to predation on gamebirds. *Journal of Zoology*, **179:** 219–224.

Tapper, S. (1979). The effect of fluctuating vole numbers (*Microtus agrestis*) on a population of weasels (*Mustela nivalis*) on farmland. *Journal of Animal Ecology*, **48:** 603–617.

Tapper, S. (1982). Using estate records to monitor population trends in game and predator species, particularly weasels and stoats. *Proceedings of the International Congress of Game Biologists*, **14:** 115–120.

Tapper, S. (1992). *Game heritage. An ecological review from shooting and gamekeeping records*. Fordingbridge; The Game Conservancy Ltd.

Tapper, S.C., Green, R.E. & Rands, M.R.W. (1982). Effects of mammalian predators on partridge populations. *Mammal Review*, **12:** 159–167.

Tapper, S.C., Potts, G.R. & Brockless, M.H. (1996). The effect of an experimental reduction in predation pressure on the breeding success and population density of grey partridges *Perdix perdix*. *Journal of Applied Ecology*, **33:** 965–978.

Taylor, R.H. & Tilley, J.A.V. (1984). Stoats (*Mustela erminea*) on Adele and Fisherman Islands, Abel Tasman National Park and other offshore islands in New Zealand. *New Zealand Journal of Ecology*, **7:** 139–145.

Trout, R.C., Tapper, S.C. & Harradine, J. (1986). Recent trends in the rabbit population in Britain. *Mammal Review*, **16:** 117–123.

Wardle, J.A. (1984). *The New Zealand beeches: ecology, utilization and management*. Wellington (NZ); New Zealand Forest Service.

Wilson, P.R., Karl, B.J., Toft, R.J., Beggs, J.R. & Taylor, R.H. (1998). The role of introduced predators and competitors in the decline of kaka (*Nestor meridionalis*) populations in New Zealand. *Biological Conservation*, **83:** 175–185.

Wodzicki, K.A. (1950). *Introduced mammals of New Zealand* (*DSIR Bulletin No. 98*). Wellington (NZ); Department of Scientific and Industrial Research.

CHAPTER 3

The conservation status of New World mustelids

Steven W. Buskirk

Abstract

New World mustelids, reviewed in this chapter, are a moderately speciose, endemic and secure group of species, placed in the context of Carnivora. The family comprises 30 species: the skunks, weasels, otters, marten, fisher, tayra, grison, wolverine, and American badger. Several forms are, by various accounts, siblings or subspecies of holarctic species that have exchanged genes across the Bering Land Bridge during the Quaternary. Others are in monotypic genera restricted to the Americas. Virtually all New World mustelids have been affected, mostly negatively, by human actions, including trapping, timber cutting, agriculture and pollution. One plausible species, the sea mink, is extinct, the black-footed ferret is critically endangered, several species (American marten, fisher, North American river otter, sea otter, wolverine) are threatened or absent over substantive parts of their presettlement geographic ranges, and a few species (striped skunks, American badgers, some weasels) are apparently unaffected or benefited by human actions. I describe the status, trends in distribution and apparent threats to selected species, representing a range of habitats occupied and apparent threats faced. Trapping and hunting generally are under control as threats to nearctic species, but continue as threats to neotropical forms. Broad-scale clearcutting has virtually ceased at north temperate latitudes but continues farther north, potentially affecting martens, fishers, wolverines and river otters. Pollution in general, and water pollution in particular is thought to limit the distribution of various freshwater otter species. Changes in community structure are emerging as threats to various species. These changes include increases in predators of some mustelids, illustrated by killer whales killing sea otters, and increases in generalist competitors, such as coyotes, which affect terrestrial species in ways we are just beginning to understand.

Introduction

The mustelids of the New World comprise a moderately speciose and endemic group that is intermediate, among the Carnivora, in its conservation security. Thirty species (Table 1) are recognised by Wilson & Reeder (1993); others have been described (e.g. sea mink, *Mustela macrodon* [Hall, 1981]; western spotted skunk, *Spilogale gracilis* [Jones *et al.*, 1997]), but have been "clumped" into other species by other taxonomists and are treated here as issues at the subspecific level. The nine skunks (Subfamily Mephitinae) were proposed as members of a separate family, Mephitidae, by Dragoo & Honeycutt (1997), a distinction that may soon be accepted. If so, the exclusion of the skunks, a relatively secure group, would alter our perception of the status of the remaining Mustelidae considerably for the worse. Of the remaining 21 New World mustelids, ten are listed on a CITES appendix, at least

Mustelids in a modern world
Management and conservation aspects of small carnivore: human interactions
edited by Huw I. Griffiths, pp. 41–52
© *2000 Backhuys Publishers, Leiden, The Netherlands*

over a part of their range, a similar proportion to that for Old World mustelids. Considered world-wide, mustelids are intermediate in their conservation status between the relatively secure canids and the more threatened felids (Fig. 1).

Virtually all New World mustelids have been affected by the actions of humans at local or regional levels. Historically (1600 - 1900), the harvest of mustelid furs was a major geopolitical force in temperate and boreal North America, and led to the scarcity of various species, notably the sea otter, *Enhydra lutris*, of the North Pacific rim, which neared extinction in the early 20th century.

Table 1. Mustelids (Wilson & Reeder, 1993) of the New World. CITES appendices are from Wilson & Reeder (1993), IUCN listings are from IUCN (1996).

Name	Distribution	Old World	CITES Append.	IUCN
Mustela africana	n. South America (S.A.)			DD
M. erminea	n. North America (N.A.)	Present		
M. felipei	n S.A.			T
M. frenata	Temp. N.A to n. S.A.			
M. nigripes	Temp. N.A.	sibling: *M. eversmanni*	I	
M. nivalis	n. N.A.	present		
M. vison	Temp. and n. N.A.			
Martes americana	n. N.A.	siblings: *M. zibellina* and *M. melampus*		
M. pennanti	n. N.A.			
Eira barbara	s. N.A. to S.A.		III (Honduras)	SP
Galictis cuja	S.A.			
G. vittata	s. N.A. to S.A.		III (Costa Rica)	
Lyncodon patagonicus	S.A. grasslands			
Gulo gulo	n.N.A.	Present		T
Taxidea taxus	Temp. N.A.			
Mephitis macroura	s. N.A.			
M. mephitis	Temp. N.A.			
Spilogale putorius	s. N.A.			
S. pygmaea	s. N.A.			
Conepatus chinga	S.A.			
C. humboldtii	S.A.		II	
C. leuconotus	s. N.A.			
C. mesoleucus	s. N.A.			SP
C. semistriatus	s. N.A., n. S.A.			
Lontra canadensis	Temp. and n. N.A.		II	
L. felina	w. S.A.		I	
L. longicaudis	s. N.A. to S.A.		I	
L. provocax	S.A.		I	
Pteronura brasiliensis	S.A.		I	
Enhydra lutris	Nw. N.A.	Present	I	

DD = data deficient
T = threatened
Mustela felipei (Colombia, Ecuador)
Gulo gulo (Canada, U.S.A.)
SP = subspecies or population threatened

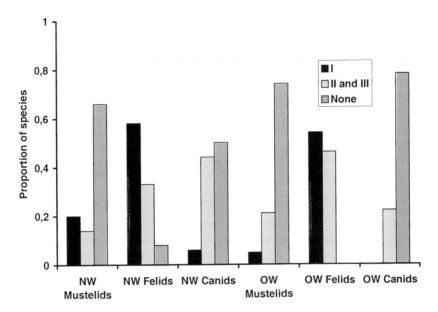

Fig. 1. The distribution of New World and Old World mustelids, felids, and canids in CITES appendices (I, II, III, and not listed). A species must be listed over most of its geographic range to be included in the listed category. The status of mustelids is similar between the New World and Old World, with about 30% of species being listed on a CITES appendix. Mustelids are intermediate between canids and felids in their conservation status.

Likewise, trapping reduced the distribution of the American marten, *Martes americana*, and the fisher, *Martes pennanti*. Much later, the giant otter, *Pteronura brasiliensis*, was severely overhunted in South America, which eradicated the species from the southern part of its range (Carter & Rosas, 1997). Even today, trapping for fur harvest accounts for the majority of total mortality for some mustelid populations, 90% for American martens in one area of northern Maine in the early 1990s (Hodgman *et al.*, 1994).

Settlement and development, including agriculture, reduced the abundance of various mustelids, including the black-footed ferret, *Mustela nigripes* (Vargas *et al.*, this volume) and wolverine, *Gulo gulo* (Banci, 1994), and increased that of others. Retrogressional changes in forests have changed the distribution and abundance of some forest species, particularly the American marten (Thompson, 1991; Kucera *et al.*, 1995) and fisher (Gibilisco, 1994) in the north-central and western U.S. The American badger, *Taxidea taxus*, is among the few nearctic mustelids to occupy a larger range now than in pre-settlement times (Lindzey, 1982).

New World otters pose a particular conservation challenge, as reflected by the listing of all six species on CITES appendices, five on Appendix I. This is partly due to the connectivity of aquatic systems; pollution, including mine-generated silt and metals can affect rivers many miles downstream from the discharge. Similarly, rivers are conduits for people seeking to harvest otters for their furs. In some respects, the inherently high connectivity of rivers is a liability in the conservation of otters in riverine systems, where water-borne pollutants and fur hunters travel long distances easily. Together, mustelids of the New World represent a full range of conservation conditions, including relative security, those once reduced or endangered but now recovered, and those now in peril to varying degrees and from various factors.

This assessment of the conservation status of New World mustelids must consider the taxonomic unit of concern. If regarded as a single holarctic species and if the species is the scale of analysis, the wolverine must be regarded as highly secure, with a vast boreal and arctic range in the New and Old Worlds. By contrast, if one considers only distributional losses for the nearctic wolverine, effects seem more severe: the wolverine has been eradicated from its southern range, including the Sierra Nevada Mountains of California (Banci, 1994), the southern Rocky Mountains, and possibly Vancouver Island (Banci, 1994). The possible loss of the species from Vancouver Island would represent the extinction of a generally recognised subspecies, *Gulo gulo vancouverensis* (Hall, 1981), for reasons that are not understood.

Of the 30 New World Mustelids, six (short-tailed weasel – stoat [both *Mustela erminea*], American marten – sable [*Martes zibellina*], black-footed ferret – steppe polecat [*Mustela eversmannii*], least weasel - weasel [both *Mustela nivalis*], wolverine, and sea otter) are native to the Old World either as single or sibling species. Indeed, these six species, except for the sea otter, represent truly holarctic taxa with broad distributions across the Northern Hemisphere (Corbet, 1978). These similarities are reflections of past genetic exchange via the Bering Land Bridge, either by land or sea, during the Quaternary and plausibly more recently for sea otters. Still, most of the New World mustelids, particularly neotropical species, are endemic. Their conservation therefore is a regional problem with global significance.

Conserving New World mustelids is a problem confounded by several factors. First, mustelids tend to be habitat specialists and vulnerable to habitat change. Other carnivores, e.g. Canidae and Ursidae, include some habitat generalists able to shift from grassland to forest to tundra, and relatively indifferent to successional stage. Second, mustelids tend to be rare, even considering their high trophic levels. Martens, for example, have population densities about one tenth that expected for a carnivore of their size (Buskirk & Ruggiero, 1994). Third, even considering their rarity, mustelids tend to be highly cryptic and difficult to monitor at the population level (Zielinski & Kucera, 1995). As a result, our information about the distribution and abundance of many species is very incomplete, so that arguing for their rarity is difficult. Fourth, some skunks excepted, New World mustelids tend not to become commensal with humans. Some skunks eat human waste and agricultural products, and various mustelids kill small domestic animals, but mustelids cause little damage to human enterprise, compared to the bear, cat and dog families. So, conflicts with humans tend to be few, but mustelids other than skunks tend not to benefit, at the population level, from human enterprise.

Species-specific problems

North American river otter

The North American river otter, *Lontra canadensis*, has undergone drastic range reductions in the temperate part of its range (Fig. 2). In the contiguous United

States, the original range of the otter was reduced by 43% by the early 1900s, including the almost complete loss of the range of subspecies *Lontra canadensis sonora*. The reasons for the loss of river otters from the Southwest include trapping and water development. Weber (1968) described the near-extinction of river otters by overtrapping in the Rio Grande by 1838, which led to prohibitions on trapping. Records of otters in the Southwest are almost entirely restricted to a few major rivers (Hoffmeister, 1986). Impoundments and modifications to instream flow, which are widespread along these rivers, probably contributed to losses as well. Continent-wide, the reduction in the distribution of otters, most noticeable in low elevation areas dominated by agriculture (Toweill & Tabor, 1982), has been attributed to overtrapping incidental to that of beavers, *Castor canadensis*, impoundment of rivers and simplification of shoreline habitat structure and water pollution. As in Europe (Macdonald & Mason, 1983), contamination of water and bioaccumulation of metals in aquatic animals is suspected of having caused declines in various piscivorous vertebrates, including river otters (Mowbray *et al.*, 1979; Szumski, 1988).

Fig. 2. The area from which the North American river otter (*Lontra canadensis*) was extirpated, shown with its pre-settlement distribution (based on Manville & Young 1965; Toweill & Tabor, 1982; Melquist & Dronkert 1987). Local populations have been established in many states by transplantation.

In spite of these problems, river otters appear to be expanding their ranges in some areas, especially as a result of translocations. Reintroductions to and translocations within various states (e.g. Indiana, Nebraska, Colorado, New York, Pennsylvania) have produced many local populations the status of which is poorly understood. Otters enjoy high public appeal and support for their conservation as a result of their endearing appearance, but recovery of lost range may be difficult and slow because of the sensitivity of otters to aquatic and shoreline environments. Twenty-nine of the United States and all Canadian provinces currently allow harvest of otters (Novak *et al.*, 1987).

American marten

One of the most habitat-specialised mammals in North America, this species is restricted to conifer-dominated forests and habitats, including deciduous forest and non-forest, nearby. Martens attain their highest abundances in coniferous forests with complex physical structure near the ground (Buskirk & Powell, 1994), which in drier regions like western North America, tends to be limited to late-successional stands. In a few areas of eastern North America, particularly Maine, martens attain high densities in insect-killed mid-successional stages; a similar pattern is found in post-fire seres in the taiga. The species receded in the face of land conversion to agriculture in the north-central states and New England, but has recovered in both these areas as a result of afforestation (Buskirk & Ruggiero, 1994). The subspecies along the north coast of California (Humboldt marten, *Martes americana humboldtensis*) apparently became extinct during the last 50 years (Kucera *et al.*, 1995), likely as a result of timber harvest. Insular populations, on montane (Buskirk & Ruggiero, 1994) and oceanic islands (Gibilisco, 1994) also are foci of conservation concern, with the Newfoundland Island (*Martes americana atrata*) population (estimated N = 150) forecast to become extinct within 50 years (Thompson, 1991). This subspecies is endangered as a result of overtrapping, timber harvest, and a depauperate island prey base (Schneider, 1997). Management of forests for martens, which are assumed to be closely associated with old-growth coniferous forests, is an issue throughout the western contiguous United States (Macfarlane, 1994), south-east Alaska (US Dept. Agriculture Forest Service, unpubl. report) and the eastern Canadian Provinces (Thompson, 1991). In Maine, landscape-scale effects of forest cutting on martens are becoming apparent (Chapin *et al.*, 1998). Trapping of martens is banned in southern New England, California, New Mexico, Utah and, recently, Colorado. Although the species is secure in most areas of its original range, public interest in the species is low, likely because of its small body size and obscurity.

Sea mink

This taxon of uncertain rank (e.g. *Mustela macrodon* [Hall, 1981], *M. vison macrodon* [Manville, 1966]) was described (Prentiss, 1903) after or around the time of its extinction, between 1860 and 1920 (Black *et al.*, 1998). It is known only from skeletal fragments found in archaeological midden sites, particularly shell heaps, along the east coast from near Cape Cod to the western Bay of Fundy. Considering that these two points are separated by a straight-line distance of <480 km and the coastline is by definition narrow, the range must have been very small since

European colonisation. Most specimens are from archaeological sites in Maine, thought to be the source for bones found farther north, and possibly farther south (Black *et al.*, 1998). The sea mink is variously described as 1.2 - 2 times that of other minks from eastern North America, and as having coarser fur, redder in colour, than other American minks. The scant natural history of the taxon is derived from oral history and suggests that it occurred in coastal habitats (Anderson, 1946), where its flesh was eaten by aboriginal peoples - hence the appearance of bones in shell middens. In the 19th century, its fur apparently was valued more highly than that of other American mink and a higher price paid, which may have sped its extirpation. Lacking more detailed knowledge, some have speculated that the sea mink became extinct because of human exploitation over a restricted range. Further, its high endemism may have reflected limited coastline habitats during the Pleistocene, because late Wisconsinan glaciers extended to tidewater. Thus, the sea mink likely was the first mustelid aided to extinction in the New World by European descendants.

Spotted skunk

This species of small skunk illustrates the strongly commensal relationships with humans, of which a few mustelids are capable. Small-scale farming is credited with facilitating the expansion of spotted skunks, *Spilogale putorius*, northward into Minnesota and Iowa in the early part of the 20th century (Boppel & Long, 1994). By 1946, over 19,000 spotted skunks were harvested, mostly by trap, from Minnesota yearly. With the decline of small-scale farming over the next 50 years, however, this pattern was reversed. By 1992, only 11 spotted skunks were taken from that state (Boppel & Long, 1994). This species likewise has become rare or threatened in other Midwestern states, including Missouri, Oklahoma, Kansas and Nebraska, presumably a result of the decline of small farms.

Giant otter

The giant otter is considered the most threatened otter species in the world by the Otter Specialist Group of IUCN (Carter & Rosas, 1997). A large-bodied, diurnal occupant of rivers with low suspended solids, this species once occupied most riverine habitats of South America. Today its distribution is restricted to a few sites within each region. The causes of its decline are reviewed by Chehébar (1990) and Carter & Rosas (1997) and include hunting for fur, water pollution, and impoundment of rivers, usually for power generation. Increased hunting pressure has accompanied expansions of the road systems of formerly pristine areas. Water pollution tends to result from agriculture and industry, especially gold mining. This latter activity tends to release large volumes of sediment into rivers, reducing their value to giant otters. Further, as for the North American river otter, mining releases metals that bioaccumulate in piscivores. Because of the rapid development of South America and weak regulatory infrastructure, measures to protect remaining giant otter populations have met with little success, and the prognosis for the species is poor.

Sea otter

Once endangered in the eastern Pacific Ocean (population size likely <2,000 [Murie, 1959; Ralls *et al.*, 1983]), this otter has recovered to a level (estimated North American population: 100,000 - 150,000 [Gorbics *et al.*, 1998]) that now permits harvests (about 1,300 in 1993) from several areas of Alaska. The role of sea otters as keystone species in nearshore communities is the most dramatic case for functional importance for any mustelid, resembling the trophic cascade model that has been described for other aquatic systems (Brett & Goldman, 1996). Recent reports (Estes *et al.*, 1998) of predation on sea otters by killer whales, *Orcinas orca*, which has nearly decimated the populations of some Aleutian Islands, reminds us that "top predator" is a context-specific term, and that trophic cascades can be reversed or altered by adding or removing participants. Sea otters also are considered highly vulnerable to oil spills (Ralls *et al.*, 1983), as shown by the Exxon Valdez spill in Prince William Sound of Alaska in 1989 (Garshelis, 1997), although a single spill capable of endangering the species is not plausible. Public interest in the species is high, with several regional organisations focused on its well-being.

Challenges to mustelids

Mustelids of the New World will face challenges of widely varying kind and severity in the 21st century. The conservation situation in the Western Hemisphere resembles that in the east in that the most serious human population growth, poverty, non-sustainable development and poor conservation practices correspond with the centres of highest biodiversity. Not coincidentally, lack of opportunities for women and political instability tend to be worst in these same areas. Human populations in temperate areas of North and South America (e.g. Canada, United States, Chile, Argentina) are growing slightly or moderately. By contrast, tropical and subtropical countries (e.g. Mexico, Colombia, Venezuela) exhibit faster population growth, and a few countries with small land areas but high biotic diversity (e.g. Guatemala, Nicaragua), are growing most rapidly of all (World Resources Institute, unpubl.). Of course, exceptions to these patterns, notably Costa Rica, are apparent. But in contrast to the Old World, the area of subtropical habitat is more limited, especially in the isthmus of Central America. Here, the conservation drama is being played out on a small stage indeed. We have few chances to correct and prevent problems before species are ecologically irrelevant or extinct.

In the United States and Canada, forestry practices have been implicated in a range of vertebrate conservation issues (Hunter, 1990). A number of reforms have been implemented at temperate latitudes, but large-scale clear-cutting is still common at boreal latitudes, and along the north-west coast, where timber values are exceptionally high. Agriculture occupies large areas of temperate and subtropical land, and has had corresponding effects on mustelids. About 20% of the area of the United States is in crop agriculture (Allen, 1995). However, major changes in the agriculture industry in the last 50 years have affected land use patterns and wildlife habitat. These include the decline of small farms in many areas (McDonald & Coffman, 1980), with the consolidation of some farms into larger ones (Allen,

1995), and the reversion of others to pre-settlement cover types (e.g. Litvaitis, 1993). In most areas, agricultural land use is larger-scale, emphasising monocultures, leaving less area in untilled borders and using more chemicals than 80 years ago (Allen, 1995). As an example of the latter, use of nitrogen fertiliser increased from about 200 million metric tons in 1940 to over 30 times that in 1970 (Allen, 1995). This has increased water pollution from non-point sources, affecting food chains that terminate in otters, mink and other piscivorous vertebrates (Szumski, 1998). On the other hand, point-source water pollution in the U.S. and Canada has decreased sharply since 1970 (Hesselberg & Gannon, 1995), reflecting strict regulation.

Another major trend in land use in North America is to construct primary or vacation residences in wildlands - areas little altered by humans. This has occurred at the same time as a broad human migration from farms and towns to cities. Such developments affect a wide range of vertebrates, including migratory species, for example wolverines, that are behaviourally sensitive to human presence (Knight *et al.*, in press). A related change is that in successional stages of fire-prone forests and shrublands of North America as a result of altered fire regimes (mostly reduced fire frequency) since the early 1900s. This has increased stem densities, altered stand structure, and raised fuel loads in many forests and shrublands, affecting fire intensity and habitat management (Ferry *et al.*, 1995). The effects of stands from which fire has been excluded, and of more intense, less frequent fires on mustelids are hard to predict, and are likely to be species-specific.

A factor, not sufficiently appreciated in my view, that affects mustelids is the expansion in ranges and growth in numbers of generalist terrestrial predators, including the coyote, *Canis latrans*, red fox, *Vulpes vulpes*, cougar, *Felis concolor*, great-horned owl, *Bubo virginianus*, and raccoon, *Procyon lotor*. Generalist predators tend to tolerate if not benefit from humans, have wide habitat niches and switch prey readily. These species tend to dominate the carnivore fauna in moderately to highly fragmented landscapes, sometimes even occurring in urban areas (Atkinson & Shackleton, 1991). In wildlands, some species concentrate their activities near edges, and collectively they have been implicated in declines or high mortality rates of various species of conservation concern (see reviews by Goodrich & Buskirk, (1995) and Buskirk *et al.* (in press)).

Conclusion

Mustelids in the New World represent a morphologically and ecologically diverse group that varies greatly in its conservation security. They include species that are critically endangered (black-footed ferret), endangered but still present over wide areas (giant otter), widespread and apparently stable (most species), formerly in peril but now secure (sea otter), and formerly extensive because of human actions, but now returning to presumed pre-settlement abundance (spotted skunk). Several subspecies apparently have become extinct in recent times, and several more are threatened. Clearly, the highest priorities for conservation action are the black-footed ferret and the various otters, especially the neotropical forms. In the case of the former, the key issues in conservation are protection of its primary prey, prairie dogs, and presumed limited ability to respond to changing environments, after the severe population bottleneck of the 1980s. The importance of subspecies to the survival of mustelid species is hard to assess. However, we must consider that subspecies are likely reservoirs of ecotypic variation, which is inherently adaptive (Krebs *et al.*, in press). The extinction of subspecies probably has, and will continue to reduce the range of environmental tolerances of mustelid species at a time of rapid global climate change, and could prove critical to species survival. For neotropical otters, the issue of species survival is complex and widespread, involving regulatory infrastructure, water development, pollution abatement and possible *ex situ* measures over the vast South American continent. This complexity does not mean intractability, however. It requires us to consider and determine how the aquatic resources of Latin America can be planned and managed to preserve some of the most sensitive elements of the neotropical aquatic systems.

References

Allen, A.W. (1995). Agricultural ecosystems. In: E.T. LaRoe, G.S. Farris, C.E. Puckett, P.D. Doran & M.J. Mac (eds.), *Our living resources*: 423-426. Washington (DC); US Department of the Interior National Biological Service.

Anderson, R.M. (1946). *Catalogue of Canadian Recent mammals (National Museum of Canada, Bulletin No. 102, Biological Series No. 31)*. Toronto (Ontario); National Museum of Canada.

Atkinson, K.T. & Shackleton, D.M. (1991). Coyote, *Canis latrans*, ecology in a rural-urban environment. *Canadian Field-Naturalist*, **105:** 49-54.

Banci, V. (1994). Wolverine. In: L.F. Ruggiero, K.B. Aubry, S.W. Buskirk, L.J. Lyon & W.J. Zielinski (eds.), *The scientific basis for conserving forest carnivores, American marten, fisher, lynx and wolverine in the western United States (US Department of Agriculture Forest Service General Technical Report RM-254)*: 99-127.

Black, D.W., Reading, J.E. & Savage, H.G. (1998). Archaeological records of the extinct sea mink, *Mustela macrodon* (Carnivora: Mustelidae), from Canada. *Canadian Field-Naturalist*, **112:** 45-49.

Boppel, P.J. & Long, C.A. (1994). Status of the spotted skunk (*Spilogale putorius*) in its northeastern range, north-central United States. *Small Carnivore Conservation*, **11:** 11-12.

Brett, M.T. & Goldman, C.R. (1996). A meta-analysis of the freshwater trophic cascade. *Proceedings of the National Academy of Sciences of the USA*, **93:** 7723-7726.

Buskirk, S.W., Romme, W.H., Smith, F.W. & Knight, R.L. (in press). An overview of forest fragmentation in the central Rocky Mountains. In: R.L. Knight, F.W. Smith, S.W. Buskirk, W.H. Romme & W.L. Baker (eds.), *Forest fragmentation in the central Rocky Mountains*. Boulder (Colorado); University Press of Colorado.

Buskirk, S.W. & Powell, R.A. (1994). Habitat ecology of fishers and American martens in North America. In: S.W. Buskirk, A.S. Harestad, M.G. Raphael & R.A. Powell (eds.), *Martens, sables, and fishers: biology and conservation*: 283-296. Ithaca (NY); Cornell University Press.

Buskirk, S.W. & Ruggiero, L.F. (1994). Marten. In: L.F. Ruggiero, K.B. Aubry, S.W. Buskirk, L.J. Lyon & W.J. Zielinski (eds.), *The scientific basis for conserving forest carnivores, American marten, fisher, lynx and wolverine in the western United States (US Department of Agriculture Forest Service General Technical Report RM-254)*: 7-37.

Carter, S.K. & Rosas, F.C.W. (1997). Biology and conservation of the giant otter *Pteronura brasiliensis*. *Mammal Review*, **27:**1-26.

Chapin, T.G, Harrison, D.J. & Katnik, D.D. (1998). Influence of landscape pattern on habitat use by American marten in an industrial forest. *Conservation Biology*, **12:** 1327-1337.

Chehébar, C. (1990). Action Plan for Latin American otters. In: P. Foster-Turley, S. Macdonald & C. Mason (eds.), *Otters: an Action Plan for their conservation*: 64-73. Gland; IUCN.

Chilelli, M.E., Griffith, B. & Harrison, D.J. (1996). Interstate comparisons of river otter harvest data. *Wildlife Society Bulletin*, **24:** 238-246.

Corbet, G.B. (1978). *The mammals of the Palaearctic Region: a taxonomic review*. Ithaca (NY); Cornell University Press.

Dragoo, J.W. & Honeycutt, R.L. (1997). Systematics of mustelid-like carnivores. *Journal of Mammalogy*, **78**: 426-443.

Estes, J.A., Tinker, M.T., Williams, T.M. & Doak, D.F. (1998). Killer whale predation on sea otters linking oceanic and nearshore ecosystems. *Science*, **282**: 473-476.

Ferry, G.W., Clark, R.G., Montgomery, R.E., Mutch, R.W., Leenhouts, W.P. & Zimmerman, G.T. (1995). Altered fire regimes within fire adapted ecosystems. In: E.T. LaRoe, G.S. Farris, C.E. Puckett, P.D. Doran & M.J. Mac (eds.), *Our living resources*: 222-223. Washington (DC); US Department of the Interior National Biological Service.

Garshelis, D. (1997). Sea otter mortality estimated from carcasses collected after the Exxon Valdez oil spill. *Conservation Biology*, **11**: 905-916.

Gibilisco, C.J. (1994). Distributional dynamics of Modern *Martes* in North America. In: S.W. Buskirk, A.S. Harestad, M.G. Raphael & R.A. Powell (eds.), *Martens, sables, and fishers: biology and conservation*: 59-71. Ithaca (NY); Cornell University Press.

Goodrich, J.M. & Buskirk, S.W. (1995). Control of abundant native vertebrates for conservation of endangered species. *Conservation Biology*, **9**: 1357-1364.

Gorbics, C.F., Garlich-Miller, J.L. & Schliebe, S.L. (1998). *Draft Alaska marine mammal stock assessment 1998: sea otter, polar bear and walrus*. Unpubl. Report. Anchorage (Alaska); US Department of the Interior Fish & Wildlife Service (Alaska Region).

Hall, E.R. (1981). *The mammals of North America* (2nd ed.). New York; John Wiley & Sons.

Hesselberg, R.J. & Gannon, J.E. (1995). Contaminant trends in Great Lakes fish. In: E.T. LaRoe, G.S. Farris, C.E. Puckett, P.D. Doran & M.J. Mac (eds.), *Our living resources*: 242-244. Washington (DC); US Department of the Interior National Biological Service.

Hodgman, T.P., Harrison, D.J., Katnik, D.D. & Elowe, K.D. (1994). Survival in an intensively trapped marten population in Maine. *Journal of Wildlife Management*, **58**: 593-600.

Hoffmeister, D.F. (1986). *Mammals of Arizona*. Tucson (Arizona); University of Arizona Press.

Hunter, M.L. (1990). *Wildlife, forests and forestry*. Englewood Cliffs (NJ); Prentice Hall.

IUCN (1996). *The IUCN 1996 Red List of threatened animals*. Gland; International Union for the Conservation of Nature & Natural Resources.

Jones, C., Hoffmann, R.S., Rice, D.W., Engstrom, M.D., Bradley, R.D., Schmidly, D.J., Jones, C.A. & Baker, R.J. (1997). Revised checklist of North American mammals north of Mexico, 1997. *Occasional Papers of the Museum of Texas Technical University*, **173**: 1-19.

Knight, R.L., Smith, F.W., Buskirk, S.W., Romme, W.H. & Baker, W.L. (in press). *Forest fragmentation in the central Rocky Mountains*. Boulder (Colorado); University Press of Colorado.

Krebs, C.J., Ruggiero, L.F., Schwartz, M.K., Stanley, A. & Buskirk, S.W. (in press). Species conservation and natural variation among populations. In: L.F. Ruggiero, K.B. Aubry, S.W. Buskirk, K. McKelvey & C.J. Krebs (eds.), *The scientific basis for lynx conservation* (*US Department of Agriculture Forest Service General Technical Report RMRS-30*).

Kucera, T.E., Zielinski, W.J. & Barrett, R.G. (1995). Current distribution of the American marten, *Martes americana*, in California. *California Fish and Game*, **81**: 96-103.

Lindzey, F.G. (1982). Badger. In J.A. Chapman & G.A. Feldhamer (eds.), *Wild mammals of North America*: 653-663. Baltimore (Maryland); Johns Hopkins University Press.

Litvaitis, J.A. (1993). Response of early successional vertebrates to historic changes in land use. *Conservation Biology*, **7**: 866-873.

Macfarlane, D. (1994). National Forest System status information. In: L.F. Ruggiero, K.B. Aubry, S.W. Buskirk, L.J. Lyon & W.J. Zielinski (eds.), *The scientific basis for conserving forest carnivores, American marten, fisher, lynx and wolverine in the western United States* (*US Department of Agriculture Forest Service General Technical Report RM-254*): 176-184

Manville, R.H. (1966). The extinct sea mink, with taxonomic notes. *Proceedings of the United States National Museum*, **1222** (3584): 1-12.

Manville, R.H. & Young, S.P. (1965). *Distribution of Alaskan mammals (Circular 211)*. US Department of the Interior, Bureau of Sport Fisheries & Wildlife

Macdonald, S.M. & Mason, C.F. (1983). Some factors influencing the distribution of otters (*Lutra lutra*). *Mammal Review*, **13**: 1-10.

McDonald, T. & Coffman, G. (1980). Fewer, larger farms by year 2000 - and some consequences. *US Department of Agriculture, Agriculture Information Bulletin*, **1980** (Oct.): 439.

Melquist, W.E. & Dronkert, A. (1987). River otter. In: M. Novak, J.A. Baker, M.E. Obbard & B. Malloch (eds.), *Wild furbearer management and conservation in North America*: 627–641. North Bay (Ontario); Ontario Trappers' Association/Ontario Ministry of Natural Resources.

Mowbray, E.E., Jr., Pursley, D. & Chapman, J.A. (1979). The status, population characteristics and harvest of the river otter in Maryland. *Maryland Wildlife Administration, Publications in Wildlife Ecology*, **2**: 1-16.

Murie, O.J. (1959). *Fauna of the Aleutian Islands and Alaska Peninsula* (*North American Fauna Series No. 61*). US Department of the Interior, Fish & Wildlife Service.

Novak, M., Obbard, M.E., Jones, J.G., Newman, R., Booth, A., Satterthwaite, A.J. &. Linscombe, G. (1987). *Furbearer harvests in North America, 1600-1984*. North Bay Ontario); Ontario Trappers' Association/Ontario Ministry of Natural Resources.

Prentiss, D.W. (1903). Description of an extinct mink from the shell-heaps of the Maine coast. *Proceedings of the United States National Museum*, **26**: 887-888.

Ralls, K., Ballou, J. & Brownell, R.L., Jr. (1983). Genetic diversity in California sea otters: theoretical considerations and management implications. *Biological Conservation*, **25**: 209-232.

Schneider, R. (1997). Simulated spatial dynamics of martens in response to habitat succession in the Western Newfoundland Model Forest. In: G. Proulx, H.N. Bryant & P.M. Woodard (eds.), *Martes: taxonomy, ecology, techniques, and management*: 419-436. Edmonton (Alberta); Provincial Museum of Alberta.

Szumski, M.J. (1998). *The effects of mining related metals contamination on piscivorous mammals along the upper Clark Fork River, Montana*. PhD thesis. Laramie (Wyoming); University of Wyoming.

Thompson, I.D. (1991). Could marten become the spotted owl of eastern Canada? *Forestry Chronicle*, **67**: 136-140.

Toweill, D.E. & Tabor, J.E. (1982). River otter. In: J.A. Chapman & G.A. Feldhamer (eds.), *Wild mammals of North America*: 688-703. Baltimore (Maryland); Johns Hopkins University Press.

Weber, D.J. (1968). *The Taos trappers*. Norman (Oklahoma); University of Oklahoma Press.

Wilson, D.E. & Reeder, D.M. (Eds.) (1993). *Mammal species of the world: a taxonomic and geographic reference* (2nd ed.). Washington (DC); Smithsonian Institution Press.

Zielinski, W.J. & Kucera, T.E. (Eds.) (1995). *American marten, fisher, lynx and wolverine: survey methods for their detection* (*US Department of Agriculture, Forest Service General Technical Report PSW-157*).

CHAPTER 4

The impact of human activities on North American mustelids

Gilbert Proulx

Abstract

In North America mustelids are found from the Arctic tundra to the rain forests, in freshwaters and the sea. Although relatively unimportant to prehistoric human populations, mustelids have gained importance to the fur trade in the 20th century. While trapping aims to remove a surplus of mustelids each year, whilst maintaining viable and productive populations, it does affect population dynamics. In the past, over-trapping has caused the decline or extirpation of some mustelid populations, however, a variety of monitoring programmes and new management concepts are now being used. These programmes, along with the use of trapping devices that address animal welfare concerns, contribute to the maintenance of a market for mustelid pelts. Habitat loss through forestry or agriculture may also cause declines in population densities or shifts in species distributions. On the other hand, maintaining or producing habitat mosaics of early-, mid- and late successional stages, interspersed with natural openings and riparian habitats, can meet the ecological needs of all mustelid species. In spite of increased fur harvest pressure and greater habitat loss in the 20th century, all the mustelid species that inhabited North America at the beginning of this century are still present today. Land improvement and protection, better pest control programmes, and the use of special conservation efforts (refugia, translocations, captive breeding), all contribute to the maintenance of a diverse mustelid community and the perpetuation of human: mustelid interactions.

Introduction

In North America Family Mustelidae is represented by 15 species. Mustelids occupy virtually every type of terrestrial habitat from the Arctic tundra to the rain forests, and also occur in rivers, lakes and the sea (Vaughan, 1978). Considering their ubiquitous distribution, it is not surprising that interactions have occurred between North American mustelids and humans throughout time.

Archaeological sites across North America indicate that, with few exceptions, the species that are valued today as furbearers were relatively unimportant to prehistoric human populations. Mustelids present in the faunal assemblages from archaeological sites are usually represented by few individuals. On occasion, the occurrence of skulls/mandibles or the skull and phalanges together have led to suggestions that they were used as religious medicine bundles, a practice recorded in historical times (Wright, 1987). What were more important were major food species such as ungulates, pinnipeds, fish, molluscs and birds (Wright, 1987).

Mustelids in a modern world.
Management and conservation aspects of small carnivore: human interactions
edited by Hw I. Griffiths, pp. 53–75
© 2000 Backhuys Publishers, Leiden, The Netherlands

During the "ethnographic present" (a concept used by anthropologists to refer to the period in which reliable descriptions of peoples occur - in this case after 1500) the use of furbearers by aboriginal North Americans has often been reported (McGee, 1987). Mustelid furs were used for prestigious cloaks (Kroeber, 1925; Drucker, 1951; McClellan, 1975), garment decorations (C. Osgood, 1937; Mandelbaum, 1979), and footwear (Steward, 1938); however, American mink, *Mustela vison*, American marten, *Martes americana*, and North American river otter, *Lontra canadensis*, were not usually eaten (Radin, 1923; Drucker, 1951). As with many other wildlife species, many of the mustelids were accorded religious or spiritual significance. For many aboriginal tribes, mustelids such as river otter and wolverine, *Gulo gulo*, were spiritually powerful and dangerous animals, deserving of respect (McClellan, 1975; Wright, 1987).

The view aboriginal hunters had of furbearers changed when they began to provide furs to the European colonists. Faced with tempting rewards such as European luxury goods and guns, aboriginals were forced to balance their primary role as providers of meat and hides to their families and communities, with a secondary role as trappers (Wright, 1987). By the 18th century mustelid pelts held an important place in the fur trade (see Obbard *et al.*, 1987) and the vast boreal forests of North America became its core region.

Today, the fur industry remains active throughout North America. However, as humans also exploit timber and mineral resources, and transform land for farming, their impact on mustelids is now much greater than in the early days of the fur trade. This paper reviews the impacts of human activities on North American mustelids. Particular emphasis is placed on fur trapping, forestry and agriculture, and on responsive management strategies. Recent population management efforts and concepts are also presented.

The fur industry

In most decades Canadian harvests have contributed more than 50% of the total North American harvest of fisher, *Martes pennanti*, marten, wolverine and weasels (long-tailed weasel, *Mustela frenata*; short-tailed weasel, *Mustela erminea*; and least weasel, *Mustela nivalis rixosa* (Obbard *et al.*, 1987)). Statistics Canada's Annual Reports show that mustelid harvests have been considerable in the 20th century (Fig. 1), and Obbard *et al.* (1987) note that for most furbearers, current annual harvest levels exceeded those of the past three centuries.

However, as market demand replaced individual need in controlling the size of the mustelid fur harvest, market forces led to significant fluctuations in the number of pelts sold annually. For example, low harvests of American badger, *Taxidea taxus*, since the beginning of this century were a reflection of weak demand (Obbard *et al.*, 1987). Furthermore, the large increase in the number of ranched American mink may partially explain the recent decline in the harvest of wild mink. On the other hand, the general decline in wolverine trapped since 1930 probably is due to over-trapping and/or habitat degradation and loss (Van Zyll de Jong, 1975, 1979a). As the harvest of some species (e.g. marten and fisher) has increased considerably over the years (Fig. 1a,b) the impact of harvest and the need for conser-

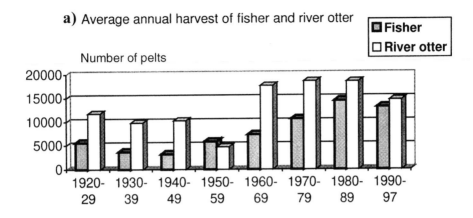

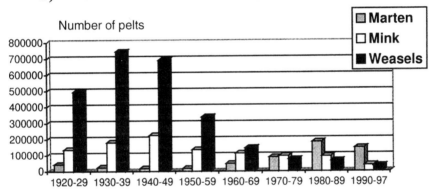

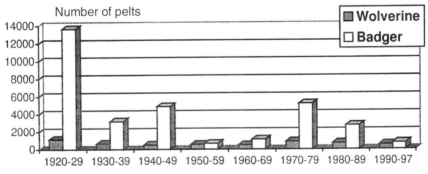

Year Classes

Fig. 1. Average annual Canadian harvests from 1920-1997: (a) fisher and river otter, (b) American marten, mink and weasels, and (c) wolverine and badger (after Obbard et al., 1987; Statistics Canada, 1998).

vation programmes for these species have often been the subject of scientific delib-
erations (Buskirk *et al.*, 1994; Ruggiero *et al.*, 1994; Proulx *et al.*, 1997).

Effect of trapping on mustelid populations

Banci & Proulx (1999) review the effects of trapping on furbearer populations.
They note that typical furbearer harvests contain a preponderance of juveniles and
males. Juveniles are more vulnerable to trapping because of their inexperience and
dispersal behaviour, and males of all ages are over-represented because of their typically greater movements and larger home ranges. Examples of the effects of trapping on American mustelid population structures have been reported for marten
(Soukkala, 1983; Strickland & Douglas, 1987), fisher (Yeager, 1950; Quick, 1953;
Kelly, 1977; Krohn *et al.*, 1994), wolverine (Banci, 1994), badger (Messick *et al.*,
1981), mink (Hibbard, 1957) and otter (Tabor & Wight, 1977).

Compensatory mortality and natality, and recolonisation of depleted areas,
might enable some species to withstand trapping mortality (Northcott *et al.*, 1974;
Sargeant *et al.*, 1982; Schowalter & Gunson, 1982; Raymond & Bergeron, 1989).
However, cases of over-exploitation have been reported for many North American
mustelid populations (e.g. Errington, 1943; McCabe, 1949; Quick, 1956; Toweill &
Tabor, 1982; Strickland & Douglas, 1977, 1987; Douglas & Strickland, 1987;
Paragi, 1990). Mustelids are vulnerable to trapping in general, and not only to those
traps set specifically for them. For example, fisher are easily caught in traps set for
coyote, *Canis latrans*, and for lynx, *Lynx canadensis* (Coulter, 1960; Cole & Proulx,
1994). Although the trapping season for the threatened Newfoundland marten
(*Martes americana atrata*) has been closed since 1934, animals are still accidental-
ly killed in traps set for other furbearers and in snowshoe hare, *Lepus americanus*,
snares (Canadian-Newfoundland Marten Recovery Team, 1995). Otter mortality
due to incidental captures in beaver, *Castor canadensis*, trap sets has also been well-
documented (Knudsen, 1957; Zackheim, 1982; Anderson & Woolf, 1984).

Management actions

Furbearers, like most other wildlife, produce an annual surplus (Errington, 1945;
Allen, 1954). The primary aim (and immediate effect) of trapping furbearers is to
remove a harvestable surplus. Harvesting the annual surplus may reduce competition among animals for food and cover, increase the chances of survival of the
remaining population, and improve the health and fecundity of individuals within
populations (Payne, 1980; Todd, 1981). Furthermore, while trapping provides basic
data on the health and dynamics of mustelid populations, it is a socio-economic
activity that is important to both aboriginal and non-aboriginal people (Proulx &
Barrett, 1991a). However, whereas trapping is part of the historical relationships
existing between humans and mustelids, actions are needed to ensure that the
advantages associated with trapping outweigh any potential negative impacts on
their populations.

It is critical that trapping is monitored and controlled according to population
constraints. Pelt registration, trade transaction reports, export permits, fur-taker
reports, population sample surveys, catch per unit effort indices and harvest data

that cover many years all may be used to recognise geographical and temporal shifts in species abundances and distributions (Erickson, 1982).

Banci & Proulx (1999) propose that species and their populations be classified along a gradient of resilience, which is the capability of a species to recover from a reduction in their population. This approach recognises the flexibility in responses among and within populations. Resilience is not static but can change, depending on conditions. A species that is highly resilient under normal conditions may become a low resilience species if it has been affected by loss of critical habitat or by intensive and widespread mortality. Within the mustelids, weasels represent one of the most resilient species (Banci & Proulx, 1999). On the basis of her work on *Mustela nivalis*, King (1989) believes that weasels are naturally resistant to control because of their normally high mortality rates and their skill at recolonisation. To remove more weasels than can be replaced naturally, a huge proportion, probably higher than 80%, of the target population has to be removed. In any large or inaccessible area, or where a weasel has only a low chance of encountering a trap or being shot, such intensive mortality usually is impossible. Thus, attempts at weasel control usually turn into harvesting, which allows a yield but does not affect density (King, 1989).

At the other end of the resilience spectrum are fisher and wolverine. Both species occur at low densities and are highly susceptible to trapping because they travel widely, are readily attracted to baits, and may be caught in traps set for other furbearers (Hornocker & Hash, 1981; Cole & Proulx, 1994). In the case of fisher, a harvest rate >25% of the pre-trapping population is believed to lead to decreases in the next year's population (Coulter, 1966; Douglas & Strickland, 1987). It has been estimated that wolverine populations can sustain harvests amounting to <10% of the pre-trapping population (Dauphiné, 1989; Gardner *et al.*, 1993; Yukon Renewable Resources, undated) although this has not been verified.

Once estimates of the density and resilience of a mustelid population are available, the harvest can be managed. This involves registering traplines, establishing trapping seasons and harvest limits, and registering pelts (Banci & Proulx, 1999). Monitoring is necessary for species on the low end of the resilience scale. Carcasses may be analysed to assess annual productivity, age and sex ratios, and the condition of the animals. In an adaptive approach to management, this information is used to adjust estimates of population abundance and harvest levels.

Ethical concerns

King (1989) wrote that "if there are times and places where it is worth trying to control a local population of weasels in order to protect birds, then it makes sense to work out the most humane, economical and efficient method". There is general concern within the public and scientific communities regarding the treatment of trapped furbearers (Proulx & Barrett, 1989, 1991a). Proulx & Barrett (1994) point out that if trapping of marten and fisher is to continue in North America, trap technology must evolve with public sentiments and thus meet the challenges of humane trapping; this applies to all mustelids.

Traditional traps

Scientific studies have demonstrated that the devices commonly used to trap mustelids on land or in water, *i.e.* foothold traps (used as live-holding and killing devices) and standard Conibear-type (rotating-jaw/body-gripping) traps, neither kill animals quickly or hold them without causing serious, often non-lethal, injuries (Proulx, 1999a).

Alternatives

Trapping technology for mustelids has been improved greatly in the last decade. For example, traps that are markedly superior to the traditional killing devices have been developed for marten (Barrett *et al.*, 1989; Proulx *et al.*, 1989; Proulx, 1999b), fisher (Proulx & Barrett, 1993a) and mink (Proulx *et al.*, 1990; Proulx & Barrett, 1991b, 1993b) and it is fortunate that the trapping industry has started to use these (Currie & Robertson, 1992; DNRNWT, 1993). With these new traps, improved trapping standards have been developed for marten and mink (Proulx, 1997a) which should be used when determining national and international trap standards.

When properly monitored, mesh or box live traps remain a valuable means of capturing mustelids without causing serious injuries (de Vos & Guenther, 1952; Irvine *et al.*, 1964; King, 1973; Kelly, 1977; Copeland *et al.*, 1995; Larivière & Messier, 1999). They provide trappers with an opportunity to determine the sex, age and pelt primeness of an animal before deciding whether to harvest it (Strickland, 1994). In long-lived species such as fisher and marten, population management may be improved by harvesting juveniles and manipulating sex ratios to preserve breeding females (Novak, 1987). Live traps also allow the release of non-target species (Fagerstone, 1987); for example, in areas where long-tailed weasel is in decline but frequently caught in furbearer sets, live traps may be used to minimise the impact of trapping on this species.

The development of better traps must also address the issue of catch selectivity. For example, Proulx *et al.* (1994a) developed a snowshoe hare snare system that minimises the risk of capturing marten. Trap research and development aimed at reducing the risk of incidental capture of non-target species is essential.

Forestry

Marten, fisher, wolverine, short-tailed weasel and least weasel, otter and mink commonly are found in forest ecosystems. Marten and fisher are associated with forests such as mature and old coniferous and mixed coniferous-deciduous forests that provide both vertical and horizontal habitat structure (Ruggiero *et al.*, 1994). Weasel species inhabit a variety of habitats associated with early- and mid-successional vegetation stages (Simms, 1979 a,b). Wolverine inhabit mosaics of structured forests featuring early successional vegetation stages (Hornocker & Hash, 1981). Finally, otter and mink are associated with riparian habitats (Melquist & Hornocker, 1983; Eagle & Whitman, 1987).

Past mustelid population declines often have been related to habitat changes. Habitat loss has been suggested as the primary cause whereby marten populations have become extinct or are currently threatened (Yeager, 1950; Bergerud, 1969; Dods & Martell, 1971; Thompson, 1991). Douglas & Strickland (1987) note that by the early 1900s, the removal of forests through settlement, logging and fire reduced the occurrence of fisher, particularly in the southern part of their original range. Banci (1994) suggests that wolverine populations that have been, or now are on the edge of extinction, now survive only in the last few available habitats that have not been developed, extensively modified, or otherwise disturbed by humans. Melquist & Dronkert (1987) also indicate that habitat destruction negatively affected the distribution of river otter. In contrast, there is some evidence that the range of the badger is expanding northwards and eastwards (Long & Killingley, 1983) and that the increase in the geographic range of the striped skunk, *Mephitis mephitis*, in North America is related to the clearing of forests (Rosatte, 1987).

Knowledge of the impact of natural disturbances on mustelids helps in the assessment of the severity of the impact of timber harvesting. Although studies of the effects of natural disturbances on mustelids are lacking, it has been noted that extensive fires could cause the disappearance of marten (Seton, 1929; Yeager, 1950; Edwards, 1954; Miller *et al.*, 1955; Bailey, 1981; Fager, 1991) and fisher (Coulter, 1966; Earle, 1978); Latour *et al.* (1994) found that marten home ranges in a 21 year-old burn were larger than those reported in undisturbed areas. On the other hand, high local densities of marten have been reported in post-fire vegetation assemblages with complex physical structure, *i.e.* horizontal boles or dense herbaceous vegetation (Magoun & Vernam, 1986; Johnson & Paragi, 1993). Furthermore, small clearings caused by low-severity fires and with remnants of the canopy cover remaining may not adversely affect marten (Koehler *et al.*, 1975). Similarly, small-scale disturbances caused by insects or wind may improve habitats for marten, fisher and other mustelids by increasing prey densities and the number of den sites (Yeager, 1950; Clough, 1987; Douglas & Strickland, 1987; Jones & Garton, 1994; Powell & Zielinski, 1994). Chapin *et al.* (1997) note that forest stands featuring significant mortality from spruce budworm, *Choristoneura fumiferana*, were preferred by marten, despite typically having <30% mature tree canopy closure. These naturally-disturbed stands were characterised by increased numbers of tree stumps, windblown trees and root mounds.

Impact of logging on mustelid populations

Data on the impact of logging on mustelid populations are biased towards studies of marten and fisher, and primarily were collected from eastern populations. Although the exact nature of a species' response may be unknown, considerable evidence exists to show that large-scale clearcutting (*i.e.* the removal of an entire stand of trees from an area of 1 ha or more, and greater than two tree heights wide) has a negative impact on mustelids that are ecologically dependent upon mature or old-growth forests. The impacts of timber harvest on mustelids are noticeable at the levels of population density and distribution, animal movements and home ranges.

Population densities and distribution

Although estimates of population densities vary between habitat, season and year, and trapping pressure, and also depend on the inventory techniques used, clearcuts have often caused declines in mustelid population densities. For example, in the coniferous-hardwood forests of Maine, Soutiere (1979) found that the density of resident adult marten was 1.2 individuals/km^2 in undisturbed and partially disturbed forests, but only 0.4 ind./km^2 in commercial clearcuts. In the Ontario boreal forest, Thompson (1994) found a 90% reduction in marten abundance in several areas in which more than 90% of the forest was cut and the remainder was in small isolated patches. The removal of canopy cover in logging creates suboptimal habitat conditions for marten, and may result in a higher rates of predation (Thompson, 1994; Potvin & Breton, 1997) and lower reproduction rates (animals do not live long enough to breed) (Thompson, 1994).

Selective cutting appears to be less deleterious to marten and fisher than clearcutting because it does not cause the changes in ground conditions that lead to decreases in preferred small mammal prey populations (Campbell, 1979; Buck *et al.*, 1994). Soutiere (1979) suggests that the retention of 20-25 m^2/ha basal area in pole and larger trees provides adequate habitat for marten (pole = trees 7.5–12.4 cm diameter at breast height, dbh = *c*. 1.3 m).

Short-tailed weasel prefer early successional stage vegetation communities and usually benefit from timber harvest (Sullivan & Sullivan, 1980; Wilson & Carey, 1996). Timber harvest also may be beneficial to semi-aquatic mustelids; patch cuts in riparian habitats regenerate aspen, *Populus tremuloides*, stands which are beneficial to beaver (Slough & Sadleir, 1977; Thompson, 1988) and indirectly help to maintain river otter habitat. However, clearcuts that remove riparian vegetation impact on the maintenance of habitats for fish, crayfish and waterfowl, all of which are found in the diet of the river otter (Toweill & Tabor, 1982) and mink (Proulx *et al.*, 1987).

Animal movements and home range

Openings created by timber harvest (or other disturbances) may not be crossed by marten if they are >250 m wide (Koehler & Hornocker, 1977; Soutiere, 1979; Spencer *et al.*, 1983). Marten home ranges in successional forests are larger (for both sexes) than are those in old forests (Soutiere, 1979; Thompson & Colgan, 1987, 1991; Potvin & Breton, 1997). Because fisher avoid large non-forested areas, large clearcuts are likely to impact on their resting and foraging habits (Powell & Zielinski, 1994), particularly in winter when snow interferes with their movements (Leonard, 1980; Raine, 1983). It is also likely that extensive logging and high habitat fragmentation are detrimental to wolverine – habitats become disconnected and, increasingly, animals must travel across open ground (Banci, 1994).

Management actions

The impacts of logging on mustelids are sometimes similar to those from natural disturbances. When disturbance (whether natural or man-made) is extensive and removes most of the canopy cover, mustelids found in late-successional forests are affected by habitat change. On the other hand, low-severity fires and selective and patch cutting may create habitat conditions that favour mustelids inhabiting early- and late-successional vegetational stages.

While clearcutting is a commonly used harvest method in North America (Gingras, 1993) selective and patch cutting should be used more often. During clearcutting ≥50% of the area should be left uncut (Lofroth & Steventon 1990; Potvin, 1998). Slash, stumps and downfall should be retained in the cut blocks to allow mustelids to utilise subnivean zones and logged areas (Campbell, 1979; Soutiere, 1979; Gyug, 1998) and to provide habitat for mustelid prey species (Hayes & Cross, 1987; Thompson & Curran, 1995). However, despite the inclusion of such recommendations in forest harvest regulations, there has been little attempt to monitor whether such actions actually are successful in maintaining species such as marten. Furthermore, such provisions will have little benefit if other issues are not addressed, notably the rate of cut, the spatial and temporal distribution of cut blocks, and silvicultural guidelines.

Thompson & Harestad (1994) propose a model for the relationship between carrying capacity and the age of forest stands in boreal conifer-dominated forest. Although developed for marten, it is likely that the model is applicable to all mustelids inhabiting mature and old forests. The model predicts a low carrying capacity for marten in boreal forests for the first 70-80 years. Carrying capacity increases dramatically in late maturity and finally declines as the stand converts to a younger forest through windfall, insect infestations and fire. The actual time periods involved vary with prevalent ecological conditions and forest type. Because canopy closure, downed woody debris and horizontal and vertical cover all increase with forest age, implementing Thompson & Harestad's model ensures the maintenance of proper habitats for mustelids inhabiting late-successional stages.

In reality, thinned and planted stands are often harvested before they can develop the attributes that are important to mustelids (Powell & Zielinski, 1994; Thompson & Harestad, 1994). Chapin *et al.* (1997) believe that the structural requirements of late-successional stage mustelids, although sometimes correlated with stand age and degree of canopy closure, could be maintained in a variety of successional stands without a closed canopy of mature trees. For example, on Vancouver Island, Baker (1992) found that marten preferred 10- to 40-year old post-cutting Douglas fir, *Pseudotsuga menziesii*, to old-growth. The use of young, managed forests by marten was possibly related to the abundance of large-diameter, coarse woody debris; this provided structure not ordinarily found in second-growth stands. Jones & Garton (1994) also found that in winter fisher preferred young forests with a high ratio of large-diameter trees, stumps (snags) and logs to that found in mature forests. Badry *et al.* (1997) found that in aspen parkland sites used by fisher, there was an average of 25 woody stems/m^2. They suggest that a dense understory may compensate for a lack of conifers by providing fisher with thermal niche advantages and access to prey species.

In contrast, there are studies that show that marten or fisher either use less or avoid young regenerating forests (Kelly, 1977; Snyder & Bissonette, 1987). These differences between results may relate to the local differences in prey availability, predator densities, snow accumulations and microclimatic conditions. Because of the variability in the responses of mustelids to diverse environmental conditions, it is necessary to plan forest management at the landscape level so as to ensure an adequate supply of all age classes and all ecosystem and community types (Thompson & Harestad, 1994; Larsen *et al.*, 1997) and to allow for animal movements within and between forest patches (see Wiens *et al.*, 1993). In this respect, Phillips (1994) compared marten population performance indices between a forest preserve site and a logged forest site in which 45% of the landscape was comprised of recently cut or regenerating clearcuts (Katnik, 1992). Phillips detected no significant differences in the percentages of lactating females and in the degree of home range overlap between resident adult females in the two study sites. His findings suggest that marten occupying patchy habitat mosaics in logged landscapes may maintain productivities comparable to those in unlogged landscapes, if trapping harvests are managed conservatively, and if residual forests are large enough to exceed the species' spatial requirements (Chapin *et al.*, 1997).

On the basis of what is known of mustelid ecological requirements, a diversity of forest communities is more advantageous than a homogenous landscape of mature forests. A mosaic of early-, mid- and late-successional vegetation stages will accommodate the needs of the mustelid community. Such mosaics give access to canopy cover, and promote the use of openings and ecotones for foraging. They also provide mustelids with a diversity of horizontal and vertical vegetation covers that ensures safe dispersal and promotes the maintenance of a diversified prey base.

Agriculture

Agriculture is a major industry in North America and billions of hectares are devoted to livestock and crop production. Farm habitats consist of tilled and untilled land, *i.e.* permanent and temporary habitats (Moen, 1983). Mustelids inhabiting agricultural environments must deal with rapidly-changing habitats in the spring, summer and autumn; arable land goes from exposed soil to lush young growth, to mature crops and to harvested stubble through each growing season. Thus a hayfield has lush, green cover one day, but on the next (when cut) this is reduced to leafless, 3 cm-high stems (Moen, 1983).

Impact of agriculture on mustelid populations

Long-tailed weasel, badger, striped skunk and mink are commonly found in agricultural regions. Free-standing water with woodlots, brush thickets, shelter belts, hayfields, rangelands, grassy meadows, summer fallow and pastures are characteristic habitats of long-tailed weasel (Hall, 1951; Fagerstone, 1987; Proulx & Drescher, 1993; Proulx, 1997b) and badger (Lindzey, 1982; Goodrich & Buskirk, 1998). Mink are found in a variety of streams and wetlands with trees, shrubs and emergent aquatic vegetation (Marshall, 1936; Arnold, 1986). Skunks live in a range of habitats but prefer early successional areas and forest ecotones (Godin, 1982) with well-drained grounds for nesting (Scott & Selko, 1939; Verts, 1967). All these species require a series of appropriate interconnected habitats that provide them with dens and prey, so the availability of habitat and prey are major concerns in the management of mustelids in agricultural environments.

Availability of habitats

In farming country, wildlife is confined to odds and ends of unused land, *i.e.* abandoned farmsteads and weedy roadside ditches, undrainable marshland creeks (sloughs) and unploughable corners, woodlands and tree-lined stream banks (Poston & Schmidt, 1981). The agricultural transformation of the parkland belt of the prairies contributed to the extensive fragmentation of habitats used by long-tailed weasels and their prey (Gamble, 1982; Forman & Gordron, 1986). The large openings created by agriculture have been beneficial to species like the striped skunk. However, while land clearance may have encouraged the movement of badgers into new areas, cultivation probably has excluded them from areas that they inhabited previously (Messick, 1987). In sub-urban areas, Racey & Euler (1983) show that the removal of trees, shrubs, and emergent and submerged aquatic vegetation impact negatively on the activities of mink. This is also true for farms where the banks of streams have been deforested.

Availability of prey

The local distribution or activity of badgers depends on the occurrence of fossorial prey such as prairie dogs, *Cynomys* spp., and ground squirrels, *Spermophilus* spp. (Johnson *et al.*, 1977; Clark *et al.*, 1982; Goodrich & Buskirk, 1998). There are apparently also close prey-predator relationships between northern pocket gopher, *Thomomys talpoides*, and long-tailed weasel (Proulx & Drescher, 1993; Proulx & Cole, 1998; Proulx, unpubl.). Prey (small mammal) density correlates with weasel occurrence (Osgood, 1935; De Van, 1982).

Unfortunately, the ephemeral nature of crops and hayfields affects small mammal populations and their predators. Monocultures do not support the diversity of small mammal species that is characteristic of mustelid diets (Fagerstone, 1987; Messick, 1987). The management of rodents in agricultural fields also often involves the use of non-selective toxic compounds that can kill a diversity of prey and predators (Wood, 1965; Hegdal *et al.*, 1981; Gamble, 1982; Uresk *et al.*, 1987; Proulx, 1998). The greatest cause of death of black-footed ferret, *Mustela nigripes*, has been the widespread use of sodium fluoroacetate (Compound 1080) to control prairie dogs, and the destruction of prairie dog colonies and secondary poisoning have almost exterminated this species (Svendsen, 1982).

Management actions

A mosaic of diverse habitats provides better conditions for mustelids than a homogenous landscape of crops and hayfields. Protecting or partially cutting woodlots, maintaining riparian shelter belts and brushland, making potholes, ponds and marshes with emergent aquatic vegetation, and leaving coarse woody debris and rock piles at the edges of fields and crops, all help to provide mustelids and their prey with adequate habitat all year round (Poston & Schmidt, 1981; Proulx *et al.*, 1987; Hafner & Brittingham, 1993; Dallaire, 1996; Proulx, 1997b).

In North America land diversion programmes have been used to convert millions of hectares of croplands into permanent vegetative cover for variable periods of time (Isaacs & Howell, 1988; Prairie Habitat Joint Venture, 1990; Frawley & Walters, 1996). These retired lands help to reduce the soil erosion caused by agricultural practices, and are relatively free of haymaking and grazing and have the potential to provide habitat for a variety of wildlife species (Farmer *et al.*, 1988).

Along with the improvement of agricultural land for mustelids, farmers are now considering improved pest management programmes. The selective removal of rodents and the manipulation of habitat characteristics are valuable control methods being implemented on farms and plantations at present (Proulx, 1996, 1997c; Engeman *et al.*, 1997).

Special conservation efforts

Trapping, timber harvesting and cultivation can individually impact on mustelid populations and distributions. However, when more than one of these activities occur together, the resilience of some populations may decrease to a point that special conservation efforts must be implemented.

Refugia (large areas free from trapping and land-use impacts) have been identified as important components of mustelid management programmes (Archibald & Jessup, 1984; Thompson & Colgan, 1987; Blood, 1989; Banci, 1994; Strickland, 1994). De Vos (1951) points out that the difficult and inferential nature of population monitoring for marten requires landscape designs that assure population persistence. Areas with low mustelid population densities could therefore be replenished with animals dispersing out from protected areas. However, the optimal size and habitat qualities of refugia relative to areas where trapping or logging occurs, and the distances between these refugia, must still be evaluated (Buskirk & Ruggiero, 1994).

The viability of metapopulations may suffer if emigrants never reach other population reservoirs because mortality in the areas between the reservoirs is high (Buskirk, 1993; Lyon *et al.*, 1994). For example, Hodgman *et al.* (1997) found that nearly half (eight out of 17) of the martens leaving a forest preserve died, primarily from trapping and intra- and interspecific aggression occurring outside the reserve. Arthur *et al.* (1993) found that dispersal by fisher juveniles allows them to quickly replace adults removed by fur trapping. However, the short dispersal distances they observed suggest that fisher will not readily recolonise large areas from which they have been extirpated, and that the expansion of isolated populations will be slow.

The refugium concept assumes tacitly that the spatial arrangement of refugia and trapped areas is such that refugial populations are persistent and that together they collectively compose a metapopulation (Gilpin, 1987). This must have better persistence than the same subpopulations in the absence of exchange. However, refugial populations that are too small to persist individually, and that are too far from each other to receive episodic immigration, will not persist unless animals are artificially translocated into them (Buskirk, 1993). Many mustelid translocation programmes have been carried out over the last 50 years. Although the results of these translocations have not always been published or evaluated over the long term, attempts to re-establish mustelid populations have often been successful (Berg, 1982; Jameson *et al.*, 1982; Proulx *et al.*, 1994b; Slough 1994; Bluett *et al.*, 1995).

To re-establish some mustelid populations successfully it may be necessary to use both refugia and translocation programmes together. In the case of the black-footed ferret, refugia that protect ferret habitat and maintain well-established colonies of black-tailed prairie dog, *Cynomys ludovicianus*, are as important as the ferret reintroduction attempts (Maguire *et al.*, 1988; Reading *et al.*, 1997; Vargas *et al.*, this volume).

The release of adult female martens and their captive-born young has been an important component of some translocation programmes (Quann, 1985; Hobson *et al.*, 1989). Captive breeding has been essential to the implementation of a black-footed ferret recovery, even though continued inbreeding could lead to problems with fertility, survivorship, and deformities in the future (Reading *et al.*, 1997). The development of greater skill in the live-capturing, handling and caring-for of mustelids (Cole & Proulx, 1991; Frost & Krohn, 1994; Mitcheltree *et al.*, 1997) has contributed significantly to the research and development of translocation programmes.

An outlook to the future

Human attitudes towards mustelids vary greatly and are often incompatible (cf. Birks, this volume). For example, because of their importance in the fur trade, mustelids receive special management considerations from government agencies (e.g. Anderson, 1987; Slough *et al.*, 1987). On the other hand, their habitats are placed at risk because of the activities of other valuable industries, such as agriculture, forestry, mining and oil exploration. Relative to other forms of land use, the market value of fur is small, almost insignificant (Adamowicz & Condon, 1987). However, trappers do represent a socio-political force that may be used to protect wilderness areas from industrial development (Proulx & Barrett, 1991a). Also, the market value of species like marten reflects only a small portion of their social value, since these species are also of value for their contribution to ecosystems and their role in enhancing recreational experiences (Adamowicz & Condon, 1987). Finally, while researchers are documenting the impact of mustelids on rodent populations (e.g. Sullivan & Sullivan, 1980; Proulx 1997b; Proulx & Cole, 1998) antipathy exists amongst farmers towards mustelids or their prey (e.g. black-tailed prairie dog), and this negatively affects conservation programmes (Messick, 1987; King, 1989; Miller *et al.*, 1990; Reading, 1993).

In spite of increased fur harvest pressure (Fig. 1) and greater habitat loss (Hummel, 1989) in the 20th century, all those mustelid species that inhabited North America at the beginning of this century are still present today. Their abundance and distribution may have changed but all of them will be part of human-wildlife interactions in the early 21st century. Therefore, even if management actions are required to improve environmental conditions and promote the growth of mustelid populations, they have not come too late. Indeed, recovery plans are already in place for species with endangered status (e.g. Canadian-Newfoundland Marten Recovery Team, 1995; Reading *et al.*, 1997). Harvest programmes are monitored (e.g. Anderson, 1987; Hamilton & Fox, 1987; Slough *et al.*, 1987; Garant *et al.*, 1996) and modified as judged necessary (e.g. Banci, 1992). Although government agencies could aid mustelid conservation through stronger fur departments (Proulx & Barrett, 1991a) mustelids are the focus of various scientific meetings and network groups such as the IUCN's Mustelid, Viverrid and Procyonid Specialist Group, the *Martes* Working Group, the Northeast Fur Resources Technical Committee Workshop, the Midwest Furbearer Workshop, the Northwestern Furbearer Conference, the Western Forest Carnivore Committee, and others. Legal groups and public organisations also apply pressure upon governments to enhance conservation efforts (Biodiversity Legal Foundation, 1994a,b; Yassa & Edelson, 1994). Improved forest management guidelines (e.g. Watt *et al.*, 1996) and the use of mustelids as indicator species for timber management planning (e.g. Thompson, 1995; Proulx & Banci, 1999) are developments that will contribute to the conservation of mustelid habitats in the future.

Fur harvest monitoring programmes, recovery efforts, scientific research and consultation, and the socio-economic value of mustelids, all contribute to the proper management of mustelids and the maintenance of human: mustelid interactions. There will always be the threat that some populations may be extirpated or subjected to further stress because of overharvest or habitat loss. However, with scientifically sound management and conservation programmes, the future of all North American mustelid species should be ensured.

Acknowledgements

I am grateful to Pauline Feldstein and Vivian Banci for reviewing an earlier version of this manuscript.

References

Adamowicz, W.L. & Condon, B.S. (1997). Socio-economic aspects of marten management. In: G. Proulx, H.N. Bryant & P.M. Woodard (eds.), *Martes: taxonomy, ecology, techniques, and management*: 395-406. Edmonton (Alberta); Provincial Museum of Alberta.

Allen, D.L. (1954). *Our wildlife legacy*. New York; Funk & Wagnalls Co.

Anderson, E.A. & Woolf, A. (1984). *River otter (Lutra canadensis) habitat utilization in northwestern Illinois (Final Report)*. Springfield (Illinois); Illinois Department of Conservation.

Anderson, S.B. (1987). Wild furbearer management in eastern Canada. In: M. Novak, J.A. Baker, M.E. Obbard & B. Malloch (eds.), *Wild furbearer management and conservation in North America*: 1040-1048. North Bay (Ontario); OntarioTrappers' Association/Ontario Ministry of Natural Resources.

Archibald, W.R. & Jessup, R.H. (1984). Population dynamics of the pine marten (*Martes americana*) in the Yukon Territory. In: R. Olson, R. Hastings & F. Geddes (eds.), *Northern ecology and resource management: memorial essays honouring Don Gill*: 81-97. Edmonton (Alberta); University of Alberta Press.

Arnold, T.W. (1986). *The ecology of prairie mink during the waterfowl breeding season*. MS thesis. Columbia (Missouri); University of Missouri.

Arthur, S.M., Paragi, T.F. & Krohn, W.B. (1993). Dispersal of juvenile fishers in Maine. *Journal of Wildlife Management*, **57**: 868-874.

Badry, M.J., Proulx, G. & Woodard, P.M. (1997). Home range and habitat use by fishers translocated to the aspen parkland of Alberta. In: G. Proulx, H.N. Bryant & P.M. Woodard (eds.), *Martes: taxonomy, ecology, techniques, and management*: 233-251. Edmonton (Alberta); Provincial Museum of Alberta.

Bailey, T.N. (1981). Factors influencing furbearer populations and harvest on the Kenai National Moose Range, Alaska. In: J.A. Chapman & D. Pursley (eds.), *Proceedings of the World Furbearer Conference, Frostburg, Maryland, USA*: 249-272.

Baker, J.M. (1992). *Habitat use and spatial organization of pine marten on southern Vancouver Island, British Columbia*. MS Thesis. Burnaby (BC); Simon Fraser University.

Banci, V. (1992). Fisher fact sheet. *The New B.C. Trapper*, **3** (2): 10-11.

Banci, V. (1994). Wolverine. In: L.F. Ruggiero, K.B. Aubry, S.W. Buskirk, L.J. Lyon & W.J. Zielinski (eds.), *The scientific basis for conserving forest carnivores: American marten, fisher, lynx and wolverine in the Western United States* (*US Department of Agriculture Forest Service General Technical Report RM-254*): 99-127.

Banci, V. & Proulx, G. (1999). Resiliency of furbearers to trapping. In: G. Proulx (ed.), *Mammal trapping*: 175-203. Sherwood Park (Alberta); Alpha Wildlife Research & Management Ltd.

Barrett, M.W., Proulx, G., Hobson, D., Nelson, D. & Nolan, J.W. (1989). Field evaluation of the C120 Magnum trap for marten. *Wildlife Society Bulletin*, **17**: 299-306.

Berg, W.E. (1982). Reintroduction of fisher, pine marten, and river otter. In: G.C. Sanderson (ed.), *Midwest furbearer management* (*Proceedings of the 43rd Midwest Fish & Wildlife Conference, Wichita, Kansas, USA*): 159-173.

Bergerud, A.T. (1969). The status of pine marten in Newfoundland. *Canadian Field-Naturalist*, **83**: 128-131.

Biodiversity Legal Foundation (1994a). *Petition to list the North American fisher* (*Martes pennanti*). Boulder (Colorado); Biodiversity Legal Foundation.

Biodiversity Legal Foundation (1994b). *Petition to list the North American wolverine* (*Gulo gulo luscus*). Boulder (Colorado); Biodiversity Legal Foundation.

Blood, D.A. (1989). *Marten. Management guidelines for British Columbia*. Victoria (BC); Ministry of the Environment, Wildlife Branch.

Bluett, R., Hubert, G., Jr., Anderson, E., Kruse, G., Lauzon, S. & Glosser, D. (1995). *Illinois river otter recovery plan* (*Technical Bulletin 7*). Springfield (Illinois); Illinois Department of Natural Resources, Division of Wildlife Resources.

Buck, S.G., Mullis, C., Mossman, A.S., Show, I & Coolahan, C. (1994). Habitat use by fishers in adjoining heavily and lightly harvested forest. In: S.W. Buskirk, A.S. Harestad, M.G. Raphael & R.A. Powell (eds.), *Martens, sables, and fishers: biology and conservation*: 368-376. Ithaca (NY); Cornell University Press.

Buskirk, S.W. (1993). The refugium concept and the conservation of forest carnivores. In: I.D. Thompson (ed.), *Proceedings of the XXI Congress of the International Union of Game Biologists, Halifax, Nova Scotia, Canada*: 242-245.

Buskirk, S.W., Harestad, A.S., Raphael, M.G. & Powell, R.A. (Eds.) (1994). *Martens, sables, and fishers: biology and conservation*. Ithaca (NY); Cornell University Press.

Buskirk, S.W. & Ruggiero, L.F. (1994). American marten. In: L.F. Ruggiero, K.B. Aubry, S.W. Buskirk, L.J. Lyon & W.J. Zielinski (eds.), *The scientific basis for conserving forest carnivores: American marten, fisher, lynx and wolverine in the Western United States* (*US Department of Agriculture Forest Service General Technical Report RM-254*): 7-37.

Campbell, T.M. (1979). *Short-term effects of timber harvests on pine marten ecology*. MS Thesis. Fort Collins (Colorado); Colorado State University.

Canadian-Newfoundland Marten Recovery Team (1995). *National recovery plan for the Newfoundland marten*. Ottawa (Ontario); Canadian Nature Federation.

Chapin, T.G., Harrison, D.J. & Phillips, D.M. (1997). Seasonal habitat selection by marten in an untrapped forest preserve. *Journal of Wildlife Management*, **61**: 707-717.

Clark, T.W., Campbell, T.M., III, Socha, D.G. & Casey, D.E. (1982). Prairie dog colony attributes and associated vertebrate species. *Great Basin Naturalist*, **42**: 572-582.

Clough, G.C. (1987). Relations of small mammals to forest management in northern Maine. *Canadian Field-Naturalist*, **101**: 40-48.

Cole, P.J. & Proulx, G. (1991). The care of mustelids in experimental research. *Midwest Furbearer Workshop*, **9**: 27.

Cole, P.J. & Proulx, G. (1994). Leghold trapping: a cause of serious injuries to fishers. *Martes Working Group Newsletter*, **2**: 14-15.

Copeland, J.P., Cesar, E., Peek, J.M., Harris, C.E., Long, C.D. & Hunter, D.L. (1995). A live trap for wolverine and other forest carnivores. *Wildlife Society Bulletin*, **23**: 535-538.

Coulter, M.W. (1960). The status and distribution of fisher in Maine. *Journal of Mammalogy*, **41**: 1-9.

Coulter, M.W. (1966). *Ecology and management of fishers in Maine*. PhD Thesis. New York; Syracuse University.

Currie, D. & Robertson, E. (1992). *Alberta wild fur management study guide*. Edmonton (Alberta); Alberta Forest Lands and Wildlife.

Dallaire, F.J. (1996). *Tree filter literature review*. Red Deer (Alberta); County of Red Deer Agricultural Services Board, CAESA Project.

Dauphiné, C. (1989). *Status report on the wolverine Gulo gulo in Canada*. Ottawa (Ontario); Committee on the Status of Endangered Wildlife in Canada.

DNRNWT (1993). *Summary of trapping regulations* (*Mimeograph*). Yellowknife (NWT); Department of Natural Resources of the Northwest Territories.

De Van, R. (1982). *The ecology and life history of the long-tailed weasel* (*Mustela frenata*). PhD thesis. Cincinnatini (Ohio); University of Cincinnati.

de Vos, A. (1951). Overflow and dispersal of marten and fisher in Ontario. *Journal of Wildlife Management*, **15:** 164-175.

de Vos, A. & Guenther, S.E. (1952). Preliminary live-trapping studies of marten. *Journal of Wildlife Management*, **16:** 207-214.

Dods, D.G. & Martell, A.M. (1971). The recent status of the marten, *Martes americana americana* (Erxleben), in Nova Scotia. *Canadian Field-Naturalist*, **85:** 63-65.

Douglas, C.W. & Strickland, M.A. (1987). Fisher. In: M. Novak, J.A. Baker, M.E. Obbard & B. Malloch (eds.), *Wild furbearer management and conservation in North America*: 511-529. North Bay (Ontario); OntarioTrappers' Association/Ontario Ministry of Natural Resources.

Drucker, P. (1951). The northern and central Nootkan tribes. *Bureau of American Ethnology Bulletin*, **144:** 1-480.

Eagle, T.C. & Whitman, J.S. (1987). Mink. In: M. Novak, J.A. Baker, M.E. Obbard & B. Malloch (eds.), *Wild furbearer management and conservation in North America*: 615-624. North Bay (Ontario); OntarioTrappers' Association/Ontario Ministry of Natural Resources.

Earle, R.D. (1978). *The fisher-porcupine relationship in Upper Michigan*. MS thesis. Houghton (Michigan); Michigan Technical University.

Edwards, R.Y. (1954). Fire and the decline of a mountain caribou herd. *Journal of Wildlife Management*, **18:** 521-526.

Engeman, R.M., Barnes, V.G., Jr., Anthony, R.M. & Crupper, H.W. (1997). Effect of vegetation management for reducing damage to lodgepole pine seedlings from northern pocket gophers. *Crop Protection*, **16:** 407-410.

Erickson, D.W. (1982). Estimating and using furbearer harvest information. In: G.C. Sanderson (ed.), *Midwest furbearer management* (*Proceedings of the 43rd Midwest Fish and Wildlife Conference, Wichita, Kansas, USA*): 53-65.

Errington, P.L. (1943). An analysis of mink predation upon muskrats in north-central United States. *Iowa State College Agricultural Experimental Station Research Bulletin*, **320:** 798-924.

Errington, P.L. (1945). Some contributions of a fifteen-year local study of the northern bobwhite to a knowledge of population phenomena. *Ecological Monographs*, **15:** 1-34.

Fager, C.W. (1991). *Harvest dynamics and winter habitat use of the pine marten in southwest Montana*. MS thesis. Bozeman (Montana); Montana State University.

Fagerstone, K.A. (1987). Black-footed ferret, long-tailed weasel, short-tailed weasel, and least weasel. In: M. Novak, J.A. Baker, M.E. Obbard & B. Malloch (eds.), *Wild furbearer management and conservation in North America*: 549-573. North Bay (Ontario); Ontario Trappers' Association/Ontario Ministry of Natural Resources.

Farmer, A.H., Hays, R.L. & Webb, R.P. (1988). Effects of the Conservation Reserve Program on wildlife habitat: a co-operative monitoring study. *Transactions of the North American Wildlife & Natural Resources Conference*, **53:** 232-238.

Forman, R.T.T. & Gordron, M. (1986). Patches. In: R.T.T. Forman & M. Gordron (eds.), *Landscape ecology*: 83-120. New York; John Wiley & Sons.

Frawley, B.J. & Walters, S. (1996). Reuse of annual set-aside lands: implications for wildlife. *Wildlife Society Bulletin*, **24:** 655-659.

Frost, H.C. & Krohn, W.B. (1994). *Capture, care, and handling of fishers* (*Martes pennanti*) (*Maine Agricultural & Forestry Experimental Station Technical Bulletin 157*). Orono (Maine); University of Maine.

Gamble, R.L. (1982). *Status report on the prairie long-tailed weasel Mustela frenata longicauda*. Ottawa (Ontario); Committee of the Status of Endangered Wildlife In Canada.

Garant, Y., Lafond, R. & Courtois, R. (1996). *Analyse du système de suivi de la martre d'Amérique* (*Martes americana*) *au Québec*. Québec; Ministère d'Environnement et Faune.

Gardner, C.L., McNay, M.E. & Tobey, R. (1993). Estimates of wolverine densities and sustainable harvests in the Melchina Basin in southcentral Alaska. In: *Proceedings of the 7th Northern Furbearer Conference, Whitehorse, Yukon, Canada*: unpaginated abstract.

Gilpin, M.E. (1987). Spatial structure and population vulnerability. In: M.E. Soulé (ed.), *Viable populations for conservation*: 126-139. Cambridge; Cambridge University Press.

Gingras J.F. (1993). Coupe à blanc avec la conscience tranquille. *Opérations Forestières et de Scierie*, **28**: 20-26.

Godin, A.J. (1982). Striped and hooded skunks. In: J.A. Chapman & G. Feldhamer (eds.), *Wild mammals of North America: biology, management, and economics*: 674-687. Baltimore (Maryland); Johns Hopkins University Press.

Goodrich, J.M. & Buskirk, S.W. (1998). Spacing and ecology of North American badgers (*Taxidea taxus*) in a prairie-dog (*Cynomys leucurus*) complex. *Journal of Mammalogy*, **79**: 171-179.

Gyug, L.W. (1998). Marten winter use of slash piles in clearcuts in southern interior British Columbia. *Martes Working Group Newsletter*, **6** (1): 6.

Hafner, C.L. & Brittingham, M.C. (1993). Evaluation of a stream-bank fencing program in Pennsylvania. *Wildlife Society Bulletin*, **21**: 307-315.

Hall, E.R. (1951). American weasels. *Publications of the University of Kansas Museum of Natural History*, **4**: 1-466.

Hamilton, D.A. & Fox, L.B. (1987). Wild furbearer management in the midwestern United States. In: M. Novak, J.A. Baker, M.E. Obbard & B. Malloch (eds.), *Wild furbearer management and conservation in North America*: 1100-1116. North Bay (Ontario); Ontario Trappers' Association/Ontario Ministry of Natural Resources.

Hayes, J.P. & Cross, S.P. (1987). Characteristics of logs used by western red-backed voles, *Clethrionomys gapperi*, and deer mice, *Peromyscus maniculatus*. *Canadian Field-Naturalist*, **101**: 534-546.

Hegdal, P.L., Gatz, T.A. & Fite, E.C. (1981). Secondary effects of rodenticides on mammalian predators. In: J.A. Chapman & D. Pursley (eds.), *Proceedings of the World Furbearer Conference, Frostburg, Maryland, USA*: 1781-1793.

Hibbard, E.A. (1957). Age ratios in wild mink populations. *Journal of Mammalogy*, **38**: 412-413.

Hobson, D.P., Proulx, G. & Dew, B.L. (1989). Initial post-release behavior of marten, *Martes americana*, introduced in Cypress Hills Provincial Park, Saskatchewan. *Canadian Field-Naturalist*, **103**: 398-400.

Hodgman, T.P., Harrison, D.J., Phillips, D.M. & Elowe, K.D. (1997). Survival of American marten in an untrapped forest preserve in Maine. In: G. Proulx, H.N. Bryant & P.M. Woodard (eds.), *Martes: taxonomy, ecology, techniques, and management*: 86-99. Edmonton (Alberta); Provincial Museum of Alberta.

Hornocker, M.G. & Hash, H.S. (1981). Ecology of the wolverine in northwestern Montana. *Canadian Journal of Zoology*, **59**: 1286-1301.

Hummel, M. (Ed.) (1989). *Endangered spaces. The future for Canada's wilderness*. Toronto (Ontario); Key Porter Books Ltd.

Irvine, G.W., Magnus, L.T. & Bradle, B.J. (1964). The restocking of fisher in lake states forests. *Transactions of the North American Wildlife & Natural Resources Conference*, **29**: 307-315.

Isaacs, B. & Howell, D. (1988). Opportunities for enhancing wildlife benefits through the Conservation Reserve Program. *Transactions of the North American Wildlife & Natural Resources Conference*, **53**: 222-231.

Jameson, R.J., Kenyon, K.W., Johnson, A.M. & Wight, H.M. (1982). History and status of translocated sea otter populations in North America. *Wildlife Society Bulletin*, **10**: 100-107.

Johnson, D.R., Smith, G.W., Cobb, E.M. & Woodley, C.E. (1977). Population ecology and habitat requirements of Townsend ground squirrels. In: *Snake River birds of prey research project* (*Annual Report*): 143-163. Boise (Idaho); US Department of the Interior Bureau of Land Management.

Johnson, W.N. & Paragi, T.F. (1993). *The relationship of wildfire to lynx and marten populations and habitat in interior Alaska* (*Koyukuk/Nowitna Refuge Complex, Annual Report, 1992*). Galena (Alaska); US Department of the Interior Fish & Wildlife Service.

Jones, J.L. & Garton, O.E. (1994). Selection of successional stages by fishers in northcentral Idaho. In: S.W. Buskirk, A.S. Harestad, M.G. Raphael & R.A. Powell (eds.), *Martens, sables, and fishers: biology and conservation*: 377-387. Ithaca (NY); Cornell University Press.

Katnik, D.D. (1992). *Spatial use, territoriality, and summer-autumn selection of habitats in an intensively harvested population of martens on commercial forestland in Maine*. MS thesis. Orono (Maine); University of Maine.

Kelly, G.M. (1977). *Fisher (Martes pennanti) biology in the White Mountain National Forest and adjacent areas*. PhD thesis. Amherst (Massachusetts); University of Massachusetts.

King, C.M. (1973). A system for trapping and handling live weasels in the field. *Journal of Zoology*, **17**: 448-453.

King, C.M. (1975). The sex ratio of trapped weasels (*Mustela nivalis*). *Mammal Review*, **5**: 1-8.

King, C.M. (1989). *The natural history of weasels and stoats*. Ithaca (NY); Cornell University Press.

Knudsen, G.J. (1957). *Preliminary otter investigations – Wisconsin (Pittman-Robertson Project W-79-R-1)*. Madison (Wisconsin); Wisconsin Department of Natural Resources.

Koehler, G.M. & Hornocker, M.G. (1977). Fire effects on marten habitat in the Selway-Bitteroot Wilderness. *Journal of Wildlife Management*, **41**: 500-505.

Koehler, G.M., Moore, W.R. & Taylor, A.R. (1975). Preserving the pine marten: management guidelines for western forests. *Western Wildlands*, **2**: 31-36.

Kroeber, A.L. (1925). *Handbook of the Indians of California* (1970 reprint). New York; Dover Press.

Krohn, W.B., Arthur, S.M. & Paragi, T.F. (1994). Mortality and vulnerability of a heavily trapped fisher population. In: S.W. Buskirk, A.S. Harestad, M.G. Raphael & R.A. Powell (eds.), *Martens, sables, and fishers: biology and Conservation*: 137-145. Ithaca (NY); Cornell University Press.

Larivière, S. & Messier, F. (1999). Review and perspective of methods used to capture and handle skunks. In: G. Proulx (ed.), *Mammal trapping*: 141-154. Sherwood Park (Alberta); Alpha Wildlife Research & Management Ltd.

Larsen, D.R., Shifley, S.R., Thompson, F.R., III, Brookshire, B.L., Dey, D.C., Kurzejeski, E.W. & England, K. (1997). 10 guidelines for ecosystem researchers: lessons from Missouri. *Journal of Forestry*, **95**: 4-8.

Latour, P.B., MacLean, N. & Poole, K. (1994). Movements of martens, *Martes americana*, in burned and unburned taiga in the Mackenzie Valley, Northwest Territories. *Canadian Field-Naturalist*, **108**: 351-354.

Leonard, RD (1980). *The winter activity and movements, winter diet and breeding biology of the fisher (Martes pennanti) in southeastern Manitoba*. MS thesis. Winnipeg (Manitoba); University of Manitoba.

Lindzey, F.G. (1982). Badger. In: J.A. Chapman & G.A. Feldhamer (eds.), *Wild mammals of North America*: 653-663. Baltimore (Maryland); Johns Hopkins University Press.

Lofroth, E.C. & Steventon, J.D. (1990). Managing for marten winter habitat in interior forests of British Columbia. In: *Proceedings of the Forestry & Wildlife Workshop (Canada-BC Forestry Research Agreement Publication 160)*: 66-76. Victoria (BC); Forestry Canada & British Columbia Forestry Service.

Long, C.A. & Killingley, C.A. (1983). *The badgers of the world*. Springfield (Illinois); Charles C. Thomas Publishers.

Lyon, L.J., Aubry, K.B., Zielinski, W.Z., Buskirk, S.W. & Ruggiero, L.F. (1994). The scientific basis for conserving forest carnivores: considerations for management. In: L.F. Ruggiero, K.B. Aubry, S.W. Buskirk, L.J. Lyon & W.J. Zielinski (eds.), *The scientific basis for conserving forest carnivores: American marten, fisher, lynx and wolverine in the Western United States (US Department of Agriculture Forest Service General Technical Report RM-254)*: 128-137.

Magoun, A.J. & Vernam, D.J. (1986). *An evaluation of the Bear Creek burn as marten (Martes americana) habitat in interior Alaska (Unpubl. Report of Special Project AK-950-CAH-0)*. Fairbanks (Alaska); US Department of the Interior Bureau of Land Management.

Maguire, L.A., Clark, T.W., Crete, R., Cada, J., Groves, C., Shaffer, M.L. & Seal, U. (1988). Black-footed ferret recovery in Montana: a decision analysis. *Wildlife Society Bulletin*, **16**: 111-120.

Mandelbaum, D.G. (1979). *The Plains Cree: an ethnographic, historical and comparative study*. Regina (Saskatchewan); Canadian Plains Research Centre.

Marshall, W.H. (1936). A study of the winter activities of the mink. *Journal of Mammalogy*, **17**: 382-392.

McCabe, R.A. (1949). Notes on live-trapping mink. *Journal of Mammalogy*, **30**: 416-423.

McClellan, C. (1975). *My old people say: an ethnographic survey of southern Yukon Territory* (2 vols.). *National Museum of Canada Publications in Ethnology*, **6**: 1-637.

McGee, H.F. (1987). The use of furbearers by native North Americans after 1500. In: M. Novak, J.A. Baker, M.E. Obbard & B. Malloch (eds.), *Wild furbearer management and conservation in North America*: 13-20. North Bay (Ontario); Ontario Trappers' Association/Ontario Ministry of Natural Resources.

Melquist, W.E. & Dronkert, A.E. (1987). River otter. In: M. Novak, J.A. Baker, M.E. Obbard & B. Malloch (eds.), *Wild furbearer management and conservation in North America*: 627-641. North Bay (Ontario); Ontario Trappers' Association/Ontario Ministry of Natural Resources.

Melquist, W.E. & Hornocker, M.G. (1983). Ecology of river otter in west central Idaho. *Wildlife Monographs*, **83**: 1-60.

Messick, J.P. (1987). North American badger. In: M. Novak, J.A. Baker, M.E. Obbard & B. Malloch (eds.), *Wild furbearer management and conservation in North America*: 587-597. North Bay (Ontario); Ontario Trappers' Association/Ontario Ministry of Natural Resources.

Messick, J.P., Todd, M.C. & Hornocker, M.G. (1981). Comparative ecology of two badger populations. In: J.A. Chapman & D. Pursley (eds.), *Proceedings of the Worldwide Furbearer Conference, Frostburg, Maryland, USA*: 1290-1304.

Miller, B.G., Wemer, C., Biggins D.E. & Reading, R.P. (1990). A proposal to conserve black-footed ferrets and the prairie dog ecosystem. *Environmental Management*, **14**: 763-769.

Miller, R.G., Ritchey, R.W. & Edwards, R.Y. (1955). Live-trapping marten in British Columbia. *Murrelet*, **36**: 1-18.

Mitcheltree, D.H., Serfass, T.L., Whary, M.T., Tzilkowski, W.M., Brooks, R.P. & Peper, R.L. (1997). Captive care and clinical evaluation of fishers during the first year of a reintroduction project. In: G. Proulx, H.N. Bryant & P.M. Woodard (eds.), *Martes: taxonomy, ecology, techniques, and management*: 317-328. Edmonton (Alberta); Provincial Museum of Alberta.

Moen, A.N. (1983). *Agriculture and wildlife management.* Lansing (Michigan); Corner Brook Press.

Northcott, T.H., Payne, N.F. & Mercer, E. (1974). Dispersal of mink in insular Newfoundland. *Journal of Mammalogy*, **30**: 243-248.

Novak, M. (1987). Wild furbearer management in Ontario. In: M. Novak, J.A. Baker, M.E. Obbard & B. Malloch (eds.), *Wild furbearer management and conservation in North America*: 1049-1061. North Bay (Ontario); Ontario Trappers' Association/Ontario Ministry of Natural Resources.

Obbard, M.E., Jones J.G., Newman, R., Booth, A., Satterhwaite, A.J. & Linscombe, G. (1987). Furbearer harvests in North America. In: M. Novak, J.A. Baker, M.E. Obbard & B. Malloch (eds.), *Wild furbearer management and conservation in North America*: 1005-1034. North Bay (Ontario); Ontario Trappers' Association/Ontario Ministry of Natural Resources.

Osgood, C. (1937). The ethnography of the Tataina. *Yale University Publications in Anthropology*, **16**: 1-229.

Osgood, F.L. (1935). Fluctuations in small mammal populations. *Journal of Mammalogy*, **16**: 156.

Paragi, T.F. (1990). *Reproductive biology of female fishers in southcentral Maine.* MS thesis. Orono (Maine); University of Maine.

Payne, N.F. (1980). Furbearer management and trapping. *Wildlife Society Bulletin*, **8**: 345-348.

Phillips, D.M. (1994). *Social and spatial characteristics, and dispersal pattern of marten in a forest preserve and industrial forest.* MS thesis. Orono (Maine); University of Maine.

Poston, H.J. & Schmidt, R.K. (1981). *Wildlife habitat: a handbook for Canada's prairies and parklands.* Ottawa (Ontario); Environment Canada.

Potvin, F. (1998). *La martre d'Amérique (Martes americana) et la coupe à blanc en forêt boréale: une approche télémétrique et géomatique.* PhD thesis. Québec; Université de Laval.

Potvin, F. & Breton, L. (1997). Short-term effects of clearcutting on marten and their prey in the boreal forest of western Quebec. In: G. Proulx, H.N. Bryant & P.M. Woodard (eds.), *Martes: taxonomy, ecology, techniques, and management*: 452-474. Edmonton (Alberta); Provincial Museum of Alberta.

Powell, R.A. & Zielinski, W.J. (1994). Fisher. In: L.F. Ruggiero, K.B. Aubry, S.W. Buskirk, L.J. Lyon & W.J. Zielinski (eds.), *The scientific basis for conserving forest carnivores: American marten, fisher, lynx and wolverine in the Western United States (US Department of Agriculture Forest Service General Technical Report RM-254)*: 38-73.

Prairie Habitat Joint Venture (1990). *Prairie habitat: a prospectus.* Edmonton (Alberta); North American Waterfowl Management Plan.

Proulx, G. (1996). *Biology and control of the northern pocket gopher (Thomomys talpoides) in Alberta (Leaflet).* Red Deer County (Alberta); Counties' Pocket Gopher Control Research Programme.

Proulx, G. (1997a). Improved trapping standards for marten and fisher. In: G. Proulx, H.N. Bryant & P.M. Woodard (eds.), _Martes: taxonomy, ecology, techniques, and management_: 362-371. Edmonton (Alberta); Provincial Museum of Alberta.

Proulx, G. (1997b). Long-tailed weasels as biological control agents of northern pocket gophers. In: _Annual Report of the Battle River Research Group_: 129-130. Camrose (Alberta); Battle River Research Group.

Proulx, G. (1997c). A northern pocket gopher (_Thomomys talpoides_) border control strategy: promising approach. _Crop Protection_, **16:** 279-284.

Proulx, G. (1998). Evaluation of strychnine and zinc phosphide baits to control northern pocket gopher populations in alfalfa fields, in Alberta, Canada. _Crop Protection_, **17:** 405-408.

Proulx, G. (1999a). Review of current mammal trap technology in North America. In: G. Proulx (ed.), _Mammal trapping_: 1-46. Sherwood Park (Alberta); Alpha Wildlife Research & Management Ltd.

Proulx, G. (1999b). The Bionic: an effective marten trap. In: G. Proulx (ed.), _Mammal Trapping_: 79-87. Sherwood Park (Alberta); Alpha Wildlife Research & Management Ltd.

Proulx, G. & Banci, V. (1999). _American marten as a potential indicator of forest structural complexity and biodiversity in Weyerhaeuser's Grande Prairie/Grande Cache Forest Management Area_. Report Prepared for Weyerhaeuser Canada, Alberta Operations Edmonton. Sherwood Park (Alberta); Alpha Wildlife Research & Management Ltd.

Proulx, G. & Barrett, M.W. (1989). Animal welfare concerns and wildlife trapping: ethics, standards and commitments. _Transactions of the Western Section of the Wildlife Society_, **25:** 1-6.

Proulx, G. & Barrett, M.W. (1991a). Ideological conflict between animal rightists and wildlife professionals over trapping wild furbearers. _Transactions of the North American Wildlife & Natural Resources Conference_, **56:** 387-399.

Proulx, G. & Barrett, M.W. (1991b). Evaluation of the Bionic trap to quickly kill mink (_Mustela vison_) in simulated natural environments. _Journal of Wildlife Diseases_, **27:** 276-280.

Proulx, G. & Barrett, M.W. (1993a). Evaluation of the Bionic trap to quickly kill fisher (_Martes pennanti_) in simulated natural environments. _Journal of Wildlife Diseases_, **29:** 310-316.

Proulx, G. & Barrett, M.W. (1993b). Field testing the C120 Magnum trap for mink. _Wildlife Society Bulletin_, **21:** 421-426.

Proulx, G. & Barrett, M.W. (1994). Ethical considerations in the selection of traps to harvest American martens and fishers. In: S.W. Buskirk, A.S. Harestad, M.G. Raphael & R.A. Powell (eds.), _Martens, sables, and fishers: biology and conservation_: 192-196. Ithaca (NY); Cornell University Press.

Proulx, G. & Cole, P.J. (1998). Identification of northern pocket gopher, _Thomomys talpoides_, remains in long-tailed weasel, _Mustela frenata longicauda_, scats. _Canadian Field-Naturalist_, **112:** 345-346.

Proulx, G. & Drescher, R.K. (1993). Distribution of the long-tailed weasel, _Mustela frenata longicauda_, in Alberta as determined by questionnaires and interviews. _Canadian Field-Naturalist_, **107:** 186-191.

Proulx, G., McDonnell, J.A. & Gilbert, F.F. (1987). Effect of water level fluctuations on muskrat, _Ondatra zibethica_, predation by mink, _Mustela vison_. _Canadian Field-Naturalist_, **101:** 89-92.

Proulx, G., Barrett, M.W. & Cook, S.R. (1989). The C120 Magnum: an effective quick-kill trap for marten. _Wildlife Society Bulletin_, **17:** 294-298.

Proulx, G., Barrett, M.W. & Cook, S.R. (1990). The C120 Magnum with pan trigger: a humane trap for mink (_Mustela vison_). _Journal of Wildlife Diseases_, **26:** 511-517.

Proulx, G., Bryant, H.N. & Woodard, P.M. (Eds.) (1997). _Martes: taxonomy, ecology, techniques, and management_. Edmonton (Alberta); Provincial Museum of Alberta.

Proulx, G., Kolenosky, A.J., Badry, M.J., Cole, P.J. & Drescher, R.K. (1994a). A snowshoe hare snare system to minimize capture of marten. _Wildlife Society Bulletin_, **22:** 639-643.

Proulx, G., Kolenosky, A.J., Badry, M.J., Cole, P.J., Drescher, R.K., Seidel, K. & Cole, P.J. (1994b). Post-release movements of translocated fishers. In: S.W. Buskirk, A.S. Harestad, M.G. Raphael & R.A. Powell (eds.), _Martens, sables, and fishers: biology and conservation_: 197-203. Ithaca (NY); Cornell University Press.

Quann, J.D. (1985). _American marten reintroduction program 1985. Progress Report_. Fundy National Park (New Brunswick); Natural Resources Conservation Section.

Quick, H.F. (1953). Wolverine, fisher, and marten studies in a wilderness region. _Transactions of the North American Wildlife Conference_, **18:** 512-533.

Quick, H.F. (1956). Effects of exploitation on a marten population. *Journal of Wildlife Management*, **20**: 267-274.

Racey, G.D. & Euler, D.L. (1983). Changes in mink habitat and food selection as influenced by cottage development in central Ontario. *Journal of Applied Ecology*, **20**: 387-402.

Radin, P. (1923). *The Winnebago tribe* (1970 Reprint). Lincoln (Nebraska); University of Nebraska Press.

Raine, R.M. (1983). Winter habitat use and responses to snow cover of fisher (*Martes pennanti*) and marten (*Martes americana*) in southeastern Manitoba. *Canadian Journal of Zoology*, **61**: 25-34.

Raymond, M. & Bergeron, J.-M. (1989). Réponse numérique de l'hermeline aux fluctuations d'abondance de *Microtus pennsylvanicus*. *Canadian Journal of Zoology*, **60**: 25-34.

Reading, R.P. (1993). *Toward an endangered species reintroduction paradigm: a case study of the black-footed ferret*. PhD thesis. New Haven (Connecticut); Yale University.

Reading, R.P., Clark, T.W., Vargas, A., Hanebury, L.R., Miller, B.J., Biggins, D.E. & Marinari, P.E. (1997). Black-footed ferret (*Mustela nigripes*): conservation update. *Small Carnivore Conservation*, **17**: 1-6.

Rosatte, R.C. (1987). Striped, spotted, hooded, and hog-nosed skunk. In: M. Novak, J.A. Baker, M.E. Obbard & B. Malloch (eds.), *Wild furbearer management and conservation in North America*: 599-613. North Bay (Ontario); Ontario Trappers' Association/Ontario Ministry of Natural Resources.

Ruggiero, L.F., Aubry, K.B., Buskirk, S.W., Lyon L.J. & Zielinski, W.J. (Eds.) (1994). *The scientific basis for conserving forest carnivores: American marten, fisher, lynx and wolverine in the Western United States* (*US Department of Agriculture Forest Service General Technical Report RM-254*).

Sargeant, A.B., Greenwood, R.J., Piehl, J.L. & Bicknell, W.B. (1982). Recurrence, mortality, and dispersal of prairie striped skunks, *Mephitis mephitis*, and implications to rabies epizootiology. *Canadian Field-Naturalist*, **96**: 312-316.

Schowalter, D.B., & Gunson, J.R. (1982). Parameters of population and seasonal activity of striped skunks, *Mephitis mephitis*, in Alberta and Saskatchewan. *Canadian Field-Naturalist*, **96**: 409-420.

Scott, T.G. & Selko, L.F. (1939). A census of red foxes and striped skunks in Clay and Boone Counties, Iowa. *Journal of Wildlife Management*, **3**: 92-98.

Seton, E.T. (1929). *Lives of game animals, Vol. II, Part 2*. New York; Doubleday, Doran & Co. Inc.

Simms, D.A. (1979a). Studies of an ermine population in southern Ontario. *Canadian Journal of Zoology*, **57**: 824-832.

Simms, D.A. (1979b). North American weasels: resource utilization and distribution. *Canadian Journal of Zoology*, **57**: 504-520.

Slough, B.G. (1994). Translocations of American martens: an evaluation of factors in success. In: S.W. Buskirk, A.S. Harestad, M.G. Raphael & R.A. Powell (eds.), *Martens, sables, and fishers: biology and conservation*: 165-178. Ithaca (NY); Cornell University Press.

Slough, B.G., Jessup, R.H., McKay, D.I. & Stephenson, A.B. (1987). Wild furbearer management in western and northern Canada. In: M. Novak, J.A. Baker, M.E. Obbard & B. Malloch (eds.), *Wild furbearer management and conservation in North America*: 1062-1076. North Bay (Ontario); Ontario Trappers' Association/Ontario Ministry of Natural Resources.

Slough, B.G. & Sadleir, R.M.F.S. (1977). A land capability classification system for beaver (*Castor canadensis*). *Canadian Journal of Zoology*, **55**: 504-520.

Snyder, J.E. & Bissonette, J.A. (1987). Marten use of clear-cutting and residual forest in western Newfoundland. *Canadian Journal of Zoology*, **65**: 169-174.

Soukkala, A.M. (1983). *The effects of trapping on marten populations in Maine*. MS thesis. Orono (Maine); University of Maine.

Soutiere, E.C. (1979). Effects of timber harvesting on marten in Maine. *Journal of Wildlife Management*, **43**: 850-860.

Spencer, W.D., Barrett, R.H. & Zielinski, W.J. (1983). Marten habitat preferences in the northern Sierra Nevada. *Journal of Wildlife Management*, **51**: 616-621.

Statistics Canada (1998). *Furs, number and value of wildlife pelts sold, by type, by Province, Territory and Canada, 1980-1997*. Ottawa (Ontario); Agriculture Canada, Livestock Statistics.

Steward, J.H. (1938). *Basin-Plateau aboriginal sociopolitical groups* (1970 Reprint). Salt Lake City (Utah); University of Utah Press.

Strickland, M.A. (1994). Harvest management of fishers and American martens. In: S.W. Buskirk, A.S. Harestad, M.G. Raphael & R.A. Powell (eds.), *Martens, sables, and fishers: biology and conservation*: 149-164. Ithaca (NY); Cornell University Press.

Strickland, M.A. & Douglas, C.W. (1977). More information on fisher and marten. *Canadian Trapper*, **4:** 8-11.

Strickland, M.A. & Douglas, C.W. (1987). Marten. In: M. Novak, J.A. Baker, M.E. Obbard & B. Malloch (eds.), *Wild furbearer management and conservation in North America*: 531-546. North Bay (Ontario); Ontario Trappers' Association/Ontario Ministry of Natural Resources.

Sullivan, T.P. & Sullivan, D.S. (1980). The use of weasel for natural control of mouse and vole populations in a coastal coniferous forest. *Oecologia (Berlin)*, **47:** 125-129.

Svendsen, G.E. (1982). Weasels. In: J.A. Chapman & G.A. Feldhamer (eds.), *Wild mammals of North America*: 613-628. Baltimore (Maryland); Johns Hopkins University Press.

Tabor, J.E. & Wight, H.M. (1977). Population status of river otter in western Oregon. *Journal of Wildlife Management*, **41:** 692-699.

Thompson, I.D. (1988). Habitat needs of furbearers in relation to logging in boreal Ontario. *Forestry Chronicle*, **64:** 251-261.

Thompson, I.S. (1991). Will marten become the spotted owl of the east? *Forestry Chronicle*, **67:** 136-140.

Thompson, I.D. (1994). Marten populations in uncut and logged boreal forest in Ontario. *Journal of Wildlife Management*, **58:** 272-280.

Thompson, I. (1995). Ontario makes marten a featured indicator species for timber management planning. *Martes Working Group Newsletter*, **3** (1): 12-13.

Thompson, I.D. & Colgan, P.W. (1987). Numerical responses of martens to a food shortage in north-central Ontario. *Journal of Wildlife Management*, **51:** 824-835.

Thompson, I.D. & Colgan, P.W. (1991). Effects of logging on home range characteristics and hunting activity of marten in Ontario. In: B. Bobek, K. Perzanowski & W. Regelin (eds.), *Global trends in wildlife management* (*Transactions of the 18th Congress of the International Union of Game Biologists, Krakow, 1987*): 371-374.

Thompson, I.D. & Curran, W.J. (1995). Habitat suitability for marten of second-growth balsam fir forests in Newfoundland. *Canadian Journal of Zoology*, **73:** 2059-2064.

Thompson, I.D. & Harestad, A.S. (1994). Effects of logging on American martens, and models for habitat management. In: S.W. Buskirk, A.S. Harestad, M.G. Raphael & R.A. Powell (eds.), *Martens, sables, and fishers: biology and conservation*: 355-367. Ithaca (NY); Cornell University Press.

Todd, A.W. (1981). Ecological arguments for fur-trapping in boreal wilderness regions. *Wildlife Society Bulletin*, **9:** 116-124.

Toweill, D.E. & Tabor, J.E. (1982). River otter. In: J.A. Chapman & G.A. Feldhamer (eds.), *Wild mammals of North America*: 688-703. Baltimore (Maryland); Johns Hopkins University Press.

Uresk, D.W., King, R.M., Apa, A.D., Deisch, MS & Linder, R.L. (1987). Rodenticidal effects of zinc phosphide and strychnine on nontarget species. In: D.W. Uresk, G.L. Schenbeck & R. Cefkin (tech. co-ords.), *Proceedings of the 8th Great Plains Wildlife Damage Control Workshop* (*US Department of Agriculture, Rocky Mountain Range & Experimental Station General Technical Report RM-154*): 57-63.

Van Zyll de Jong, C.G. (1975). The distribution and abundance of the wolverine (*Gulo gulo*) in Canada. *Canadian Field-Naturalist*, **89:** 431-437.

Vaughan, T.A. (1978). *Mammalogy* (2nd ed.). Philadelphia (Pennsylvania); W.B. Saunders Company.

Verts, B.J. (1967). *The biology of the striped skunk*. Urbana (Illinois); University of Illinois Press.

Watt, W.R., Baker, J.A., Hogg, D.M., McNicol, J.G. & Naylor, B.J. (1996). *Forest management guidelines for the provision of marten habitat*. Sault Ste. Marie (Ontario); Ontario Ministry of Natural Resources.

Wiens, J.A., Stenseth, N.C., Van Horne, B. & Ims, R.A. (1993). Ecological mechanisms and landscape ecology. *Oikos*, **66:** 369-380.

Wilson, T.M. & Carey, A.B. (1996). Observations of weasels in second-growth Douglas-fir forests in the Puget Through, Washington. *Northwest Naturalist*, **77:** 35-39.

Wood, J.E. (1965). Response of rodent populations to controls. *Journal of Wildlife Management*, **29:** 425-427.

Wright, J.V. (1987). Archeological evidence for the use of furbearers in North America. In: M. Novak, J.A. Baker, M.E. Obbard & B. Malloch (eds.), *Wild furbearer management and conservation in North America*: 3-12. North Bay (Ontario); Ontario Trappers' Association/Ontario Ministry of Natural Resources.

Yassa, S. & Edelson, D.B. (1994). *Petition to USDA Forest Service for amendments to the regional guide and forest plans for sensitive furbearers and other old growth-associated wildlife in the Sierra Nevada National Forests.* San Francisco (California); Natural Resource Defence Council.

Yeager, L.E. (1950). Implications of some harvest and habitat factors on pine marten management. *Transactions of the North American Wildlife Conference*, **15**: 319-334.

Yukon Renewable Resources (undated). *Managing your wolverine trapline.* Leaflet. Yellowknife (Yukon); Government of Yukon.

Zackheim, H. (1982). *Ecology and population status of the river otter in southwestern Montana.* MS thesis. Missoula (Montana); University of Montana.

CHAPTER 5

Management and conservation of mustelids in Ontario and eastern Canada

Jean-François Robitaille

Abstract

For the last 100 years, Ontario and eastern Canada have collected data from the annual harvest of a large and consistent community of mustelid species. However, details of the procedures used, and the successes of the management programme are just beginning to be published, and remain still relatively hard to track down. Hence, the objective of this paper is to provide a review of the ecology and management of mustelid populations across the six eastern Canadian provinces.

Ontario and eastern Canada (including Labrador Territory) are inhabited by nine mustelid species: the long-tailed weasel, *Mustela frenata*, the ermine (or stoat), *M. erminea*, the least weasel, *M. nivalis rixosa*, the American mink, *M. vison*, the American marten, *Martes americana*, the fisher, *M. pennanti*, the North American river otter, *Lontra canadensis*, the striped skunk, *Mephitis mephitis*, and endangered populations of wolverines, *Gulo gulo*. All species but the wolverine are generally abundant, legally harvested furbearers. The recognition of the need for sustainable harvests and advances in wildlife management techniques have made habitat applied studies, wildlife population monitoring, and conservation efforts more numerous during the last half of the 20th century, especially with economically profitable species. A review of the past and current management of mustelids across the varied eastern Canadian landscape shows a range of regional goals, methods, and concerns. However, it is now admitted that different demography-related patterns tend to emerge at different scales, hence the necessity of a multi-scale approach (Bissonette, 1997).

Introduction

Nine species of Mustelidae occur in Ontario and eastern Canada, including three cursorial weasels: long-tailed weasel, *Mustela frenata*, ermine (or stoat), *M. erminea*, and least weasel, *M. nivalis rixosa*; the forest-dwelling American marten, *Martes americana*, and fisher, *M. pennanti*; the semi-aquatic American mink, *Mustela vison*, and North American river otter, *Lontra canadensis*; one generalist, the striped skunk, *Mephitis mephitis*; and small, endangered populations of wolverines, *Gulo gulo*. Except for the last, all species are abundant in most parts of eastern Canada and are legally harvested as furbearers. In eastern Canada, the American badger, *Taxidea taxus*, occurs only in the southern part of Ontario and has never been widely distributed. In eastern Canada, the striped skunk can barely qualify as a furbearer in a commercial sense; its distribution is known mostly from studies related to rabies epidemiology and control programs which cost between 15-20 million Canadian dollars (CAN$) per year (Rosatte, 1987). Rabies control programs across North America

Mustelids in a modern world
Management and conservation aspects of small carnivore: human interactions
edited by Huw I. Griffiths, pp. 77–96
© *2000 Backhuys Publishers, Leiden, The Netherlands*

may provide the data required to develop monitoring techniques applicable to other mustelid species. However, because of their marginal economic value on the fur market, both badger and striped skunk are not considered further in this paper.

Trapping in Canada is a traditional, albeit sometimes controversial, source of income and hence, way of survival and life for Canadians. Despite the depreciation of the Canadian dollar and declines in fur demand and fur prices, fur trapping in Ontario and eastern Canada has become more of a recreational/cultural activity, but still represents a significant source of income, especially in the more isolated regions of eastern Canada. For wildlife managers, trapping in Canada also represents a *de facto* "experiment" on the sustainable exploitation of (potentially) abundant species, although the methods and results of this experiment have largely been unpublicised. Nowadays, because of the high level of public concern for ecological issues, a misunderstanding of the ins and outs of a nearly three-centuries-old practice (trapping) may easily lead to political strife, and to economic disasters such as the ban and subsequent collapse of the harp seal, *Phoca groenlandica*, industry in eastern Canada in the 1980s (Canada, 1986). One particular benefit from trapping as a landscape-level human intervention is a better understanding of the challenges involved in, and possible solutions to, managing exploited mustelid populations. This chapter illustrates how commercial trapping data provide the basis for much of wildlife management in eastern Canada. This treatment may be rather superficial for the specialised Canadian reader, however, this paper is addressed particularly to outside readers curious about the large-scale management and conservation of mustelids in the context of generally abundant and exploited wildlife resources. Few monographs deal with conservation of North American mustelids, but for further reading on *Martes* species, I strongly recommend Buskirk *et al.* (1994) and Proulx *et al.* (1997).

A variable landscape

Provincial landscapes

Canada has ten provinces and two territories, and covers nearly ten million square kilometres (Table 1). Eastern Canada (*sensu* Anderson, 1987) includes five provinces and one territory (Labrador Territory, under Newfoundland's jurisdiction) and covers nearly one third of the country (21 %), including Quebec, Newfoundland, New Brunswick, Nova Scotia and Prince Edward Island.

Together, Ontario and Quebec comprise one quarter (10.7 and 15.5 %, respectively) of the country (Table 1). Ontario and eastern Canada have proportionally more forested areas (42 %) than the Canadian average. Most of the forests in Ontario and in eastern Canada are available for timber production (silviculture and harvest, current or future) except in Newfoundland (Table 1). Except for Nova Scotia, Ontario and eastern Canada have less farmland area than Canada as a whole, and farmland area decreased in Ontario, Quebec and New Brunswick between 1991 and 1996. Three provinces exceed the proportion (8 %) of freshwater area found in Canada. Ontario and eastern Canada include low mountain ranges (e.g. Appalachians in Quebec and New Brunswick) and associated drainage basins (e.g. St. Lawrence River), seashore in five provinces, and part of the Canadian Shield. Ontario and Quebec share a strong mining- and forestry-based economy in the north. Five percent of eastern Canada is insular.

Table 1. Land and water areas (1000 km sq.) in Eastern Canada, by province.

	Forested areas				Farmland*	%	Freshwater	%	Other	%	subtotal	total	%
	Productive	%	Non-productive	%									
Canada	2445,7	24,5	1730,1	17,4	680,5	6,8	755,2	7,6	4359,1	43,7	5611,5	9970,6	100,0
Eastern Canada	1174,6	37,3	572,9	18,2	102,0	3,2	399,3	12,7	900,8	28,6	2248,8	3149,6	31,6
Quebec	539,9	35,0	299,1	19,4	34,6	2,2	183,9	11,9	483,2	31,4	1057,5	1540,7	15,5
Ontario	422,0	39,5	158,0	14,8	56,2	5,3	177,4	16,6	255,0	23,9	813,6	1068,6	10,7
Newfoundland	112,7	27,8	112,5	27,7	0,4	0,1	34,0	8,4	146,1	36,0	259,7	405,7	4,1
New Brunswick	59,5	81,0	1,6	2,2	3,9	5,3	1,4	1,8	7,1	9,7	66,3	73,4	0,7
Nova Scotia	37,7	67,9	1,5	2,7	4,3	7,7	2,7	4,8	9,4	16,9	46,1	55,5	0,6
Prince Edward Island	2,8	49,1	0,2	3,5	2,7	46,5	0,0	0,0	0,0	0,8	5,7	5,7	0,1

* = Data from 1996

Source: Statistics Canada, Natural Resources Canada, Canadian Centre of Teledetection, Geoaccess.

Climate

Ontario and eastern Canada also experience a wide range of climatic conditions (Annex 1). Both maximum and minimum temperatures decrease gradually towards the north, but minimum temperatures show more local variation (e.g. Thunderbay = 16.7°C). Sable Island has an exceptionally mild minimum temperature (4.7°C). Annual rainfalls tend to decrease towards northern locations (e.g. Sable Island = 1280 mm, Kuujjuaq = 262 mm) while they tend to increase eastbound (e.g. Thunderbay = 547 mm, St-John's = 1163 mm). Snowfall tends to increase north-ward (Sable Island = 122 cm, Kuujjuaq = 271 cm) largely as a function of annual average temperature. It also increases eastward (Thunderbay = 196 cm, St-John's =322.1 cm), albeit with much regional variation. The combination of temperature and snowfall results in a wide variation in the amount of snow cover (range: Sable Island = 3 cm; Churchill Falls = 119 cm) with the insular areas having less (Annex 1). The geographical ranges of mustelids in Ontario and eastern Canada vary among species, possibly because each species shows a different tolerance threshold to annual temperature and snowfall regimes. Hence, management of populations of mustelids within a province may require different management regimes for different target population levels.

Geographical ranges of mustelids

Mustelids are common across the eastern Canadian landscape. Ermine and mink are found throughout Ontario and eastern Canada as far north as the 60th parallel, and share their range with least weasels which occur sporadically above the 47th parallel (Hall, 1951), and with long-tailed weasels found only below 48°N in Ontario and Quebec. Feral American mink have established populations in insular Newfoundland (Northcott et al., 1974).

The otter formerly inhabited aquatic ecosystems throughout much of North America (Hall & Kelson, 1959). However, progressive human encroachment, habitat destruction, and overharvest eliminated river otter from portions of their range (Nilsson, 1980). Otters now inhabit the eastern provinces, except for Prince Edward Island (Melquist & Dronkert, 1987).

Wolverine is probably the Canadian mustelid with the most marked retrogression of its original distribution. Wolverines once inhabited most of Ontario and eastern Canada, except for insular areas. Northward restriction of its historical range started in the 1840s with expanding colonisation, fur trade, settlement and declines in the herds of bison, Bison bison, and caribou, Rangifer tarandus (Hash, 1987). Today, small, isolated populations occur in the northwest corner of Ontario and in the uninhabited upper third of Quebec (>50°N) (Novak 1975; van Zyll de Jong 1975; Kelsall, 1981; Prescott, 1983). General reports have indicated reoccupation of some of the historical range where suitable habitat occurs, but no sightings have been confirmed in eastern Canada.

Habitat degradation as a result of land-use practices and the spread of chemical pollutants probably pose a threat to mink populations, at least in the southern part of its range. Mink near uranium mines showed higher radionuclide levels in their tissues than those from control areas (Dewitt, 1998) while other semi-aquatic species such as beaver, *Castor canadensis*, showed higher levels of heavy metals near industrial areas (Hillis & Parker, 1993). Mink is considered to be a sensitive bioindicator of environmental mercury levels (Wren *et al.*, 1986).

The Newfoundland population of marten, *Martes americana atrata*, is currently on the list of endangered species (Table 2), most likely due to habitat loss through landscape disturbance (Sturtevant *et al.*, 1996). From the point of view of trappers who are concerned by a decrease in harvests, expanding road access, particularly due to logging operations on Crown land, intensifies trapping pressure by facilitating access to remote areas which act as natural refuges (Strickland & Douglas, 1987; B. Olivier, pers. comm.).

By the early 1900s, the removal of forests through logging, fire, and settlement had reduced the fisher's occurrence. Protective legislation, habitat improvement, and reintroductions into areas where the species had been extirpated have since resulted in the restoration of viable fisher populations throughout much of their primordial range (Berg, 1982; Douglas & Strickland, 1987).

Ecology of exploited mustelid populations

Harvest

Not all Canadian mustelid species are equally targeted as furbearers. There is a general lack of interest from trappers and provincial managers in weasels, and currently the economic value of weasel pelts is low. However, weasels are relatively easy to trap and can be targeted locally where other furbearers are few, or if they become nuisance animals. Mink are at least partly harvested in all jurisdictions of Ontario and eastern Canada. Decreasing mink annual harvests in Ontario and Quebec suggest a gradual decline in mink populations. However, fur prices have also decreased, which suggests that trappers may have decreased their efforts (Fig. 1). In the last eight to ten years in Quebec, however, harvest levels varied with the number of trappers (hence, with capture effort) rather than fur prices (R. Lafond, pers. comm.). The steady levels of harvest of wild mink in the last two decades in New Brunswick (New Brunswick, 1997) and in Ontario and Quebec (Fig. 1) suggest that mink populations generally are not overharvested.

Mink season regulations or catch limits apparently are set by tradition, by previous harvest records, or by the primeness of pelts. Demand for wild mink varies with the demand for fur and the ranch mink markets, but the wild mink populations of Ontario and eastern Canada experience a particular pressure because of the high quality of their fur (Obbard, 1987). According to Eagle & Whitman (1987), management strategies seem to yield sustainable mink harvests and are probably adequate, in part due to the natural resilience of the species.

Martens have been, and still play, a major part in the fur harvest of Ontario and Quebec (Fig. 1). Here marten harvests reached an increasing average of 59,950 inds./year (n = 10) between 1987 and 1997 (Fig. 1). Strickland & Douglas (1987) suggested that abundant marten harvest data reflect population trends and that Ontario marten populations were able to sustain trapping pressure and habitat loss. In New Brunswick, marten annual harvests were low before 1961 because of closed

a)

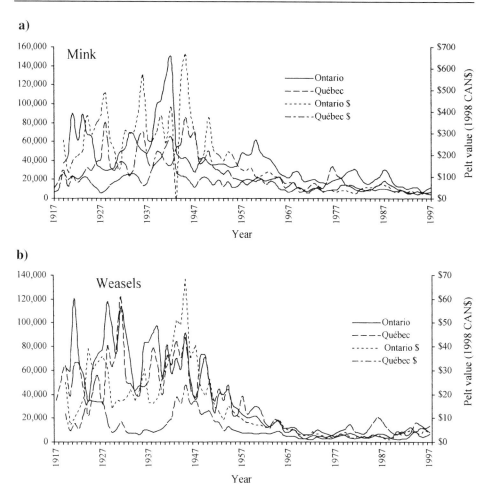

Fig. 1a, b. Harvest data and fur prices trends 1919-1997 for Ontario and Quebec for (a) mink, (b) weasels.

seasons, but rapidly increased until 1985 when a record 5,800 inds./year were caught. Marten harvests in New Brunswick have since averaged approximately 2,000 inds./year (New Brunswick, 1997). Only five martens were caught in PEI between 1919-1921, and three martens were caught in Nova Scotia between 1958-1961, shortly after a re-introduction effort (Dodds & Martell, 1971a). Between 1950-1977 in Newfoundland, marten harvests averaged 40 inds./year and increased to reach thousands in the 1980s.

Fisher status has varied rather more than that of marten. Fishers were nearly extirpated from Nova Scotia, but 104 animals were successfully re-introduced in 1947/48 and in 1963/66 (Dodds & Martell, 1971b; Table 2), although populations appear to remain geographically disjunct. Novak (1987) reported annual harvests of 25-64 animals between 1976 and 1983 in Nova Scotia. In Ontario and Quebec respectively, fisher harvest reached a peak of over 5,400 inds./year in 1927, and fluctuated about

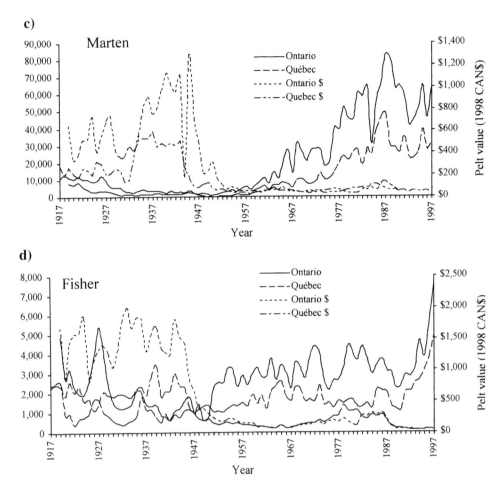

Fig. 1c, d. Harvest data and fur prices trends 1919-1997 for Ontario and Quebec for (c) marten and (d) fisher.

a current annual harvest of 3,000 and 2,000 inds./year (Fig. 1). Fisher harvests recently increased in both provinces despite poor fur prices (Fig. 1) and the number of incidental captures (*i.e.* of non-target animals) is increasing (C. Heydon, pers. comm.; Robitaille, unpubl.). Trappers' councils are lobbying for increased fisher quotas (catch limits), claiming that fishers keep the prey base low and disturb the natural balance of ecosystems (K. Monk, pers. comm.). In New Brunswick, fisher harvest levels paralleled an increase in fur prices until 1988, but decreased in 1990, only to increase again to a current annual harvest of *c.* 400 inds./year. Trapping success since 1964 (e.g. *c.* 500 individuals in 1995) is apparently due to successful re-introduction programmes (Dilworth, 1974; New Brunswick, 1997).

Intense harvests were detrimental to otter populations during the 19th century, but otters became widely protected during the first half of the 20th century. Otters are now widespread (see above) and harvests currently exceed 50,000 pelts in North

America. In Ontario and Quebec, otter harvests fluctuate around an average of 3,200 inds./year. In the last 25 years, New Brunswick's annual otter harvests fluctuated between 300-800 inds./year in proportion to fur prices (New Brunswick, 1997).

The wolverine has been heavily exploited, and occasionally persecuted, throughout much of its range. This was especially the case between 1840 and 1925 because of high fur demand. Furthermore, because wolverines were a nuisance to trappers, no limitations were imposed upon hunting and trapping, and even bounties were offered (Hornocker & Hash, 1981). However, the wolverine was never economically important on the international fur market of eastern Canada. In 1980, Canadian wolverine pelts sold for *c.* CAN$ 80. Wolverine fur is not popular for garments, thus the majority of pelts are sold locally by native communities. Full pelts are kept as trophies.

Research and conservation priorities

Partly because research on mustelids is challenging and expensive, a common trait in past Canadian wildlife management has been to prioritise short-term ecological studies of "problem" populations (*i.e.* "grease the wheel that squeaks"). This creates a short-term effect in new management actions, regardless of long-term implications. Hence, our ecological comprehension of economically valuable mustelids such as marten is at best fragmented and empirical. In other species, studies have been even more sporadic.

There are no immediate conservation concerns with long-tailed weasel. Nonetheless, weasels have been studied as small-sized models to improve understanding of the population dynamics of other, less tractable, mustelid species (e.g. Vaudry *et al.*, 1990; Raymond *et al.*, 1990). However, population-level studies of least weasels are rare (Fagerstone, 1987); field studies in eastern Canada (e.g. Simms, 1979; Robitaille & Raymond, 1995) have been empirical, and many population regulation factors (e.g. mortality sources and rates) are largely unknown. The effects of weasels on prey populations are not necessarily the same in all areas and animal communities (King, 1989).

Most North American mink research has been conducted on ranch mink (see Shump *et al.*, 1977; Pendleton, 1982), and relatively little is known about the ecology of wild mink populations. Most estimates of mink populations are based on fur harvest records. Unfortunately, there is no way to validate harvest data relative to actual population densities (Eagle & Whitman, 1987) unless trapper catch per unit effort data are provided (C. Heydon, pers. comm.). Other challenges include sexing and ageing techniques, censusing and estimating population numbers and growth, and regulating the harvest (Eagle & Whitman, 1987). Because the status of mink is generally secure, research funds are usually spent on other species with more urgent management requirements, as suggested by the low number of population inventories conducted (Deems & Pursley, 1983). Research into habitat relationships and the mink's response to changes in habitat, especially wetlands, would greatly benefit mink management (Eagle & Whitman, 1987). Techniques to determine population status and changes would alleviate some of the uncertainty in current decision-making processes.

Because of their relative abundance, value to the fur industry, and also because of the impact of logging on their preferred habitat (mature and late-successional forests), martens have attracted much scientific attention and their population ecology is much studied. The control of trapping towards sustained harvest requires that population levels and harvest density (proportion of population) be determined. There are no cost-effective methods for obtaining absolute densities of marten, but some methods offer the potential to monitor population trends over consecutive years: e.g. winter track counts (Thompson *et al.*, 1989), monitoring track counts on snow or trackboards over standard transects (Raphael, 1994). When used in conjunction with trapper surveys, these methods may help detect population trends. Few population monitoring methods have been validated in the field (Zielinski & Kucera, 1995).

Because determining the absolute numbers of marten in the population is impracticable, indices have been developed based on harvest data. Strickland & Douglas (1987) suggested the use of ratios of juveniles: adult females to estimate annual recruitment and preservation of a satisfactory adult component in the residual (*i.e.* post-harvest) population. However, these ratios have not been validated either for Ontario or other parts of marten distribution range (Kohn & Eckstein, 1987; Garant *et al.*, 1996). Strickland & Douglas (1987) suggested that refuges and untrapped areas (e.g. provincial parks) are important recolonisation source areas, but optimal size and spacing of such refuges are still uncertain. Enough reservoirs would eliminate the need for quota systems (Strickland & Douglas, 1987). Martens occur in a wide variety of climatic and habitat conditions, thus making it hard for managers to determine how results from particular ecological studies apply to their jurisdiction. Moreover, many studies have been short term and local. Long-term studies would help develop comparative population estimates, and measure the effects of fluctuations in habitat, food base and harvest levels (Watt *et al.*, 1996).

Powell's (1993) observations on fisher seem valid for populations of Ontario and eastern Canada. Interactions with humans are as important as any other aspect of fisher biology because of the invasive, yet pervasive, actions of humans on fisher populations. Commercial trapping, forestry practices, and small game hunting contribute in a variable, sometimes indirect, but probably additive, degree have a negative effect on fisher populations. Opposing this is the recurrent interest of forest managers in the fisher's potential ability to control porcupine, *Erethizon dorsatum*, populations.

Because of their size, spacing patterns and high mobility, otter management requires a considerable investment in money, time and expertise. Management objectives for otter populations are for conservation, except in the case of local population controls near fish hatcheries. The difficulty in finding sustainable population levels is compounded by unpredictable fluctuations in trapping pressure due to fur prices. Selective harvest by age class or sex would ensure that the reproductive portion of the population remains generally intact, but this is impossible to achieve with the current undiscriminating otter harvesting techniques. Data on demographic parameters, feeding habits, habitat requirements, spacing, behaviour and interactions with conspecifics and other species of the community (Melquist & Dronkert, 1987) are lacking, and techniques for ageing otters are still imperfect. Habitat simulation models are being developed, but because the otter is such a difficult animal to study, data are often non-targeted and limited in scope (Melquist & Dronkert, 1987). Despite all this, the future of otters in eastern Canada is promising due, in part, to an increased awareness of environmental contaminants (e.g. Wren *et al.*, 1986) and concern for loss of habitat.

Eastern populations of wolverines are now on the list of endangered species (Dauphiné, undated; Table 2). Ontario wolverine populations are considered vulnerable, although all captures occur at the north-western border with Manitoba. The first measures for recording and monitoring wolverine harvest appeared between 1925 and 1960. In the 1960s wolverines were legally protected in some jurisdictions, while in other areas management of exploited wolverine populations was based on harvest records, professional judgement, subjective information and scarce observations from site-specific research projects. Like most other mustelid species, wolverines are difficult and expensive to study. Populations never reach high densities and radio-telemetry requires the use of aeroplane and/or helicopter time (Hash, 1987). Recent western field studies have improved our understanding of wolverine ecology, but as with most large, solitary, territorial carnivore species, further work is needed to test and develop reliable practical density indicators of wolverine populations (Banci, 1987; Banci & Harestad 1988, 1990). The recovery of endangered eastern wolverine populations is currently under investigation (Wylynko, 1994; M. Huot, pers. comm.). Hash (1987) suggested that the future of the wolverine appears bright. In many areas, wolverines survived pioneer periods of unregulated trapping, hunting and predator control, and widespread habitat degradation. A greater public awareness of conservation issues, the current efforts of recovery teams, and a better knowledge of wolverine habitat needs and suitability, should increase the chances of successful re-introduction programs in the future.

Population recruitment: sociobiology, reproduction, and farming

Population management of exploited populations often relies on the assumption that post-harvest populations will generate enough offspring to sustain future population and harvest. Thus, techniques to estimate natural recruitment, furbearer captive propagation, and farming have been used at varying degrees to monitor, maintain or restore mustelid populations. Age-specific fecundity of martens has been obtained by counts of *corpora lutea*, but estimating the rate of increase requires the difficult task of determining age distribution (Strickland, 1994). Reproductive success depends not only on the physical condition of the parent population, but also on spacing patterns in both the adult and juvenile (*i.e.* dispersal) segments of the population. Density of mustelid populations is largely determined by intra-sexual territoriality/dominance and inter-sexual tolerance, resulting in adult males *vs.* adult female range overlap, tendency to philopatry in young females, wide dispersal of young males and overall, in relatively limited densities. These patterns also have implications for the different vulnerability of age/sex classes to trapping (Strickland, 1994).

Body size also influences the annual reproductive output among species. Among mustelids (and mammals in general), weasels are considered r-strategists with highly opportunistic, labile, populations having high turnover rates (King, 1989). When conditions are favourable, adult female (*i.e.* all female) weasels may produce ten young, whereas in years of low prey base, weasels will become extinct locally (Robitaille & Raymond, 1995). This pattern may be observed in other predatory mustelids as well (Merriam & Wegner, 1992; Schneider & Yodzis, 1994), although litter size decreases with increasing body size.

Farming of martens and fishers has been successful in the past (Patton, 1925; Ashbook & Harson, 1927; Brassard & Bernard, 1939; Douglas, 1943), but the increased time to maturity and smaller litter sizes of martens make it less profitable than mink farming. As a result, marten and fisher ranching has been only sporadic (e.g. *La Renardière*, E. Corcoran, pers. comm.).

Mortality factors

Non-trapping mortality rates are largely unknown for most mustelid species. In weasels, those factors include predation by red fox, *Vulpes vulpes*, and grey fox, *Urocyon cinereoargenteus* (Latham, 1952), raptors (Powell, 1973), and larger carnivores such as domestic cats, *Felis catus* (Robitaille, unpubl.). Canine distemper also may be affecting population levels (Goss, 1948). Natural mortality sources in mink include predation by a variety of large carnivores and owls, possible cannibalism, trapping, and possible bioaccumulation of lethal compounds (see above). In marten, non-trapping mortality may be higher in females and juveniles than in males, but males may be more susceptible to trapping (Soukkala, 1983). Hunting and trapping are not important mortality sources for wolverine in Ontario and eastern Canada where it is protected. Hash (1987) recommended that bait trapping be prohibited where population expansion is desired, that females and kits be protected, that improved techniques be developed to reduce incidental wolverine snare captures, and that surplus animals be taken only from viable populations.

Provincial management initiatives

Population management

In 1951, Ontario developed and implemented a quota system where each registered trapper was attributed one surveyed trapline (*c.* 10,000 ha) and allowed each year a variable number of animals, depending on the intrinsic habitat value of the land, previous harvest success, and the species. Until 1999, every trapper had their pelts sealed and recorded before fur auctions, and the possession of surplus pelts for more than one year was illegal. In Quebec, fur sealing is not mandatory and the Ministry monitors fur sales and operated (until recently) by controlling the length of the season. A reform is in process to administer the harvest on a regional basis. In other jurisdictions, methods of control of harvest include closed or short seasons. Most, if not all, jurisdictions possess a furbearer management programme that keeps exhaustive records on economically important mustelids and tends to manage using a synecological (*i.e.* ecosystem-based) approach (Douglas, 1988).

In 1989 Quebec set up a systematic trapper survey (Lafond, 1990). In this survey, a sample of trappers was asked to report on their annual fur harvest using a field booklet. This included data on fur catches, trapping activity pattern and effort, biological information (e.g. sex and age-class of the catch), and also personal opinions on the population levels of snowshoe hare, *Lepus americanus*, and some other furbearers during the season (Fig. 2; R. Lafond, pers. comm.). After a critical review, Garant *et al.* (1996) concluded that long-term analysis would improve

The Trapline Diary

**Cochrane Area
Fur Council**

MNR

Ontario

EXAMPLE

1: This trapper had no traps set for Lynx on the 11th of December, but he did install 3 traps on the 12th and bagged a female Lynx on the 14th. The last day of the Lynx trapping season, that is the 15th, he had 3 traps in operation.

2: This same trapper bagged 2 male Marten on the 12th of December, one female the next day and removed his traps on the 15th.

3: Since no Fisher were present in his area, our trapper indicated only zero for these traps during this period.

DECEMBER

SPECIES		DATES	11	12	13	14	15	16	17	
LYNX		MALE	0	0	0	0	0			
		FEMALE	0	0	0	1	0			①
		UNKNOWN								
		NB TRAPS	0	3	3	3	3			
MARTEN		MALE	0	2	0	1	0	0	0	
		FEMALE	0	0	1	0	0	0	0	②
		UNKNOWN								
		NB TRAPS	10	10	12	12	0	0	5	
FISHER		MALE								
		FEMALE								
		UNKNOWN								③
		NB TRAPS	0	0	0	0	0	0	0	

Fig. 2. Ontario's trapline diary. The diary yields furbearer harvest and capture effort and the two values can be used to calculate success of capture.

statistical trends, but that trapper information was reasonably accurate and could be used as a management tool. They recommended the use of the trapper booklet as a main source for marten population monitoring, testing derived population trends against annual fur harvests and sales, testing sex ratios against carcass data, and maintaining systematic sampling in three targeted areas to reflect regional differences (determining adequate sample size in each region after Dussault, 1990).

Ontario tested the value of furbearer harvest data obtained through mailed trapper questionnaires and obtained moderate success (C. Heydon, unpubl.). A non-mandatory trapper booklet project was still experimental in 1998 (see Fig. 2). Ontario initiated research projects aimed at testing various field methods for population monitoring (Raphael, 1994; Robitaille, unpubl.). Quebec's law on endangered species allows for the protection of the habitats of threatened or vulnerable wolverine and least weasel. In Quebec, between 1989 and 1998, the sexes of harvested mink and otter were analysed without any significance for the management of populations. Quebec's trapper booklet provides for the estimation of trapping effort and success (catch per unit effort, e.g. animals/1,000 trap-nights), while other indices are used from trappers' surveys. Local Quebec jurisdictions run marten carcass analyses (e.g. physical condition, fertility), subject to review, and the collection of fisher skulls was established in 1996. In New Brunswick, trappers were asked to return marten carcasses to the Department of Natural Resources and Energy, and this helped construct a life table analysis from which a decreasing trend in marten population growth rate was apparent. Correction measures suggested included a restricted quota system rather than any shortening of the season (Cumberland, 1992, 1993).

Habitat conservation

Habitat conservation measures vary among jurisdictions according to different socio-economic priorities, but all include lobbies for increased nature preserve areas and enhanced habitat information dissemination among foresters and biologists (Thompson & Welsh, 1993). Ontario recently developed forest management guidelines for the provision of marten habitat (Watt *et al.*, 1996), while implementing a planning process called Lands for Life (Table 2) to determine land use in its 46 million hectares of Crown land. Public hearings were completed in autumn 1998. In Ontario, forest is often divided into three zones (boreal, transition and temperate forests) and into regions (Rowe, 1972), but forests must be redefined for the purpose of integrated resource management measures (Douglas, 1988). For example, north-eastern Ontario's forests alone are now subdivided into 22 ecosystem site types (D'Eon & Watt 1994; Bowman *et al.*, 1996).

New Brunswick imposes a Conservation Fee towards the New Brunswick Wildlife Trust Fund which will support wildlife and habitat enhancement projects (Cumberland, 1992; Table 2). Furthermore, since 1992, it has incorporated quantitative, spatially explicit Marten Habitat Objectives in all forest management plans for all Crown land. Marten were used as "umbrella" species for other wildlife species with similar habitat preference (*i.e.* late-successional coniferous forest). New Brunswick implemented suggestions from Thompson & Welsh (1993) and beyond to reach landscape-level objectives. New Brunswick Forest Habitat Management Guidelines suggest future areas for research and development (New Brunswick, 1995), while Nova Scotia has a new Wilderness Areas Protection Act (Table 2).

All east Canadian jurisdictions recognise that habitat is an important aspect of the ecology of mustelids, and have made habitat management a priority. However, habitat heterogeneity and dynamics limit the capability of generic habitat models, and complicate the decision-making process for wildlife managers.

Table 2. Some internet addresses relevant to provincial conservation of Mustelids

Name	URL address
COSEWIC	http://www.cosewic.gc.ca
Environment Canada	http://www.cmc.ec.gc.ca
Greenpeace International	http://www.greenpeace.org/
New Brunswick Dept. Natural Resources & Energy	http://www.gov.nb.ca/dnre/index.htm
Nova Scotia Furbearer Program	http://www.gov.ns.ca/natr/wildlife/furbers/furbs.htm
Nova Scotia Department of Environment	http://www.gov.ns.ca/envi/dept/mission.htm#index
Ontario Ministry of Natural Resources	http://www.mnr.gov.on.ca/MNR/
Parks Canada	http://parkscanada.pch.gc.ca/parks/main_e.htm
PEI Fish and Wildlife	http://www.gov.pe.ca/te/faw-info/index.php3
Quebec territory	http://www.gouv.qc.ca/territoi/indexf.htm
Statistics Canada	http://www.StatCan.ca

Conclusion

Historically, Ontario and eastern Canada offered abundant wildlife and habitat resources and this promoted the northward colonisation of lands and waterways. However, Canadian population densities are still relatively low outside urban conglomerates, and the tradition of sustained fur harvest, even as a recreational activity, is alive and well in rural communities. The trade and sale of furs are still a vital part of the economy of rural people of the north. Furthermore, systematic harvest records have provided largely untapped data banks that provide for the better management of mustelid populations in eastern Canada.

Provincial authorities have the daunting task of managing a diversity of furbearers, most of which are mustelid species. Although provincial ministries receive a wealth of information from the fur harvest data and trappers' contributions, research projects have often been limited to sporadic attempts to solve local problems. There is a need for long-term, large-scale studies, which could possibly be implemented through research and development-oriented sampling of trapping data. Thompson & Welsh (1993) suggest steps towards an integrated approach to forest resource management: recognition of institutional short-comings, development of predictive models using a common language for foresters and wildlife managers, re-tooling with Geographical Information System technology and decision support systems, and development of habitat models that are fit for landscape-scale management plans. More integrated studies would probably contemplate using data from several human generations of seasonal and inter-annual variations in intra- and interspecific interactions, gene flow, trends in human encroachment, fire patterns, trapping, pollution, growth rates, and chaotic events (e.g. the freezing rain that transformed the landscape in southern Ontario and Quebec in February, 1998). An analysis at several spatial and temporal grain sizes is necessary to develop predictive mustelid population dynamic models (Bissonette, 1997).

Successful long-term management-oriented studies on mustelid species have taken place in various locations, including Switzerland (Debrot, 1984), Maine (Bissonette *et al.*, 1997) and Ontario (Strickland & Douglas, 1987). However, in Ontario and eastern Canada, research institutions are rarely funded for long-term research projects, and government agencies are primarily mandated to serve the public. Trapper data based on an educated, long-lasting involvement from responsible trappers and government agencies has proved, in some cases, to significantly support management operations. Further dissemination of information to research institutions would allow researchers to contribute in screening, processing, and analysing huge data banks, and to orientate data collection. Government institutions would benefit from helping to bring together knowledge (*i.e.* research results and applications) and decision-making processes, which are intimately linked.

Most mustelid species are solitary and territorial carnivores and prime members of the eastern Canadian furbearer group. Recurrent in Novak *et al.*'s (1987) compendium on furbearer conservation and management in North America is the notion that mustelids defy determination of the data fundamental to population management: estimation of population sizes, both relative and absolute, determination of annual changes in productivity or recruitment, and hence, establishment of regulation for a sustainable harvest. Despite the uncertainty in basic population parameters and in management strategies and outcomes, most mustelid populations in eastern Canada have resisted waves of heavy commercial trapping, hunting, bounties, and/or predator control programs, and still nowadays show viable populations, based on a consistent data source, the fur harvest.

Acknowledgements

This paper benefited from the generous inputs from J. Brazil (Wildlife Branch, Department of Forest Resources and Agrifoods, Newfoundland), C. Heydon (Ontario Ministry of Natural Resources), M. Huot, R. Lafond & F. Potvin (Ministère de l'Environnement et de la Faune Québec), M. O'Brien (Wildlife Division, Department of Natural Resources, Nova Scotia), M. Sullivan (Fish & Wildlife Branch, Department of Natural Resources and Energy, New Brunswick), B. Olivier (Lakeland Lodge, Skead, Ontario), and E. Corcoran (Domaine Rivière Verte, St-Raymond, Québec) whom I would like to thank. Special thanks to Mr. Karl Monk (206 Bear Lake Road, Monetville, Ontario) for sharing his knowledge of the biology of harvest of furbearers in northern Ontario. My sincere thanks also to J.C. Bowman and A.C. Landry for their thoughts and editorial help.

References

Anderson, S.B. (1987). Wild furbearer management in eastern Canada. In: M. Novak, J.A. Baker, M.E. Obbard & B. Malloch (eds.), *Wild furbearer management and conservation in North America*: 1039-1048. North Bay (Ontario); Ontario Trappers' Association/Ontario Ministry of Natural Resources.

Ashbook, F.G. & Harson, K.B. (1927). Breeding marten in captivity. *Journal of Heredity*, **18**: 499-503.

Banci, V. (1987). *Ecology and behaviour of the wolverine in Yukon.* MSc thesis. Vancouver (BC); Simon Fraser University.

Banci, V. & Harestad, A.(1988). Reproduction and natality of wolverine (*Gulo gulo*) in Yukon. *Annales Zoologici Fennici*, **25**: 265-270.

Banci, V. & Harestad, A.S. (1990). Home range and habitat use of wolverines *Gulo gulo* in Yukon, Canada. *Holarctic Ecology*, **13**: 195-200.

Berg, W.E. (1982). Reintroduction of fisher, pine marten, and river otter. In: G.C. Anderson (ed.), *Midwest furbearer management* (*Proceedings of the 43rd Symposium of the Midwest Fish and Wildlife Conference, Wichita, Kansas*): 159-173.

Bissonette, J.A (1997). Scale-sensitive ecological properties: historical context, current meaning. In: J.A. Bissonette (ed.), *Wildlife and landscape ecology: effects of pattern and scale*: 3-31. New York; Springer Verlag.

Bissonette, J.A., Harrison, D.J., Hargis, C.D. & Chapin, T.G. (1997). The influence of spatial scale and scale sensitive properties on habitat selection by American marten. In: J.A. Bissonette (ed.), *Wildlife and landscape ecology: effects of pattern and scale*: 368-385. New York; Springer-Verlag.

Bowman, J.C., Robitaille, J.-F. & Watt, W.R. (1996). Northeastern Ontario forest ecosystem classification as a tool for managing marten habitat. *Forestry Chronicle*, **72**: 529-532.

Brassard, J.S. & Bernard, R. (1939). Observations on breeding and development of marten, *Martes americana* (Kerr). *Canadian Field-Naturalist*, **53**: 15-21.

Buskirk, S.W., Harestad, A.S., Raphael, M.G. & Powell, R.A. (Eds.) (1994). *Martens, sables and fishers: biology and conservation.* Ithaca (NY); Cornell University Press.

Canada (1986). *Les phoques et la chasse au phoque au Canada - Rapport final de la Commission Royale sur les Phoques et la Chasse au Phoque.* Ottawa (Ontario); Ministère des Approvisionnements et Services.

Cumberland, R.E. (1993). *A life table analysis of American marten (Martes americana) in New Brunswick* (*Furbearer Report No. 5*). Saint John (NB); New Brunswick Department of Natural Resources & Energy.

Cumberland, R.E. (1992). *A framework for furbearer management in New Brunswick: proposed goals and objectives for the furbearer management program* (*Unpublished Report*). Saint John (NB); New Brunswick Department of Natural Resources & Energy.

D'Eon, R.G. & Watt, W.R. (1994). *A forest habitat suitability matrix for northeastern Ontario* (*Technical Manual TM-004*). Toronto (Ontario); Northeast Science and Technology, Ministry of Natural Resources.

Dauphiné, C. (undated). *Updated status on the wolverine Gulo gulo in Canada.* Ottawa (Ontario); Committee on the Status of Endangered Wildlife in Canada.

Debrot, S. (1984). The structure and dynamics of a stoat (*Mustela erminea*) population. *Revue d'Ecologie*, **39**: 77-88.

Deems, E.F., Jr. & Pursley, D. (1983). *North American furbearers: a contemporary reference.* Baltimore & Annapolis (Maryland); International Association of Fish and Wildlife Agencies/Maryland Department of Natural Resources.

Dewitt, T.J. (1998). *Ra-226 in bone of secondary consumers (mink, Mustela vison, and otter, Lutra canadensis) taken near U workings at Elliott Lake, Canada, and from control areas, with calculation of transfer parameters from some of their prey.* BSc thesis. Sudbury (Ontario); Laurentian University.

Dilworth, T.G. (1974). Status and distribution of fisher and marten in New Brunswick. *Canadian Field-Naturalist*, **88**: 495-498.

Dodds, D.G. & Martell, A.M. (1971a). The recent status of the marten, *Martes americana americana* (Turton) in Nova Scotia. *Canadian Field-Naturalist*, **85**: 61-62.

Dodds, D.G. & Martell, A.M. (1971b). The recent status of the fisher, *Martes pennanti pennanti* (Erxleben) in Nova Scotia. *Canadian Field-Naturalist*, **85**: 63-65.

Douglas, C.W. & Strickland, M.A. (1987). Fisher. In: M. Novak, J.A. Baker, M.E. Obbard & B. Malloch (eds.), *Wild furbearer management and conservation in North America*: 511-529. North Bay (Ontario); Ontario Trappers' Association/Ontario Ministry of Natural Resources.

Douglas, L.A. (1988). The development and evolution of the integrated resource management philosophy within the Ministry of Natural Resources. *Forestry Chronicle*, **64**: 267-269.

Douglas, W.O. (1943). Fisher farming has arrived. *American Fur Breeder*, **16**: 18-20.

Dussault, C. (1990). *Plan tactique: martre d'Amérique*. Québec; Ministère du Loisir, de la Chasse et de la Pêche du Québec, Direction Générale des Espèces et des Habitats.

Eagle, T.C. & Whitman, J.S. (1987). Mink. In: M. Novak, J.A. Baker, M.E. Obbard & B. Malloch (eds.), *Wild furbearer management and conservation in North America*: 615-624. North Bay (Ontario); Ontario Trappers' Association/Ontario Ministry of Natural Resources.

Fagerstone, K.A. (1987). Black-footed ferret, long-tailed weasel, short-tailed weasel, and least weasel. In: M. Novak, J.A. Baker, M.E. Obbard & B. Malloch (eds.), *Wild furbearer management and conservation in North America*: 548-573. North Bay (Ontario); Ontario Trappers' Association/Ontario Ministry of Natural Resources.

Garant, Y., Lafond, R. & Courtois, R. (1996). *Analyse du système de suivi de la martre d'Amérique (Martes americana) au Québec*. Québec; Ministère de l'Environnement et de la Faune du Québec, Direction de la Faune et des Habitats (Service de la Faune Terrestre).

Goss, L.J. (1948). Species susceptibility to the viruses of Carre and feline enteritis. *American Journal of Veterinary Research*, **9**: 65.

Hall, E.R. (1951). American weasels. *University of Kansas Publications, Museum of Natural History*, **4**: 1-466.

Hall, E.R. & Kelson, K.R. (1959). *Mammals of North America*. New York; Ronald Press.

Hash, H.S. (1987). Wolverine. In: M. Novak, J.A. Baker, M.E. Obbard & B. Malloch (eds.), *Wild furbearer management and conservation in North America*: 574-585. North Bay (Ontario); Ontario Trappers' Association/Ontario Ministry of Natural Resources.

Hillis, T.L. & Parker, G.H. (1993). Age and proximity to local ore-smelters as determinants of tissue metal levels in beaver (*Castor canadensis*) of the Sudbury (Ontario) area. *Environmental Pollution*, **80**: 67-72.

Hornocker, M.G. & Hash, H.S. (1981). Ecology of the wolverine in northwestern Montana. *Canadian Journal of Zoology*, **59**: 1286-1301.

Kelsall, J.P. (1981). *Status report on the wolverine, Gulo gulo, in Canada in 1981*. Ottawa (Ontario); Commission on the Status of Endangered Wildlife.

King, C.M. (1989). *The natural history of weasels and stoats*. New York; Comstock Publishing Associates.

Kohn, B.E. & Eckstein, R.G. (1987). *Status of marten in Wisconsin, 1985 (WDNR Research Report 143)*. Madison (Wisconsin); Wisconsin Department of Natural Resources.

Lafond, R. (1990). *Analyse du système de suivi des animaux à fourrure*. Québec; Ministère du Loisir, de la Chasse et de la Pêche Québec, Direction de la Gestion des Espèces et des Habitats.

Latham, R.M. (1952). The fox as a factor in the control of weasel populations. *Journal of Wildlife Management*, **16**: 516-517.

Melquist, W.E. & Dronkert, A.E. (1987). River otter. In: M. Novak, J.A. Baker, M.E. Obbard & B. Malloch (eds.), *Wild furbearer management and conservation in North America*: 627-641. North Bay (Ontario); Ontario Trappers' Association/Ontario Ministry of Natural Resources.

Merriam, G. & Wegner, J. (1992). Local extinctions, habitat fragmentation and ecotones. In: A.J. Hansen & F. di Castri (eds.), *Landscape boundaries: consequences for biotic diversity and ecological flows*: 151-169. New York; Springer-Verlag.

New Brunswick (1995). *Management of forest habitat in New Brunswick*. Fredericton (NB); New Brunswick Department of Natural Resources & Energy, Fish and Wildlife Branch (Forest Habitat Program).

New Brunswick (1997). *New Brunswick furbearer harvest report 1996-1997*. Fredericton (NB); New Brunswick Department of Natural Resources & Energy, Fish and Wildlife Branch.

Nilsson, G. (1980). *River otter research workshop*. Gainsville (Florida); Florida State Museum.

Northcott, T.H., Payne, N.E. & Mercer, E. (1974). Dispersal of mink in insular Newfoundland. *Journal of Mammalogy*, **55**: 243-248.

Novak, M. (1975). *Recent status of the wolverine in Ontario*. Toronto (Ontario); Ontario Ministry of Natural Resources.

Novak, M. (1987). *Furbearer harvests in North America, 1600-1984*. Toronto (Ontario); Ontario Trappers' Association.

Novak, M., Baker, J.A., Obbard, M.E. & Malloch, B. (Eds.) (1987). *Wild furbearer management and conservation in North America*. North Bay (Ontario); Ontario Trappers' Association/Ontario Ministry of Natural Resources.

Obbard, M.E. (1987). Fur grading and pelt identification. In: M. Novak, J.A. Baker, M.E. Obbard & B. Malloch (eds.), *Wild furbearer management and conservation in North America*: 717-826. North Bay (Ontario); Ontario Trappers' Association/Ontario Ministry of Natural Resources.

Patton, H. (1925). *Raising fur-bearing animals*. London; Wheldon & Wesley Ltd.

Pendleton, G.W. (1982). *A selected annotated bibliography of mink behavior and ecology (SDCWRU Technical Bulletin no. 3)*. Brooking (SD); South Dakota Co-operative Wildlife Research Unit.

Powell, R.A. (1973). A model for raptor predation on weasels. *Journal of Mammalogy*, **54**: 259-263.

Powell, R.A. (1993). *The fisher: life history, ecology and behavior* (2nd ed.). Minneapolis (Minnesota); University of Minnesota Press.

Prescott, J. (1983). Wolverine, *Gulo gulo*, in Lake St-John area, Quebec. *Canadian Field-Naturalist*, **97**: 457.

Proulx, G., Bryant, H.N. & Woodard, P.M. (Eds.) (1997). *Martes: taxonomy, ecology, techniques, and management*. Edmonton (Alberta); Provincial Museum of Alberta.

Raphael, M.G. (1994). Techniques for monitoring populations of fishers and American martens. In: S.W. Buskirk, A.S. Harestad, M.G. Raphael & R.A. Powell (eds.), *Martens, sables and fishers: biology and conservation*: 224-240. Ithaca (NY); Cornell University Press.

Raymond, M., Robitaille, J.-F., Lauzon, P. & Vaudry, R. (1990). Prey-dependent profitability of foraging behaviour of male and female ermine, *Mustela erminea*. *Oikos*, **58**: 323-328.

Robitaille, J.-F. & Raymond, M. (1995). Spacing patterns of ermine, *Mustela erminea* L., in a Quebec agrosystem. *Canadian Journal of Zoology*, **73**: 1827-1834.

Rosatte, R.C. (1987). Striped, spotted, hooded, and hog-nosed skunk. In: M. Novak, J.A. Baker, M.E. Obbard & B. Malloch (eds.), *Wild furbearer management and conservation in North America*: 598-613. North Bay (Ontario); Ontario Trappers' Association/Ontario Ministry of Natural Resources.

Rowe, J.S. (1972). *Forest regions of Canada*. Ottawa (Ontario); Canadian Forestry Service, Department of the Environment.

Schneider, R.R. & Yodzis, P. (1994). Extinction dynamics in the American marten (*Martes americana*). *Conservation Biology*, **8**: 1058-1068.

Shump, A.V., Shump, K.A., Heidt, G.A. & Aulerich, J. (1977). *A bibliography of mustelids. II. Mink*. Pittsville (Maryland); Mink Farmer's Research Foundation.

Simms, D.A. (1979). North American weasels: resource utilization and distribution. *Canadian Journal of Zoology*, **57**: 504-520.

Soukkala, A.M. (1983). *The effects of trapping on marten populations in Maine*. MSc thesis. Orono (Maine); University of Maine.

Strickland, M.A. (1994). Harvest management of fishers and American martens. In: S.W. Buskirk, A.S. Harestad, M.G. Raphael & R.A. Powell (eds.), *Martens, sables, and fishers: biology and conservation*: 149-164. Ithaca (NY); Cornell University Press.

Strickland, M.A. & Douglas, C.W. (1987). Marten. In: M. Novak, J.A. Baker, M.E. Obbard & B. Malloch (eds.), *Wild furbearer management and conservation in North America*: 548-573. North Bay (Ontario); Ontario Trappers' Association/Ontario Ministry of Natural Resources.

Sturtevant, B.R., Bissonette, J.A. & Long, J.N. (1996). Temporal and spatial dynamics of boreal structure in western Newfoundland: silvicultural implications for marten habitat management. *Forest Ecology and Management*, **87**: 13-25.

Thompson, I.D., Davidson, I.J., O'Donnell, S. & Brazeau, F. (1989). Use of track transects to measure the relative occurrence of some boreal mammals in uncut forest and regeneration stands. *Canadian Journal of Zoology*, **67**: 1816-1823.

Thompson, I.D. & Welsh, D.A. (1993). Integrated resource management in boreal forest ecosystems – impediments and solutions. *Forestry Chronicle*, **69**: 32-39.

van Zyll de Jong, C.G. (1975). The distribution and abundance of the wolverine (*Gulo gulo*) in Canada. *Canadian Field-Naturalist*, **89**: 431-437.

Vaudry, R., Raymond, M. & Robitaille, J.-F. (1990). The capture of voles and shrews by male and female ermine, *Mustela erminea*, in captivity. *Holarctic Ecology*, **13**: 265-268.

Watt, W.R., Baker, J.A., Hogg, D.M., McNicol, J.G. & Naylor, B.J. (1996). *Forest management guidelines for the provision of marten habitat*. Timmins (Ontario); Ontario Ministry of Natural Resources, Northeastern Science and Technology.

Wren, C.D., Stokes, P.M. & Fischer, K.L. (1986). Mercury levels in Ontario mink and otter relative to food levels and environmental acidification. *Canadian Journal of Zoology*, **64:** 2854-2859.

Wylynko, D. (1994). *Recovery of nationally endangered wildlife (MSS Report no. 4)*. Ottawa (Ontario); Ministry of Supply and Services.

Zielinski, W.J. & Kucera, T.E. (1995). *American marten, fisher, lynx, and wolverine: survey methods for their detection (US Department of Agriculture Forest Service Technical Bulletin PSW-GTR-157)*.

Annex 1. Climatic characteristics in selected cities of eastern Canada

City	Lat N	Lon W	Max temp (°C)	Min temp (°C)	Average temp (°C)	Rainfall (mm)	Snowfall (cm)	Max snow cover (cm)	Sunshine (h)	Wind speed (km/h)
Ontario										
Moosonee	51°16'	80°39'	4,7	-7,4	-1,3	499,8	225,4	64	1777,4	12
Ottawa	45°19'	75°40'	10,7	0,8	5,8	701,8	221,5	31	–	14
Sudbury	46°37'	80°48'	8,5	-1,6	3,5	635,8	266,6	40	–	18
Thunderbay	48°22'	89°19'	8,4	-16,7	-11,3	546,8	195,5	35	2183,3	13
Toronto	43°40'	79°38'	12,3	1,9	7,2	664,7	124,2	8	–	15
Quebec										
Baie Comeau	49°08'	68°12'	6,3	-3,4	1,5	661,6	362	69	–	16
Kuujjuaq	58°06'	68°25'	-1,3	-10,3	-5,8	262	270,5	66	–	16
Mont-Joli	48°36'	68°13'	7,4	-1,2	3,1	572,2	373	66	–	19
Montreal	45°28'	73°45'	10,9	1,2	6,1	736,3	214,2	21	–	15
Québec	46°48'	71°23'	9	-1	4	881,3	337	79	1910,4	15
Val D'Or	48°04'	77°47'	7	-4,7	1,2	630	317,6	68	1903	13
Newfoundland										
Churchill Falls	53°33'	64°06'	1,6	-8,7	-3,5	497,9	481	119	1618,4	15
Gander	48°57'	54°34'	8,3	-0,4	4	737,9	443,8	44	–	21
St-John's	47°37'	52°44'	8,6	0,8	4,7	1163,1	322,1	24	–	24
New Brunswick										
Saint John	45°20'	65°53'	9,8	-0,2	4,9	1156,4	283,2	26	1893,7	18
Moncton	46°07'	64°41'	10,3	-0,4	5	834,5	365,5	36	1939	17
Fredericton	45°55'	66°37'	10,7	-0,2	5,3	856,7	240,5	30	1928,9	12
Nova Scotia										
Halifax	44°53'	63°31'	10,7	1,4	6,1	1222,7	261,4	18	–	18
Sable Island	44	60°01'	10,1	4,7	7,5	1280	122,4	3	1471	25
Yarmouth	43°50'	66°05'	10,7	2,8	6,8	1077,1	205,3	9	1821,8	18
Prince Edward Island										
Charlottetown	46°17'	6308'	9,5	0,8	5,2	868,6	338,7	31	–	19

Source: Environment Canada

CHAPTER 6

Black-footed ferrets: recovering an endangered species in an endangered habitat

Astrid Vargas*, Pete Gober, Mike Lockhart & Paul Marinari

Abstract

The black-footed ferret, one of North America's rarest mammals, depends on an endangered ecosystem for its survival. Prairie dogs, a keystone species within this ecosystem and the black-footed ferrets' main prey, have been seriously decimated over this century. As a result, captive breeding became the only conservation avenue for black-footed ferrets (ferrets). Captive propagation efforts began in 1986 and, to date, more than 2,600 kits have been born in captivity. Since 1991, approximately 873 captive-raised black-footed ferrets have been returned to native habitats in five sites located in Wyoming, Montana, South Dakota and Arizona. Ferret reintroduction efforts in Wyoming were suspended in 1995 due to an epizootic of sylvatic plague. Research has been, and continues to be critical in directing ferret recovery, and studies on diseases, reproductive biology, behavioural development, and field biology have helped shape management efforts. Experimental work has demonstrated that a naturalistic captive environment, especially during early developmental periods, is critical for survival after release. Consequently, management efforts have been adapted to provide all reintroduction candidates with "preconditioning" experience prior to release. Efforts are presently directed towards breeding and preconditioning ferrets at reintroduction sites. With continuing success in the implementation of captive breeding and reintroduction techniques, the recovery program must now pursue conservation measures to protect and enhance large extensions of ferret habitat. Protection of prairie dog complexes to conserve black-footed ferrets would, in turn, help safeguard many other species that coexist in the imperilled prairie dog ecosystem.

Of ferrets and prairie dogs

The black-footed ferret, *Mustela nigripes*, is a habitat and prey specialist that relies on prairie dogs, *Cynomys* spp., for survival. Black-footed ferrets (ferrets) utilise prairie dogs for food and their burrows as dens (Sheets *et al.*, 1972; Campbell *et al.*, 1987). Historically, black-footed ferrets occupied a vast range across the Great Plains of North America, overlapping prairie dog habitat from southern Canada to northern Mexico (Anderson *et al.*, 1986). The cost of this high dependence on the prairie dog community was extreme vulnerability to habitat disturbance – which came in the form of prairie dog poisoning campaigns and introduced diseases. Government controlled poisoning programs began shortly after the turn of the century and,

---

* Corresponding author.

Mustelids in a modern world
Management and conservation aspects of small carnivore: human interactions
edited by Huw I. Griffiths, pp. 97–105
© 2000 Backhuys Publishers, Leiden, The Netherlands

together with conversion of prairie into agricultural land and sylvatic plague, decimated the original distribution of prairie dogs by 98% (Miller *et al.*, 1994). Sylvatic plague, an infectious disease caused by the bacterium *Yersinia pestis*, was introduced into the United States in the late 1800s (Barnes, 1993). Plague is devastating for prairie dogs and has advanced progressively from the Pacific coast across the western United States (Barnes, 1993; Cully 1993). Population recovery after a plague epizootic may take several years (Mulhern & Knowles, 1995), and some colonies never recover (Cully, 1993).

Prairie dogs are critical components of the short/mid-grass prairie ecosystem. Burrowing and grazing activities of prairie dogs benefit a number of ecosystem functions such as soil oxygenation, enhanced vegetation structure, and increased plant nutrient qualities (Uresk & Bjustad, 1983; Munn,1988; Reading *et al.*, 1989; Miller *et al.*, 1994; Wuerthner, 1997). The ecosystem created by prairie dogs is valuable to many other taxa, and more that 100 species of mammals, birds and reptiles are known associates of prairie dogs and the habitat they provide (Clark *et al.*, 1989; Reading *et al.*, 1989). Historically, ranchers believed that prairie dogs competed with cattle for forage, and they began eradication campaigns in the late 1800s (McNulty, 1971). But prairie dog impact on rangeland production is not as detrimental as many had thought, and recent studies have shown that wild and domestic ungulates prefer to graze on prairie dog colonies (Detling & Whicker, 1987; Knowles, 1986). However, negative attitudes towards prairie dogs still continue today (Roemer & Forrest, 1996).

Habitat conversion, eradication campaigns, and disease, left fragmented prairie dog complexes that were either too small or too isolated from each other to maintain viable ferret populations (Miller *et al.*, 1990). As a result, the black-footed ferret was thought to be extinct twice, once in the late 1950s and again in the late 1970s. A free-ranging ferret population was discovered during the 1960s in South Dakota and disappeared for unknown reasons in the early 1970s (Hillman, 1968; Henderson *et al.*, 1974). The last wild black-footed ferret population was discovered in Meteetsee, Wyoming, in 1981 and it collapsed due to an epizootic of canine distemper in 1985 (Williams *et al.*, 1988).

Between autumn 1985 and spring 1987, all ferrets that could be captured at Meteetsee (n = 18) were brought into captivity to initiate a breeding program at the Wyoming Game and Fish Department's (WGFD) Sybille Wildlife Research and Conservation Education Unit (Thorne *et al.*, 1987). Captive propagation has been successful, with more than 2,600 kits born during the past 11 years. From the original 18 founders, only seven have contributed to the present genetic pool but, in spite of the high population kinship, inbreeding depression has not been apparent in the propagation program. Presently, there are seven facilities involved in a Species Survival Plan (SSP®) breeding program. Half of the captive population is maintained at the US Fish & Wildlife Service, National Black-footed Ferret Conservation Center (FCC), Wyoming (formerly the WGFD Sybille Unit), while the remaining captive animals are distributed among six North American zoos (Vargas *et al.*, 1996). The Recovery Program has used scientific research to help direct recovery efforts, integrating knowledge from captive breeding and reintroduction studies, and adapting relevant findings into an effective management for the management of this endangered species.

Integrating research to manage an endangered population

Captive and field research have been essential to furthering our understanding of black-footed ferret biological needs and disease susceptibilities, ensuring the health of the captive stock, improving captive propagation methods, refining reintroduction techniques, and enhancing the survival of reintroduced animals. Disease research continues to be a program priority and efforts have been focused on learning how to manage two infectious diseases: canine distemper and sylvatic plague. Distemper is lethal to black-footed ferrets (Williams *et al.*, 1988), and the development of an adequate vaccine that ensures protection of reintroduced animals is an ongoing program challenge. For the past few years, ferrets have been immunised with a killed canine distemper vaccine developed by Dr. Max Appel (Williams *et al.*, 1996). Although the vaccine is safe and provides good antibody titres, it does not confer life-long immunity and requires repeated boosters (Williams *et al.*, 1996). Researchers are currently testing modified live virus and recombinant vaccines, both of which have yielded encouraging results in the closely-related steppe polecat, *Mustela eversmannii*, and in black-footed ferret x steppe polecat hybrids (B. Williams, chair, BFF Disease Working Group, pers. comm). Ongoing research is also directed at studying the dynamics of canine distemper at reintroduction sites (B. Williams, pers. comm.). This information will increase our understanding of how to manage free-ranging ferrets and how to predict when a distemper epizootic may occur. Sylvatic plague is fatal to prairie dogs and black-footed ferrets (Williams *et al.*, 1994), and it is perhaps the greatest biological challenge for ferret conservation and recovery. Plague research is therefore a top program priority and, although no conclusive results are presently available, studies are directed at developing an effective vaccine and understanding the dynamics of plague in prairie dog towns (B. Williams, pers. comm.).

Studies on black-footed ferret reproductive biology have improved captive breeding techniques and consequently increased the number of kits available for release. Black-footed ferrets are seasonally monoestrus and, in captivity, the breeding season extends from February to May. Female readiness to breed is detected using vaginal cytology (Williams *et al.*, 1991, 1992; Carvalho, 1992) and pairings are carried out following SSP genetic recommendations. After a 42-day gestation period, captive females whelp an average of 3.5 young/litter (range = 1-9). Historically, the program has suffered from a high incidence of pseudopregnancies, and approximately only 58% of bred females produced young. A recent study on male reproductive efficiency showed that yearling males, even if they show physical signs of breeding readiness, do not become spermic until four to six weeks later than older males (Howard *et al.*, 1998; Wolf *et al.*, 1998). Attempts to breed these males following genetic recommendations likely increased the number of false pregnancies, since aspermic males can induce ovulation after copulation (Howard *et al.*, 1998). In 1998, the detection of aspermic males *via* electro-ejaculation decreased the number of pseudopregnant females at FCC by 20%, which resulted in a significant increase in the expected number of births. This was implemented as a program-wide management tool starting in 1999.

Behavioural research has contributed to shaping program management by shedding insight into ferret developmental processes and environmental needs. Black-footed ferrets are altricial at birth, grow rapidly, and reach adult size at approximately four months of age (Vargas & Anderson, 1996a). The period of maximum growth occurs between eight and twelve postnatal weeks, which is when ferrets replace deciduous dentition for permanent teeth and begin to experiment with live prey (Vargas & Anderson, 1998, 1999). This period also coincides with a sensitive phase for the development of food preferences, and whatever type of food kits consume during this time window, will be preferred when ferrets reach adulthood (Vargas & Anderson, 1996b). From a management perspective, it is important that growing ferrets are exposed to prairie dogs during early developmental periods. Results from behavioural work indicate that the early captive environment is critical for shaping adult responses, and that upbringing has a significant effect on the development of behaviours that are necessary for survival (Miller *et al.*, 1992, 1998; Biggins *et al.*, 1993, 1998; Vargas, 1996b, 1999; Miller *et al.*, 1996).

Captive black-footed ferrets released to date have either been raised in indoor cages (with an approximate surface area of 1.5 m^2 supported on one metre legs) or exposed to preconditioning pens for varying periods of time. Preconditioning pens provide ferrets with a naturalistic environment where they can coexist with prairie dogs and live in their intricate burrow systems (Vargas & Anderson, 1998). Two years of breeding data from preconditioning pens at the National Black-footed Ferret Conservation Centre (off-site pens) showed that females allowed to whelp in pens wean an average of 1.2 more kits per litter than females that whelped in indoor cages (Vargas *et al.*, in press). The recovery program is currently evaluating pen breeding efforts in on-site pens, *i.e.* pens located at the reintroduction site. On-site pen breeding techniques have been tested in Arizona since 1997 and, in 1998, breeding was successful with survival of 18 young out of 26 kits born, a weaning success comparable to that experienced in off-site pens. Results indicate that a naturalistic pen environment can effectively increase ferret productivity in captivity.

When comparing post-release survival success captive-raised black-footed ferrets, results demonstrated that ferrets preconditioned in outdoor pens enjoyed a significant post-release survival advantage from their cage-reared counterparts (Biggins *et al.*, 1993, 1998; Vargas, 1994). Data showed that survival rates were highest for ferrets reared from early developmental stages (<60 days of age) in preconditioning pens (Biggins *et al.*, 1998). Short- and long-term survival was three and 10-times higher, respectively, for ferrets raised in preconditioning pens than for ferrets reared in indoor cages (Biggins *et al.*, 1998). Ferrets transferred to preconditioning pens at 90 days of age showed intermediate levels of survival success. Telemetry information indicated that preconditioned ferrets showed adaptive behavioural responses to the new environment by remaining closer to the release area and by minimising the amount of time spent aboveground, behaviours that would likely decrease the chances of encountering predators (Miller *et al.*, 1992; Biggins *et al.*, 1993). Cage-raised ferrets tended to travel further and often were detected in substandard habitat (Biggins *et al.*, 1993).

There are many explanations for the higher breeding and survival success for ferrets maintained in preconditioning pens. For instance, access to a large naturalistic area sharpens motor co-ordination and physical fitness (Vargas & Anderson, 1998). Prairie dog burrows provide a living area with reduced noise and a cooler, more humid and relatively stable climate; a climate that is radically different than the nest box environment (Biggins *et al.*, 1998). Burrows also provide high quality escape cover and are likely to sharpen escape reactions to threatening stimuli while enhancing prey-searching abilities (Biggins *et al.*, 1998). Large pens may enhance breeding by stimulating more exercise and reducing crowding. Crowding is an aberrant social situation for a relatively solitary carnivore like the black-footed ferret, and could potentially induce adverse behavioural and physiological changes. Ferrets raised outdoors are exposed to natural oscillations in climatic conditions and to local parasites such as fleas and ticks. Also, the development of physical endurance and specific resistances after release is probably less extreme for pen-raised black-footed ferrets than for kits reared in a benign cage setting (Vargas, 1994). Adaptation to local conditions and parasites should be greatest for animals born and reared in on-site preconditioning pens.

Research results on the effects of captive rearing on black-footed ferret post-release survival have led to management changes in the black-footed ferret recovery program. Since 1997, all ferrets destined for release in the wild have been preconditioned. Three release sites, Arizona, South Dakota and Colorado-Utah, have built on-site pens to breed and/or precondition reintroduction candidates. Montana is presently constructing pens for reintroduction efforts and the Turner Endangered Species Fund also is building off-site pens in New Mexico to provide additional ferrets for release in approved reintroduction areas. The combination of enhanced productivity and increased post-release survival for pen-born ferrets will likely lead to a more effective and expedient approach to black-footed ferret recovery.

Current recovery status

Advances in ferret breeding, reintroduction, and preconditioning techniques are encouraging and may soon lead to the establishment of viable, free-ranging populations.

Increased captive production is largely due to the adaptation of successful husbandry and research findings into management techniques. In addition, captive production has been streamlined by removing post-reproductive ferrets out of the SSP while maintaining only prime-age breeders in the program. The ferret SSP presently manages 240 (90.150) breeders one to three years of age. Every year, the program retains 85-95 kits for SSP re-stocking, and the remaining young (approximately 150 ± 30) are available for on-site pen breeding or reintroduction in suitable habitats. Ferrets that are not eligible for captive breeding or field programs, are allocated to disease research (development of vaccines) or educational displays.

Since 1991, when black-footed ferrets were first released into the wild, 873 animals have been reintroduced in five different sites within four Rocky Mountain states (Vargas *et al.*, 1998). Reintroduction was first attempted in a white-tailed prairie dog complex in Wyoming and releases in this state unfortunately were suspended in 1995 due to an epizootic of sylvatic plague that severely affected the reintroduction area. In 1994, two new sites were initiated in black-tailed prairie dog towns in Montana and South Dakota. To date, 325 ferrets have been released in plague-free habitat in South Dakota and, for the last two years, this site has preconditioned a large part of their allocated ferrets on site. The Charles Russell National

Wildlife Refuge in Montana has received 163 ferrets since 1994. This site has carried out intensive post-release monitoring every year, and is presently studying the relationship between carrying capacity and ferret reintroductions (D. Biggins, pers. comm). South Dakota and Montana have experienced multiple years of reproduction in the wild, with more than 30 litters produced in 1998 and over 100 wild-born young found between both sites (US Fish & Wildlife Service, Press Release, August 17, 1998). Arizona, which began reintroduction efforts in 1996, has received a total of 79 ferrets for release and approximately 60 for pen breeding efforts. The Arizona program has recently experienced important progress with the first-time production of kits in on-site preconditioning pens. A fifth ferret reintroduction site was established at the Fort Belknap Indian Reservation, Montana, in 1997, and a total of 78 kits have been released to date. A site in Colorado-Utah has joined black-footed ferret field conservation efforts in 1998, and will receive 20 ferrets for breeding in on-site preconditioning pens.

Post-release survival has been greatest for ferrets released in black-tailed prairie dog complexes (Biggins *et al.*, 1998), possibly due to higher prey densities in the habitat of this species. Additional reintroduction sites are being considered and preliminary efforts are being made to raise interest in ferret recovery by states/sites with potentially good habitat (Native American lands in South Dakota; Chihuahua, Mexico; Thunder Basin, Wyoming). Allocation priority will be given to sites with large, plague-free black-tailed prairie dog complexes. In addition, the program will continue to support disease research, specifically focused on the development of distemper and plague vaccines for use in the field. As wild ferret populations increase, translocations from established populations will be used to maintain or establish other wild populations and to begin new reintroductions. Such management will require determining and defining surplus wild stock and, eventually, scaling down the production of ferrets in the SSP captive population.

Although captive breeding and reintroduction capabilities have significantly improved, little progress has been accomplished in assuring the long-term protection and maintenance of prairie dog habitat for black-footed ferrets. Present prairie dog habitat may be insufficient to establish wild ferret populations free of human intervention. The National Wildlife Federation has recently petitioned the United States government to list the black-tailed prairie dog, *Cynomys ludovicianus*, as a threatened species throughout its range. The objective of the petition is to provide a legal system to protect and restore short- and mid-grass prairie habitats upon which prairie dogs, black-footed ferrets, and many other species depend (National Wildlife Federation, 1998). Prairie dog listing is a controversial issue since this endemic prairie species has been legally declared as "pest" in several western states (Miller *et al.*, 1996). The Fish & Wildlife Service supports collaborations with states and interested parties to develop conservation plans for the black-tailed prairie dog, and is currently reviewing the listing proposal. With successful captive breeding and reintroduction techniques, the greatest challenge now facing ferret recovery is whether suitable habitat can be secured to establish multiple, viable populations of black-footed ferrets in the wild.

Acknowledgements

The US Fish and Wildlife Service appreciates the valuable contributions of the many partners involved in black-footed ferret recovery efforts, including federal and state agencies, zoological parks, NGOs, universities, Native American tribes, private landowners, and partners in Canada and Mexico. Funding sources for various aspects of the discussed work included Wildlife Preservation Trust International, US Fish and Wildlife Service, US Geological Service – Biological Resources Division, National Fish and Wildlife Foundation, Smithsonian Institution, Wyoming Co-operative Fish & Wildlife Research Unit, and PIC Technologies. We are indebted to all the zoos that raise black-footed ferrets for captive breeding and reintroduction; these include the National Zoological Park – Conservation and Research Centre, Omaha's Henry Doorly Zoo, Louisville Zoological Gardens, Phoenix Zoo, Cheyenne Mountain Zoo, and Toronto Zoo. We are indebted to all the dedicated individuals working at reintroduction sites in South Dakota, Montana (Charles Russell National Wildlife Refuge and Fort Belknap Indian Reservation), Arizona, Wyoming, and Colorado-Utah. Special mention to Dean Biggins, Brian Miller, Beth Williams, and Jo Gayle Howard for their important work and contributions to black-footed ferret recovery.

References

Anderson, E., Forrest, S.C., Clark, T.W. & Richardson, L. (1986). Paleobiology, biogeography, and systematics of the black-footed ferret, *Mustela nigripes* (Audubon and Bachman, 1851). *Great Basin Naturalist (Memoirs)*, **8**: 11-62.

Barnes, A.M. (1993). A review of plague and its relevance to prairie dog populations and the black-footed ferret. In: J.L. Oldemeyer, D.E. Biggins, B.J. Miller & R. Crete (eds.), *Management of prairie dog complexes for the reintroduction of the black-footed ferret* (*US Fish & Wildlife Service Biological Report 13*): 28-37.

Biggins, D.E., Godbey, J. & Vargas, A. (1993). *Influence of pre-release experience on reintroduced black-footed ferrets* (*Mustela nigripes*) (*US Fish and Wildlife Service Report, 27 May, 1993*). Fort Collins (Colorado); US Fish & Wildlife Service, National Ecology Research Center.

Biggins, D., Godbey, J., Hanebury, L., Marinari, P., Matchett, R. & Vargas, A. (1998). Survival of black-footed ferrets. *Journal of Wildlife Management*, **62**: 643-653.

Campbell, T.M., III, Clark, T.W., Richardson, L., Forrest, S.C. & Houston, B.R. (1987). Food habits of Wyoming black-footed ferrets. *American Midland Naturalist*, **117**: 208-210.

Carvalho, C.F., Howard, J.G., Collins, L., Wemmer, C., Bush, M.& Wildt, D.E (1991). Captive breeding of black-footed ferrets (*Mustela nigripes*) and comparative reproductive efficiency in 1-year old versus 2-year old animals. *Journal of Zoo and Wildlife Medicine*, **22**: 96-106.

Clark, T.W. (1989). Conservation biology of the endangered black-footed ferret (*Mustela nigripes*). *Wildlife Preservation Trust International Special Scientific Report*, **3**: 1-175.

Cully, J.F., Jr. (1989). Plague in prairie dog ecosystems: importance for black-footed ferret management. In: T.W. Clark, D. Hinckley & T. Rich (eds.), *The prairie dog ecosystem: managing for biological diversity* (*MBLM Wildlife Technical Bulletin 2*): 47-55. Butte (Montana); Montana Bureau of Land Management.

Detling, J.K. & Whicker, A.D. (1988). A control of ecosystem processes by prairie dogs and other grassland herbivores. In: *Proceedings of the 8th Great Plains Wildlife Damage Control Workshop, April 28-30, 1987, Rapid City, South Dakota*: 23-29. Washington (DC); US Department of Agriculture Forest Service.

Henderson, F.R., Springer, P.F. & Adrian, R. (1974). *The black-footed ferret in South Dakota* (*SDDGFP Technical Bulletin 4*): 1-37. Sioux Falls (SD); South Dakota Department of Game, Fish and Parks.

Hillman, C.N. (1968a). *Life history and ecology of the black-footed ferret in the wild.* MS thesis. Brookings; South Dakota State University.

Howard, J.G., Wolf, K.N., Marinari, P.E., Kreeger, J.S., Anderson, T.R., Vargas, A. & Wildt, D.E. (1998). Delayed onset of sperm production in 1-year old male black-footed ferrets. *Proceedings of the Society for the Study of Reproduction,* **58** (Suppl): 124.

Knowles, C.J. (1986). Population recovery of black-tailed prairie dogs following control with zinc phosphide. *Journal of Range Management,* **39:** 249-251.

McNulty, F. (1971). *Must they die?* New York; Double Day & Company.

Miller, B., Wemmer, C., Biggins, D. & Reading, R. (1990). A proposal to conserve black-footed ferrets and prairie dog ecosystem. *Environmental Management,* **14:** 763-769.

Miller, B., Biggins, D., Hanebury, L., Conway, C. & Wemmer, C. (1992). Black-footed ferrets – rehabilitation of a species. *Wildlife Rehabilitation,* **9:** 183-192.

Miller, B., Ceballos, G. & Reading, R. (1994). Prairie dogs, poison, and biotic diversity. *Conservation Biology,* **8:** 677-681.

Miller, B.J., Reading, R. & Forrest, S. (1996). *Prairie night: black-footed ferrets and the recovery of endangered species.* Washington (DC); Smithsonian Institution Press.

Miller, B., Biggins, D., Vargas, A., Hutchins, M., Hanebury, L., Godbey, J., Anderson, S., Wemmer, C. & Oldemeyer, J. (1998). The captive environment and reintroduction. In: D. Shepherdson, J. Mellen & M. Hutchins (eds.), *Second nature: environmental enrichment for captive animals:* 92-112. Washington (DC); Smithsonian Institution Press.

Mulhern, D. & Knowles, C.J. (1995). *Black-tailed prairie dog status and future conservation planning.* In: *US Department of Agriculture Rocky Mountain Forest & Range Experimental Station Technical Report RM-GTR-298:* 19-29.

Munn, L. (1993). Effects of prairie dogs on physical and chemical properties of soils. In: J.L. Oldemeyer, D.E. Biggins, B.J. Miller & R. Crete (eds.), *Management of prairie dog complexes for the reintroduction of the black-footed ferret (USFWS Biological Report 13):* 11-17. Washington (DC); US Fish & Wildlife Service.

National Wildlife Federation (1998). *Petition for rule listing the black-tailed prairie dog (Cynomys ludovicianus) as threatened throughout its range (Unpublished document on file).* Washington (DC); US Department of the Interior, Fish & Wildlife Service, Office of Endangered Species.

Reading, R.P., Grensten, J.J., Beissinger, S.R. & Clark, T.W. (1989). *Attributes of black-tailed prairie dog colonies in Phillips County, MT, with management recommendations for the conservation of biodiversity (Wildlife Technical Bulletin 2):*13-27. Butte (Montana); Montana Bureau of Land Management.

Roemer, D.M. & Forrest, S.C. (1996). Prairie dog poisoning in the northern Great Plains: an analysis of programs and policies. *Environmental Management,* **20:** 349-359.

Sheets, R.G., Linder, R.L. & Dahgren, R.B. (1972). Food habits of two litters of black-footed ferrets in South Dakota. *American Midland Naturalist,* **87:** 249-251.

Thorne, E.T. (1987). Captive propagation of the black-footed ferret in Wyoming. In: *Proceedings of the AAZPA Regional Conference:* 419-424. Syracuse (NY); American Association of Zoological Parks and Aquariums Publications.

Uresk, D.W. & Bjugstad, A.J. (1983). Prairie dogs as ecosystem regulators on the northern high plains. In: *Proceedings of the 7th North American prairie conference, August 4-6, 1980, SW Missouri State University, Springfield, Missouri, USA:* 91-94.

Vargas, A, Lockhart, M., Marinari, P. & Gober, P. (1996). The reintroduction process: black-footed ferrets as a case study. In: *Proceedings of the American Zoo and Aquarium Association Western Regional Conference, May 15-19, 1996, Denver, Colorado:* 829-834.

Vargas, A. & Anderson, S.H. (1996a). Growth and development of captive-raised black-footed ferrets (*Mustela nigripes*). *American Midland Naturalist,* **135:** 43-52.

Vargas, A. & Anderson, S.H. (1996b). The effects of diet on black-footed ferret (*Mustela nigripes*) food preference. *Zoo Biology,* **15:** 105-113.

Vargas, A. & Anderson, S.H. (1998). Ontogeny of black-footed ferret predatory behavior towards prairie dogs. *Canadian Journal of Zoology,* **76:** 1692-1704.

Vargas, A. & Anderson, S.H. (1999). Effects of experience and cage enrichment on predatory skills of black-footed ferrets (*Mustela nigripes*). *Journal of Mammalogy,* **80:** 263-269.

Vargas A, Lockhart, M., Marinari, P. & Gober, P. (1998). Reintroduction of captive-raised black-footed ferrets: progress towards recovery of an endangered species. In: *Proceedings of the American Zoo and Aquarium Association's Western Regional Conference, September 14-18, 1998, Tulsa, Oklahoma* (in press).

Williams, E.S., Thorne, E.T., Appel, M.J.G. & Belitsky, D.W. (1988). Canine distemper in black-footed ferrets (*Mustela nigripes*) from Wyoming. *Journal of Wildlife Diseases*, **24:** 385-398.

Williams, E.S., Thorne, E.T., Kwiatkowski, D.R., Lutz, K & Anderson, S.L. (1991). Reproductive biology and management of captive black-footed ferrets (*Mustela nigripes*). *Zoo Biology*, **10:** 383-398.

Williams, E.S., Thorne, E.T., Kwiatkowski, D.R., Lutz, K & Anderson, S.L. (1992). Comparative vaginal cytology of the estrus cycle of black-footed ferrets (*Mustela nigripes*), Siberian polecats (*M. eversmannii*), and domestic ferrets (*M. putorius furo*). *Journal of Veterinary Diagnostic Investigation*, **4:** 38-44.

Williams, E.S., Mills, K., Kwiatkowski, D.R., Thorne, E.T. & Boerger-Fields, A. (1994). Plague in a black-footed ferret (*Mustela nigripes*). *Journal of Wildlife Diseases*, **30:** 581-585.

Williams, E.S., Anderson, S.L., Cavender, J., Lynn, C., List, K., Hearne, C. & Appel, M.J.G. (1996). Vaccination of black-footed ferret (*Mustela nigripes*) x Siberian polecat (*M. eversmannii*) hybrids and domestic ferrets (*M. putorius furo*) against canine distemper. *Journal of Wildlife Diseases*, **32:** 417-423.

Wolf, K.N., Wildt, D.E., Vargas, A., Marinari, P., Williamson, L., Ottinger, M.A. & Howard, J.G. (1998). Compromised reproductive efficiency in male black-footed ferrets. *Journal of Andrology*, **1998** (Suppl): 44.

Wuerthner, G. (1997). Viewpoint: the black-tailed prairie dog-headed for extinction? *Journal of Range Management*, **50:** 459-466.

CHAPTER 7

American river otters, *Lontra canadensis*, and humans: occurrence in a coastal urban habitat and reaction to increased levels of disturbance

Peter Giere* & Don S. Eastman

Abstract

A three part study consisting of a sign survey in an urban habitat, a study of habitat preference in coastal environments and a study of the effects of tourism on site use by coastal North American river otters, *Lontra canadensis*, is presented.

The sign survey for river otter was carried out in the urban habitat of Victoria (British Columbia, Canada) in 1993, including 30 adjacent islands. Otter sign was present intermittently throughout the 54.5 km of surveyed coastline. The density of dens on the Victoria shoreline at 0.77 dens/km was significantly lower than the density of 2.62 dens/km found on the surrounding, uninhabited islands.

In 1994, part of the former study area and two other coastal habitats (the Juan de Fuca Marine Trail and Denman Island) were examined in a study of river otter habitat preference. Habitat variables found to influence site selection by otters were: (1) cover provided by vegetation, (2) a low degree of disturbance by humans, and (3) local geomorphological features such as sheltered sections of coastline. The availability of freshwater is considered to be less important.

In 1996 the effects of increased human disturbance on site use by river otter in a coastal habitat (Vancouver Island, British Columbia) were studied in a new, long-distance hiking trail (the Juan de Fuca Marine Trail). Significantly more changes in the geographic location of otter sites were found in the new hiking trail as compared with Victoria and Denman Island.

Introduction

In times of World-wide human encroachment and habitat fragmentation, the influence of humans on wildlife populations is manifold. Apart from studies of the effects of environmental pollution on wildlife populations (e.g. Mason, 1989), the direct influences of human activities also has been examined. For example, this influence is apparent in industrial activities such as the exploitation of natural resources (e.g. McLellan, 1989a,b,c), fish farming (see papers in Gossow & Kranz, 1998), in transportation accidents such as oil spills (e.g. Bowyer *et al.*, 1995) or, on a smaller scale, in the impact of increased road traffic on wildlife populations (for Eurasian otters, *Lutra lutra*, see Stubbe *et al.*, 1993; Kruuk, 1995). Some studies have examined the direct disturbances to wildlife caused by human recreational activities, and others the

---

* Corresponding author.

Mustelids in a modern world
Management and conservation aspects of small carnivore: human interactions
edited by Huw I. Griffiths, pp. 107–125
© 2000 Backhuys Publishers, Leiden, The Netherlands

adaptation of wildlife to humans (e.g. urban wildlife). The last two aspects of human-wildlife interaction are the topic of the present study of North American river otter, *Lontra canadensis*, in coastal habitats. Like Eurasian otters, North American river otters inhabit bodies of freshwater and the sea coast; they range throughout the northern part of North America with the exception of the arid south-west of the United States and Mexico (Toweill & Tabor, 1982). In contrast to the situation in some European countries (e.g. Macdonald, 1983) no large-scale surveys have been conducted for *L. canadensis*. Despite this, the entire population was considered to be stable by Jenkins (1983), with 15,000-30,000 river otters being estimated for British Columbia (BC) in 1979 on the basis of trapping data (Munro & Jackson, 1979).

a. Urban wildlife

Among carnivores, only few species have adjusted to urban habitats, e.g. red fox, *Vulpes vulpes* (Page, 1981; Adkins & Stott, 1998), coyote, *Canis latrans* (Atkinson & Shackleton, 1991) and raccoon, *Procyon lotor* (Slate, 1985). However, with the exception of the well-documented occurrence of Eurasian badger, *Meles meles*, in the vicinity of human habitations (e.g. Harris, 1984; Aaris-Sørensen, 1987) and the long-known presence of stone marten, *Martes foina*, in several European cities (e.g. Nicht, 1969; Tester, 1986), little is known about mustelids in urban habitats. For otters (of any species) records of occurrence in human settlements are rare. Apart from Lunnon's (1989) work on *L. lutra*, data are available only as background information on the otters' presence in unusual environments, e.g. Bruce (1881), MacLoughlin (1950), Green & Green (1980, 1987) Chapman & Chapman (1982), Kranz & Toman (this volume) for *L. lutra*, and Guiguet (1962), Cowan & Guiguet (1975), Melquist & Hornocker (1983) and Shannon (1989) for *L. canadensis*. This study examines river otter distributions through the study of otter sign on the coast of Victoria, the capital of British Columbia, Canada. The influences of human disturbance as well as other habitat variables were examined in a 1994 study of river otter habitat use in Victoria and two other marine habitats (the Juan de Fuca Marine Trail and Denman Island; see Fig. 1).

b. Recreational use

Various aspects of the use of natural habitats for recreational purposes currently are of interest in the context of human-wildlife interactions. Besides recreational activities such as hunting and fishing, the impact on backcountry areas due to non-consumptive human activities has increased during recent decades. Various aspects of these activities, notably wildlife viewing (Duffus & Dearden, 1993), skiing (Dearden & Hall, 1983; Goodrich & Berger, 1994) and backcountry hiking (Dearden & Hall, 1983; Jacobs & Schloeder, 1992) have been addressed. The last of these (hiking) is the basis for the second objective of the present study. The opening of part of a new long-distance hiking trail (the Juan de Fuca Marine Trail) in 1995 allowed research into the effects of increased human presence in a backcountry area on a site used by coastal American river otters; the first part of the trail that was opened (see Wood, 1995) included the 1994 river otter habitat use study area. The study was carried out in 1994 (before the opening of the trail) and in 1996, at the close of the trail's second tourist season.

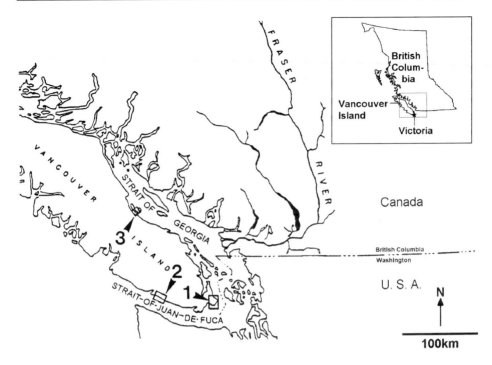

Fig. 1. Location of study areas: (1) Victoria (see Fig. 2), (2) Juan de Fuca Marine Trail (JdFMT), and (3) Denman Island.

Methods

Study Areas

Three study areas were chosen (see Fig. 1): (1) Victoria (48°25'N, 123°22'W), (2) the Juan de Fuca Marine Trail (JdFMT; 48°31'N, 124°25'W), and (3) Denman Island (49°32'N, 124°48'W). Victoria was studied in 1993 (May-July), 1994 (June-July) and 1996 (September). The JdFMT and Denman Island study areas were surveyed in 1994 (JdFMT: August-September; Denman Island: September-October) and 1996 (JdFMT: September-October; Denman Island: October).

1. Victoria

54.5 km of the Victoria shoreline were surveyed in 1993 (Figs. 1, 2). Victoria lies at the south-eastern end of Vancouver Island at the junction of the Strait of Georgia and the Juan de Fuca Strait. The study area included five large bays and several smaller coves with sandy or pebble beaches, as well as part of an inlet (the "Gorge") and 30 uninhabited islands. Most of the coastline consists of a 20-30 m wide strip of gently sloping rock. Other areas include popular beaches and waterfront parks or gardens. Driftwood (often in piles) was abundant. The Gorge area is a narrow inlet with mostly soft, muddy substrate and few coves. This inlet was the only heavily

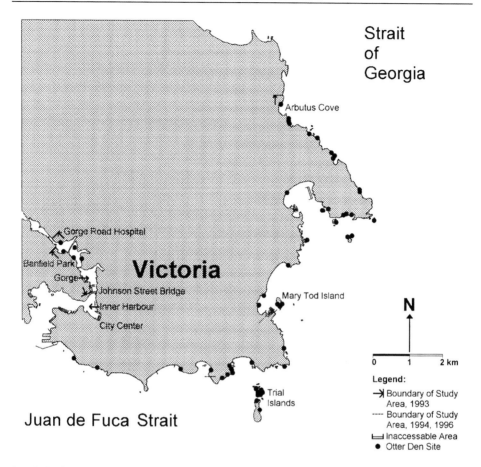

Fig. 2. Study area (1993, 1994, and 1996) and location of river otter dens (n = 54; 1993) in Victoria, British Columbia, Canada.

industrialised area surveyed. Typically, along the shoreline mature trees were rare and shrubby vegetation and herbs prevailed. The rocky intertidal zone typical of Victoria is intermediate between the protected habitats of the Strait of Georgia and the more exposed coast of the Juan de Fuca Strait (for a detailed description, see Giere, 1995). Stephenson & Stephenson (1961) and Weston & Stirling (1986) provide descriptions of the intertidal region. The 1994 and 1996 study area was an 8.1 km stretch of coastline within the 1993 survey area (Fig. 2). This includes residential areas, parks and other areas that are accessible to the public.

2. The Juan de Fuca Marine Trail (JdFMT)

The 1994 and 1996 study area extends for 6.5 km on the south-western coast of Vancouver Island (Fig. 1). In 1994 it was bordered to the west by a popular provincial park, Botanical Beach. After the Commonwealth Games of summer 1994 this, and a large part of coastal south-west Vancouver Island, became the Juan de Fuca Provincial

Park in 1995. This park implemented a long-distance hiking trail (the Juan de Fuca Marine Trail, henceforth JdFMT) offering unlimited public access in the vicinity of the popular West Coast Trail which operates a visitor quota system. Counts by BC Parks staff estimated that 60,000 persons visited the park in its first season (C. Kissinger, pers. comm.). In 1994, however, human disturbance in the study area was generally low. Some areas are sheltered from inland access by vertical 30-50 m cliffs which prevent access other than by boat (for further details, see Giere, 1995).

3. Denman Island

Denman Island (see Fig. 1) lies in the Strait of Georgia, close to the east coast of Vancouver Island. The 3.2 km 1994 and 1996 study area lay around the southern tip of the island and extended to the eastern ferry terminal. It included both the Boyle Point Provincial Park and a rural residential area with homes situated in coniferous forest. Human usage of the park is generally low. In the eastern part of the park easy access is prevented by near vertical or overhanging cliffs that separate the coastal plateau from the elevated interior of the southern tip of the island. Most of this coastal plateau is richly structured by numerous boulders.

Survey techniques

Otters are elusive and secretive, so direct observation is difficult. Thus, many studies of wild otters rely on indirect census methods (e.g. Macdonald, 1983; Macdonald & Mason, 1985; Arden-Clarke, 1986; Verwoerd, 1987; Beja, 1989; Rowe-Rowe, 1992). Only two field signs are specific to otters (Mason & Macdonald, 1986): scats (= spraints or faeces) which can be found on river banks and coastlines, and tracks, which occur only in soft substrates.

Otter surveys were conducted by walking the shoreline and recording otter signs; due to property rights this was done at low tide in built-up areas. Sites recognised as being used by otters were recorded in the field on maps (Victoria = 1:1,752, Denman Island = 1:10,000) or air photos (JdFMT = 1:15,000), all data later being transferred to topographic (1:20,000) maps for analysis.

An otter site was defined as being an area with distinct signs of otter use (usually scats) and was considered to be a separate site if the nearest signs to it were more than 10 m away. Two site categories were recorded: dens and latrines, although rolling places, runs and other field signs also were found (these were associated with one of the above categories in data analysis). Dens were found in structures such as hollows under boulders or logs, or amongst dense vegetation.

Habitat variables

In the 1994 study, several habitat variables were recorded at otter sites in the three study areas (see Table 1 for a list of the variables and their explanations). To measure the overall occurrence of habitat variables in the respective study areas, the entire coastline for each of the 1994 surveys was subdivided into 125 m sections and the predominant state of each variable (other than local features such as substrate and coastal exposure) was recorded (Table 1).

Table 1. Overview and explanation of habitat variables, their distance to or state at sites and their overall occurrence (including statistical analysis tested against occurrence at dens and latrines) in Victoria, Juan de Fuca Marine Trail and Denman Island, 1994.

habitat variable	subcategory/explanation	site/frequency	Victoria	Juan de Fuca Marine Trail	Denman Island
freshwater					
permanent	closest source (straight line distance ± s.d.: [m])[1]	den	807.4±551.0	102.7±134.4	503.2±183.3
		latrine	937.9±455.6	168.6±455.6	551.2±227.3
	permanent freshwater sources/km	frequency	0.5	1.7	0.3
temporary	closest source (straight line distance ± s.d.: [m])[1]	den	356.4±425.5	174.0±302.6	81.5±75.6
		latrine	345.4±380.7	92.0±92.3	74.4±119.3
	temporary freshwater sources/km	frequency	1.9	4.6	6.2
closest den	distance to closest den (straight line distance ± s.d.: [m])[1]	den	198.6±184.8	265.7±457.0	113.9±135.2
		latrine	110.0±76.5	135.1±162.5	128.2±136.4
closest site	distance to closest site (straight line distance ± s.d.: [m])[1]	den	53.4±26.0	78.2±66.6	44.8±50.2
		latrine	41.8±31.1	87.6±90.3	54.1±59.1
distance site-high water line	straight line distance from site to high water line ± s.d.: [m])[1]	den	10.7±6.0	14.4±12.6	12.8±6.5
		latrine	4.7±4.1	6.8±8.9	12.5±8.9
vegetation	non woody plants (presence; [%])[1]	den	66.7 χ^2=0.67; p=0.41; two-tailed:n.s.	60.0 C.-F: χ^2=6.41; d.f.=1; p=0.01	61.5 C.-F: χ^2=4.02; d.f.=1; p=0.04
		latrine	76.9 χ^2=5.45; p=0.02; two-tailed	14.3 F. e. p=0.53; two-tailed; n.s.	63.2 χ^2=8.54; p<0.01; two-tailed
		occurrence[2]	53.3	23.1	31.4
	woody plants (presence; [%])[1]	den	83.4 χ^2=4.40; p=0.04; two-tailed	70.0 F. e. p=0.32; two-tailed; n.s.	69.2 χ^2=1.39; p=0.24; two-tailed
		latrine	22.0 χ^2=10.47; p<0.01; two-tailed	14.3 χ^2=4.96; p=0.03; two-tailed	50.0 χ^2<0.01; p=0.95; two-tailed
		occurrence[2]	53.3	50.0	47.1
human disturbance	low (site inaccessible to the public, little sign of human use; [%])[1]	den	82.4 χ^2=1.70; p=0.19; two-tailed; n.s.	100.0 F. e. p=0.62, two-tailed; n.s.	100.0 n/a
		latrine	77.5 χ^2=2.11; p=0.15; two-tailed; n.s.	100.0 F. e. p=0.59; two-tailed; n.s.	100.0 n/a
		occurrence[2]	62.9	92.3	100.0
	medium (humans present at intervals; [%])[1]	den	17.6 F. e. p=0.54, two-tailed; n.s.	0.0 F. e. p=0.62, two-tailed; n.s.	0.0 n/a
		latrine	20.0 χ^2=0.28; p=0.60; two-tailed; n.s.	0.0 F. e. p=0.57, two-tailed; n.s.	0.0 n/a
		occurrence[2]	25.8	7.7	0.0

Table 1. Continued

habitat variable	subcategory/explanation	site/frequency	Victoria	Juan de Fuca Marine Trail	Denman Island
driftwood	high (site fully accessible to the public, regular human presence; [%])[1]	den	0.0	0.0; n/a	0.0; n/a
		latrine	2.5; F. e. p=0.34, two-tailed; n.s.	0.0; n/a	0.0; n/a
		occurrence[2]	11.3; F. e. p=0.14, two-tailed; n.s.	0.0	0.0
	no driftwood; [%][1]	den	44.4; χ^2=0.06; p=0.80; two-tailed; n.s.	70.0; n/a	35.7; n/a
		latrine	70.4; χ^2=8.09; p<0.01; two-tailed	71.4; n/a	31.6; n/a
		occurrence[2]	45.2	73.1	35.3
	<5 logs per 10m section of coastline; [%][1]	den	22.2; χ^2=0.09; p=0.76; two-tailed; n.s.	20.0; n/a	35.7; n/a; χ^2=1.49; p=0.22; two-tailed; n.s.
		latrine	11.1; χ^2=5.41; p=0.02; two-tailed	14.3; n/a	15.8
		occurrence[2]	29.1	7.7	33.3
	>5 and ≥ 15 logs per 10m section of coastline; [%][1]	den	27.8; n/a	10.0; n/a	21.4; n/a; χ^2=0.91; p=0.34; two-tailed; n.s.
		latrine	13.0; χ^2=1.66; p=0.19; two-tailed; n.s.	14.3; n/a	42.1; n/a
		occurrence[2]	22.5	5.8	27.5
	>15 logs per 10m section of coastline; [%][1]	den	5.6; n/a	0.0; n/a	7.2; n/a
		latrine	5.5; n/a	0.0; n/a	10.5; n/a
		occurrence[2]	3.2	13.4	3.9
substrate	sand; [%][1]	den	0.0; n/a	0.0; n/a	0.0; n/a
		latrine	4.4; n/a	0.0; n/a	0.0; n/a
		occurrence[2]	3.2	0.0	0.0
	pebbles; [%][1]	den	16.7; χ^2=1.12; p=0.29; two-tailed; n.s.	10.0; n/a	0.0; n/a
		latrine	6.7; χ^2=9.72; p<0.01; two-tailed	7.7; n/a	0.0; n/a
		occurrence[2]	32.3	25.0	13.7
	boulders; [%][1]	den	16.7; n/a	10.0; n/a	42.9; n/a
		latrine	8.9; n/a	0.0; n/a	11.1; n/a
		occurrence[2]	8.1	0.0	21.6
	bedrock; [%][1]	den	66.6; χ^2=0.29; p=0.59; two-tailed; n.s.	80.0; n/a	57.1; F. e. p=0.36; two-tailed; n.s.
		latrine	80.0; χ^2=6.38; p=0.01; two-tailed	92.3; F. e. p=0.29; two-tailed; n.s.	88.9; F. e. p=0.15; two-tailed; n.s.
		occurrence[2]	56.4	75.0	64.7
adjacent terrain	not used by humans (forest, cliff, island; [%])[1]	den	33.4; n/a	100.0; n/a	92.9; n/a
		latrine	29.7; χ^2=2.51; p=0.11; two-tailed; n.s.	100.0; n/a	68.4; χ^2=0.01; p=0.91; two-tailed; n.s.
		occurrence[2]	17.7	100.0	66.8
	used by humans (garden, park, building; [%])[1]	den	66.6; n/a	0.0; n/a	7.1; n/a
		latrine	57.4; χ^2=2.51; p=0.11; two-tailed; n.s.	0.0; n/a	31.6; χ^2=0.01; p=0.91; two-tailed; n.s.
		occurrence[2]	82.3	0.0	33.2

Table 1. Continued

habitat variable	subcategory/explanation	site/frequency	Victoria	Juan de Fuca Marine Trail	Denman Island
inland slope	measured in 5° increments ± s.d.; [°][1]	den	21.1±13.8	43.1±30.1	62.0±24.3
		latrine	26.6±18.9	36.2±22.9	36.1±29.8
		occurrence[2]	23.5±14.7	36.2±21.5	34.3±24.2
slope high water line	recorded as a measure for subtidal slope, measured in 5° increments ± s.d.; [°][1]	den	20.6±10.9	19.5±6.9	13.2±6.7
		latrine	20.8±8.6	24.1±14.6	18.3±8.2
		occurrence[2]	16.8±8.4	20.5±8.4	19.7±16.9
coastal exposure	exposed only (recorded within 10m around site; [%])[1]	den	30.0	0.0	14.3
		latrine	44.8	30.8	41.2
	sheltered available (recorded within 10m around site; [%])[1]	den	70.0	100.0	85.7
		latrine	55.2	69.2	58.8
substrate exposure	exposed only; [%][1]	den	25.0	75.0	10.0
		latrine	85.7	45.5	16.7
	sheltered available; [%][1]	den	75.0	0.0	90.0
		latrine	14.3	54.5	83.3

1 data on these habitat variable categories included in Principal Component Analysis.
2 for a definition of "occurrence" see text. Data on "occurrence" not included in Principal Component Analysis.
Statistical analysis: C.-F.: Craddock-Flood; F. e.: Fisher's exact; n/a: not applicable; statistical evaluation refers to data of either den or latrine tested against data of occurrence. Slopes excluded from analysis.

Data analysis

Differences between den distribution on islands *vs.* mainland (1993) and site use in different years (1994 and 1996) were tested for significance (χ^2). To evaluate the numbers of observations against the overall occurrence of habitat variables in the 1994 study (and because of small sample sizes), a variety of tests (χ^2, Craddock-Flood χ^2, Fisher's Exact Test) had to be employed. Some cases had to be excluded as formal statistical evaluation was inappropriate. The 1994 data were subjected to Principal Component Analysis (PCA; see Table 2) to identify factors (*i.e.* combinations of habitat variables) that influenced site use. This was carried out on pooled data sets and for all study areas and site categories separately. However, Bartlett's Test of Sphericity (carried out prior to the PCA) determined that only the pooled data sets were admissible for further calculation. The number of factors extracted was limited to those with eigenvalues greater than one, which coincided with the number of factors determined by a scree plot. Non-significant loadings and minor loadings strongly associated with other factors were omitted in Table 2 (see Stevens, 1996). BiAS 4.05 software was used for χ^2-tests and Fisher's Exact Test (Ackermann, 1994) and PCA was conducted on SPSS for Windows 7.5.2G.

Results

I. Urban river otters in Victoria, 1993

48.0 km (88.1%) of the coastline examined was on the mainland and the rest (6.5 km, 11.9%) was on the islands. Overall, 54 dens (Fig. 2) and 159 latrines were found. Most dens were 50-250 m apart (minimum = 30 m, maximum = 1180 m; see Fig. 3). Distances of dens to nearest permanent source of freshwater ranged from ≤10 m (n=7) to 1,480 m (n=2). None of the islands had a visible supply of permanent freshwater. However, freshwater is temporarily available throughout the study area in rainwater puddles, the presence of which was included in the 1994 study. Groundwater sources to dens cannot be excluded, however, their presence seems unlikely considering the topography of the study area and the low number of subterranean dens.

The abundance of dens in the city area of Victoria differed significantly from that of the surrounding islands (Fig. 4). Islands comprised only 11.9% of the coastline surveyed but held 31.5% of all the den sites found (2.62 dens/km on islands *vs.* 0.77 dens/km on the mainland).

II. River otter habitat use in coastal BC, 1994

In 1994, 18 dens and 52 latrines were found in Victoria, 10 dens and 14 latrines in the JdFMT and 14 dens and 19 latrines on Denman Island.

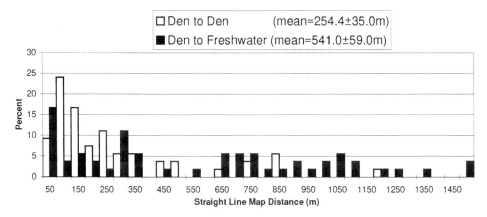

Fig. 3. Straight line map distances of dens to nearest den and of dens to nearest source of permanent freshwater in Victoria, 1993 (n = 54).

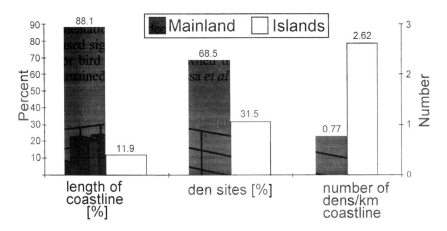

Fig. 4. Proportions of coastline, den sites (n = 54), and numbers of dens/km coastline in Victoria and surrounding, uninhabited islands (χ^2 = 19.66; p <0.01), 1993.

Habitat variables

Table 1 shows data on habitat variables for each of the three study areas, and the following section highlights results regarding these variables. Metric data (slopes and distances) were included in the PCA, however, with the exception of distance to freshwater, these variables are not described below (for details, e.g. levels of significance, see Table 1).

Mean distances to permanent freshwater sources differed considerably: 102.7 ± 134.4 m for dens in JdFMT (with 1.7 permanent freshwater sources/km) and 937.9 ± 455.6 m for latrines in Victoria (with 0.5 permanent freshwater sources/km; see Table 1). Mean distances to temporary freshwater sources were lower, ranging between 74.4 ± 119.3 m for Denman Island latrines (6.2 sources/km) and 356.4 ± 425.5 m for dens in Victoria (1.9 sources/km). This trend can be seen for both site categories in all study areas (at least 27.8% of all sites were within 50 m of a source of freshwater). However, distances were scattered, with a maximum of 1,100 m for a den in Victoria (see Giere, 1995).

Considerable differences were found between observations of particular habitat variables and their overall occurrence in the respective study areas. Woody plants were recorded significantly more often at dens in Victoria, and less often at latrines (Victoria and JdFMT) than expected from their overall occurrence. Non-woody plants, however, were found significantly more often than expected at sites in all three study areas (Victoria: latrines, JdFMT: dens, Denman Island: dens and latrines; see Table 1). The frequency of dens (82.4%) and latrines (77.5%) in low disturbance zones was much higher in Victoria than the overall occurrence of these zones (62.9%). However, these differences were not significant (Table 1). Except for its significantly higher absence at latrines in Victoria (70.4% *vs.* 45.2%; Table 1) site driftwood availability and occurrence did not differ notably. This also applies to substrate: overall occurrence was similar to the frequency of otter sites on their respective substrates throughout, although latrines in Victoria and Denman Island had an increased percentage of bedrock and the percentage of latrines with pebbles was significantly lower than the occurrence of pebble in Victoria (Table 1). Overall, no significant differences were found between the occurrence and use of the respective adjacent terrain categories.

PCA

In PCA of habitat variables for the pooled data sets of all three study areas and site categories, the number of factors extracted was limited to five by eigenvalues greater than one: the factor loadings (varimax rotation of the factor matrix) are shown in Table 2. Factors 1 and 3-5 correlate with three or four different variables whereas factor 2 is defined by two factor loadings of the variables that code for human influence ("adjacent terrain type" and "human disturbance"). Factor 1 (19.1%) and factor 2 (15.3%) account for approximately half of the overall explained variance (72.3%), whereas the remaining part is explained equally by factors 3-5 (factor 3 = 12.8%, factor 4 = 12.6%, factor 5 = 12.6%).

III. Human recreation and river otters, 1996

The 1994 survey was repeated in 1996. 18 dens and 51 latrines were found in Victoria, 14 dens and 11 latrines on JdFMT, and 11 dens and 17 latrines on Denman Island. No differences in the mean numbers of dens/km were found in Victoria (2.22; Fig. 5) between the two years, and the only increase (as dens/km) was found in the JdFMT study area (1994 = 1.54 dens/km, 1996 = 2.15 dens/km). On Denman Island the number of dens dropped from 4.38/km in 1994 to 3.44/km in 1996 (Fig. 5). There was a slight decrease in the mean number of latrines/km between 1994 and 1996 in all three study areas (Victoria = 6.42 *vs.* 6.3, JdFMT = 2.15 *vs.* 1.69, Denman Island = 5.94 *vs.* 5.31; see Fig. 5).

Table 2. Significant factor loadings of varimax rotated factor matrix of the principal component analysis carried out for pooled study areas and pooled site categories of sites used by *Lontra canadensis* in 1994. For an explanation of the variables, *cf.* Table 1.

variable (percent of explained overall variance)	factor 1 (19.1%)	factor 2 (15.3%)	factor 3 (12.8%)	factor 4 (12.6%)	factor 5 (12.6%)
distance to nearest site	–	–	0.835	–	–
nearest site category	0.613	–	–	–	–
distance to nearest den	–	–	–	–	0.558
distance to nearest permanent freshwater	–	–	–	0.622	
distance to nearest temporary freshwater	–	–	–	–	0.820
adjacent terrain slope	–	–	–	–	0.663
adjacent terrain type	–	0.875	–	–	–
human disturbance	–	0.789	–	–	–
slope at high water line	–	–	0.577	–	–
distance site to high water line	0.796	–	–	–	–
occurrence of non woody plants	0.915	–	–	–	–
occurrence of woody plants	0.943	–	–	–	–
occurrence of logs	–	–	–	0.856	–
coastal exposure	–	–	0.831	–	–
substrate type	–	–	–	–	-0.592
substrate exposure	–	–	–	0.652	

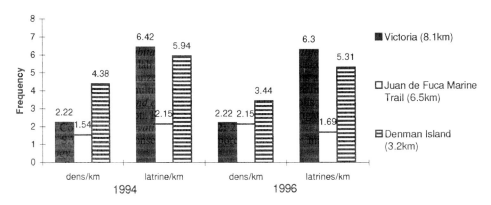

Fig. 5. Mean numbers of dens and latrines/km coastline in the three study areas in 1994 and 1996.

A detailed comparison of all changes between 1994 and 1996 is given in Fig. 6. Victoria and Denman Island show similar degrees in the "no change" category (60% and 62%, respectively) but only 34% of the sites remained unchanged in JdFMT, where the percentages of abandoned dens (6%) or latrines (23%) and the rates of new dens (11%) and latrines (20%) were highest. However, 54.5% of these new sites were in areas that were only accessible from the ocean. Further analysis also suggests that the JdFMT study area differed significantly from both Victoria and Denman Island

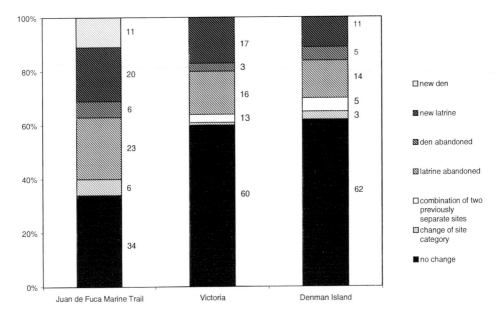

Fig. 6. Changes in site use by *Lontra canadensis* between 1994 and 1996 in the three study areas. Differences between combined data for no change in site location ("no change", "change of site category" and "combination of previously separate sites") were significant between JdFMT and Victoria ($\chi^2 = 5.10$; p = 0.02; two-tailed) and JdFMT and Denman Island ($\chi^2 = 5.50$; p = 0.02; two-tailed), whereas differences between the last two were not significant ($\chi^2 = 0.18$; p = 0.67; two-tailed).

with regard to the categories that indicated no change in site location ("no change"; "change of site category", and "combination of previously separate sites"), whereas no significant differences were found between the last (Fig. 6). It is notable that a landslide occurred prior to the 1996 study and affected two dens: both sites remained active, although one changed to a latrine site.

Discussion

I. Otters in urban habitats

Otter sign was found intermittently throughout the 1993 survey area (dens: Figs. 2, 3). It is not surprising that the area around the city centre is not extensively used by river otters considering the disturbance caused by both boat and floatplane traffic in the Inner Harbour. However, the findings of otter latrines underneath wooden docks in the city centre, plus one daytime otter sighting, are surprising, even though Melquist & Hornocker (1983) found *L. canadensis* within the city limits of McCall (Idaho) and on the intensely-used Payette Lake. Surveys of *L. lutra* in Scotland and Ireland have shown otter sign within the city limits of Dunblane (Green & Green, 1980; 1987), Dublin (Lunnon, 1989) and Dublin, Cork, Galway and Limerick (Chapman & Chapman, 1982).

Otters and other semi-aquatic mustelids such as American mink, *Mustela vison* (Hatler, 1976) have a special mode of spatial habitat utilisation which may assist in adaptation to urban habitats. Studies of coastal river otters in Alaska show that home-ranges are linear (Larsen, 1983) and radio-tracked animals rarely were found inland (Woolington, 1984). Melquist & Hornocker (1983) also note that their Idaho river otters moved mainly along waterways in linear home ranges. The river otter dens in coastal Alaska studied by Larsen (1983) were usually located within 20 m of the beach, which compares well with our 1994 study. In an urban context, the linear home ranges of otters and the restriction of sites (dens and latrines) to narrow stretches of coast, coupled with aquatic foraging, limit interactions with humans and may thus facilitate the co-existence of the two species.

The intermittent distribution of otter dens found in the 1993 study suggests certain habitat preferences. It also emphasises the significantly higher number of dens on islands that are undisturbed by humans (Fig. 4). The extensive utilisation of uninhabited islands demonstrates the general importance of undisturbed retreat areas for urban wildlife.

II. Habitat use by river otters in marine habitats of British Columbia

River otter habitat use in coastal BC was examined: (1) by a comparison of the overall occurrence of a habitat variable and its occurrence at river otter sites, and (2) by PCA of all data recorded at otter sites. Despite limitations on the detection of a localised occurrence of a habitat variable (which then is not the predominant state for the respective 125 m section), the first method employed does offer a basis for comparison. However, due to these limitations, variables that were measured on a small scale (e.g. substrate exposure) were not included in the comparison.

Significant differences between otter occurrence at sites and overall occurrence were found for vegetation (Table 1). Bushes and other woody plants were found significantly more often at Victoria den sites than expected, but latrines had significantly less woody plants and more non-woody plants than would be expected (Table 1). Both results highlight the importance of vegetation as cover for resting otters, especially in urban settings. This is also shown by factor 1 of the PCA (Table 2). Here, plant categories and the distance of sites from the high water line (*i.e.* distance from saltwater spray) can be linked to vegetational aspects of the habitat. This importance of vegetation for *L. canadensis* relates well with published data for this species (Melquist & Hornocker, 1983) and for *L. lutra* (Jenkins & Burrows, 1980; Bas *et al.*, 1984). Liers (1951) mentions the use of thickets besides burrows and cavities amongst tree roots by *L. canadensis* for giving birth. The utilisation of dense vegetation for denning has also been reported for the Cape clawless otter, *Aonyx capensis* (Arden-Clarke, 1986; Verwoerd, 1987; Rowe-Rowe, 1992) and the spot-necked otter, *Lutra maculicollis* (Rowe-Rowe, 1992).

The second factor of the PCA (Table 2) correlates with only two habitat variables coding for human use of an area ("human disturbance" and "adjacent terrain type"). This underlying factor (which explains 15.3% of the overall variance), as well as the 1993 study findings, provide evidence for the impact of human disturbance of otter site use. The non-significant differences between observed and expected occurrence of sites in low disturbance areas (Table 1) may be an artefact of the coarse measure of assessing overall availability: local disturbance may deter otters but may not be recognised as the predominant state for a 125 m section of coastline which then is considered a low disturbance section. Human disturbance acting as a limiting factor on denning was shown by Verwoerd (1987) in a study of *A. capensis*, and the preference of *L. canadensis* for areas with minimal human disturbance has been suggested by Melquist & Hornocker (1983). Nevertheless, they found otters in areas frequented by humans - provided that sufficient cover was present.

Two of the variables loading on factor 3 ("slope at high water line" and "coastal exposure") relate to coastal geomorphology, which also influences the third variable ("distance to nearest site"): an apparent trend for a preference for locally sheltered areas was observed in the JdFMT study area and, as sheltering features such as surge channels were spaced widely, the distance to nearest neighbouring sites can be linked to this variable. Furthermore, the effects of large-scale geomorphology can influence prey species' composition and abundance (see Larsen, 1983). However, neither prey nor large-scale geomorphology were recorded in this study. In contrast, Bowyer *et al.* (1995) found that otters had a slight preference for exposed coasts which had relatively less oil residue following the Exxon Valdez oil spill.

In Eurasian otters, the availability of freshwater is crucial for coat maintenance (Kruuk & Balharry, 1990). Although no data are available for *L. canadensis*, similar requirements can be assumed. Varying distances between dens and the closest permanent freshwater source in 1993 (Fig. 3), and the lack of permanent freshwater on the islands around Victoria (which have significantly higher den numbers than the mainland; Fig. 4), suggest that the influence of this habitat variable on site selection by river otters is limited. Since all but two of all 1994 dens were found above ground (Giere, 1995), non-apparent groundwater sources inside dens, as were found for *L. lutra* dens in Shetland (Moorhouse, 1988), are unlikely to provide overlooked access to freshwater. Still, in 1994 at least 27.8% of all sites were located within 50 m of the nearest freshwater source (whether temporary or permanent). However, PCA is ambiguous with regard to this variable as the two freshwater variables load onto separate factors, each explaining 12.6% of the overall variance (Table 2). Besides including the variables that code for freshwater availability, factors 4 and 5 subsume mainly variables that describe further aspects of habitat heterogeneity and geomorphology. Yet, factors 1-3 (explaining 47.2% of the total and 65.3% of the explained variance) are considered to be more important than the freshwater-influenced factors (factors 4, 5; Table 2). This agrees with Bowyer *et al.* (1995) who interpret the failure of distance to freshwater (which was substantially higher in their study areas than in the present study) in entering their model for habitat selection by the ready accessibility of freshwater within the large home ranges of otters – also suggested by observations of river otters in Louisiana more than 20 km from the nearest freshwater (Chabreck *et al.*, 1982). Thus, freshwater availability does not seem to limit habitat use in coastal environments for North American river otter as much as it does in the European species (Kruuk & Balharry, 1990; Lovett *et al.*, 1997), or its influence is masked by more important factors in the special situation offered in the present study of the effects of human presence.

Thus, it may be concluded that in British Columbia, river otter site selection in marine habitats is based primarily on three factors: (1) vegetation cover, (2) low levels of human disturbance, and (3) local geomorphology (e.g. the availability of local shelter on the coastline). Freshwater availability, the occurrence of driftwood, substrate type and exposure, as well as adjacent terrain slope and distance to the nearest den appear to be of only minor importance.

III. Human recreation and river otters

Otters are reported to revisit sites for long periods of time unless habitat conditions deteriorate (see Mason & Macdonald, 1986). In the present study, sites on southern Denman Island remained active in 1996 despite the considerable environmental disturbance of a landslide. The significantly lower number of sites with unaltered locations in Victoria and on Denman Island than in the JdFMT study area suggest a deterioration of environmental conditions in the last of these (Fig. 6). The lowest frequency of unchanged sites (34%) and the highest rate of site abandonments found in the JdFMT (29% *vs.* 19% for both Victoria and Denman Island; Fig. 6) point into the same direction. The large increase of human pressure between 1994-1996 due to the opening of the Juan de Fuca Marine Trail offers a cause for the deterioration of environmental conditions. Further support for this comes from the observation that 54.5% of the new sites in the JdFMT study area were found in areas that are not accessible from the trail. The substantial increase of dens (1994 =10, 1996 = 14) and the decrease in latrines (1994 = 14, 1996 = 11) can be interpreted as being due to an increased need for the cover provided at dens rather than at latrines. This is more likely than an increase in otter numbers, as would be expected if the findings of Moorhouse (1988) in Shetland for female *L. lutra* were transferred to the situation in western Canada.

The use of sign surveys for population studies is controversial (e.g. Kruuk *et al.*, 1986; Kruuk & Conroy, 1987; Mason & Macdonald, 1987). Objections include seasonal variation in otter marking, as shown for *L. lutra* (Conroy & French, 1987; Ruiz-Olmo & Gosálbez, 1997). Despite the different species involved and the overlap of survey months for 1994 and 1996 (see Methods), variation in scat numbers cannot be excluded as a cause for the differences in site use. *Lutra lutra* is known to defecate into the water (Kruuk & Conroy, 1987) which, transferred to a North American setting, might question some of the results of the 1996 study. This effect cannot be denied – it must nevertheless be assumed for all three study areas.

Judging from the non-significant difference between change rates in site use in Victoria and Denman Island, the Victoria otters have no increased rates of abandonment or site recruitment. Thus, it can be concluded that they have adjusted to the increased level of human disturbance in an urban habitat, and the same may eventually be expected for the new hiking trail – provided that undisturbed retreat areas similar to those on the uninhabited islands around Victoria are present.

Little published information on long-term site use is available for *L. canadensis*. Duffy *et al.* (1994) found more than three times higher site abandonment rates in oiled (15%) than in non-oiled areas (4%). These rates are low compared to those in the present study, yet Duffy *et al.* (1994) refer to abandonment alone, with no new sites being mentioned and no time frame for the change being given. Assuming that their rate for the oiled area refers to consecutive years, this compares favourably with that found in Victoria between 1993-1994 (13% abandoned sites - caused in part by extensive construction activity around a marina at the northern end of the study area; Giere, 1995). Furthermore, considering the twice as long period between the surveys, it compares with the rate found in the JdFMT in the present study. In all three studies, substantial environmental changes (oiling, construction, tourism) had occurred between the initial survey and its repetition.

Acknowledgements

We would like to thank the reviewers for valuable comments on the manuscript and to BC Parks for permitting research in the Juan de Fuca Provincial Park. A. Wasilewski (Marburg) is acknowledged for conducting the PCA and O. Gathmann (Toronto) for advice on data-handling. We thank J. Balke (Denman Island) for critical reviews of earlier drafts of part of the manuscript and for many fruitful discussions on the topic. H.-O. von Hagen (Marburg) is acknowledged for supervising the 1994 study (Diplomarbeit). Part of this study was supported by grant 40095/705.6.311 from Stifterverband für die Deutsche Wissenschaft.

References

Aaris-Sørensen, J. (1987). Past and present distribution of badgers *Meles meles* in the Copenhagen area. *Biological Conservation*, **41**: 159-165.

Ackermann, H. (1994). *Biometrische Analyse von Stichproben. Version 4*. Hochheim; Epsilon Verlag.

Arden-Clarke, C.H.G. (1986). Population density, home range and spatial organization of the Cape clawless otter, *Aonyx capensis*, in a marine habitat. *Journal of Zoology*, **209**: 201-211.

Adkins, C.A. & Stott, P. (1998). Home ranges, movements and habitat associations of red foxes *Vulpes vulpes* in suburban Toronto, Ontario, Canada. *Journal of Zoology*, **244**: 335-346.

Atkinson, K.T. & Shackleton, D.M. (1991). Coyote, *Canis latrans*, ecology in a rural-urban environment. *Canadian Field-Naturalist*, **105**: 49-56.

Bas, N., Jenkins, D. & Rothery, P. (1984). Ecology of otters in Scotland. V. The distribution of otter (*Lutra lutra*) faeces in relation to bankside vegetation on the river Dee in summer 1981. *Journal of Applied Ecology*, **21**: 507-513.

Beja, P.R. (1989). Coastal otters in southeast Portugal. *IUCN Otter Specialist Group Bulletin*, **4**: 2-7.

Bowyer, R.T., Testa, J.W. & Faro, J.B. (1995). Habitat selection and home ranges of river otters in a marine environment: effects of the Exxon Valdez oil spill. *Journal of Mammalogy*, **76**: 1-11.

Bruce, J. (1881). Otters caught in a sewer. *The Field, the Farm, the Garden*, **57**: 797.

Chabreck, R.H., Holcombe, J.E., Linscombe, R.G. & Kinler, N.E. (1982). Winter foods of river otters from saline and fresh environments in Louisiana. *Proceedings of the Annual Conference of the Southeastern Association of Fish and Wildlife Agencies*, **36**: 473-483.

Chapman, P.J. & Chapman, L.L. (1982). *Otter survey of Ireland, 1980-81*. London; The Vincent Wildlife Trust.

Conroy, J.W.H. & French, D.D. (1987). The use of spraints to monitor populations of otters (*Lutra lutra* L.). *Symposia of the Zoological Society of London*, **58**: 247-262.

Cowan, I.McT. & Guiguet, C.J. (1975). *The mammals of British Columbia*. Victoria (BC); British Columbia Provincial Museum.

Dearden, P. & Hall, C. (1983). Non consumptive recreation and the case of the Vancouver Island marmot (*Marmota vancouverensis*). *Environmental Conservation*, **10**: 63-66.

Duffus, D.A. & Dearden, P.D. (1993). Recreational use, valuation and management of killer whale (*Orcinus orca*) on Canada's Pacific coast. *Environmental Conservation*, **20**: 149-156.

Duffy, L.K., Bowyer, R.T., Testa, J.W. & Faro, J. B. (1994). Chronic effects of the Exxon Valdez oil spill on blood and enzyme chemistry of river otters. *Environmental Toxicology and Chemistry*, **13**: 643-647.

Giere, P. (1995). *Zur Habitatnutzung küstenbewohnender Otter (Lutra canadensis) in Britisch-Kolumbien.* Diplomarbeit. Marburg; Philipps-Universität Marburg.

Goodrich, J.M. & Berger, J. (1994). Winter recreation and hibernating black bears. *Environmental Conservation*, **67**: 105-110.

Gossow, H. & Kranz, A. (Eds.) (1998). *Otters and Fish Farms. Boku-Reports on Wildlife Research & Game Management*, **14**: 1-144.

Green, J. & Green, R. (1980). *Otter survey of Scotland.* London; The Vincent Wildlife Trust.

Green, J. & Green, R. (1987). *Otter survey of Scotland, 1984-85.* London; The Vincent Wildlife Trust.

Guiguet, C.J. (1962). River otter. *Victoria Naturalist*, **18** (5): 53.

Harris, S. (1984). Ecology of urban badgers *Meles meles*: distribution in Britain and habitat selection, persecution, food and damage in the city of Bristol. *Biological Conservation*, **28**: 349-375.

Hatler, D.F. (1976). *The coastal mink on Vancouver Island, British Columbia.* PhD Thesis. Vancouver (BC); University of British Columbia.

Jacobs,. M.J. & Schloeder, C.A. (1992). Managing brown bears and wilderness recreation on the Kenai Peninsula, Alaska, USA. *Environmental Conservation*, **16**: 249-254.

Jenkins, D. & Burrows, G.O. (1980). Ecology of otters in northern Scotland. III. The use of faeces as indicators of otter *Lutra lutra* density and distribution. *Journal of Animal Ecology*, **49**: 755-774.

Jenkins, J.H. (1983). The status and management of the river otter (*Lutra canadensis*) in North America. *Acta Zoologici Fennici*, **174**: 233-235.

Kruuk, H. (1995). *Wild otters: predation and populations.* Oxford; Oxford University Press.

Kruuk, H. & Balharry, D. (1990). Effects of sea water on thermal insulation of the otter, *Lutra lutra*. *Journal of Zoology*, **220**: 405-415.

Kruuk, H. & Conroy, J.W.H. (1987). Surveying otter *Lutra lutra* populations: a discussion of problems with spraints. *Biological Conservation*, **41**: 179-183.

Kruuk, H., Conroy, J.W.H., Glimmerveen, U. & Ouwerkerk, E.J. (1986). The use of spraints to survey populations of otters *Lutra lutra*. *Biological Conservation*, **35**: 187-194.

Larsen, D.N. (1983). *Habitats, movements and foods of river otters in coastal southeast Alaska.* MSc thesis. Fairbanks (Alaska); University of Alaska.

Liers, E.E. (1951). Notes on the river otter (*Lutra canadensis*). *Journal of Mammalogy*, **32**: 1-9.

Lovett, L., Kruuk, H. & Lambin, X. (1997). Factors influencing use of freshwater pools by otters, *Lutra lutra*, in a marine environment. *Journal of Zoology*, **243**: 825-831.

Lunnon, R.M. (1989). *The distribution and food of otters in the Dublin area.* BA Mod. thesis. Dublin (Trinity College); National University of Ireland.

Macdonald, S.M. (1983). The status of the otter (*Lutra lutra*) in the British Isles. *Mammal Review*, **13**: 11-23.

Macdonald, S.M. & Mason, C.F. (1985). Otters, their habitat and conservation in northeast Greece. *Biological Conservation*, **31**: 191-210.

MacLoughlin, J.H. (1950). An otter in Belfast. *Irish Naturalists' Journal*, **10**: 42.

Mason, C. (1989). Contaminants in British eels. *IUCN Otter Specialist Group Bulletin*, **4**: 38.

Mason, C.F. & Macdonald, S.M. (1986). *Otters: ecology and conservation.* Cambridge; Cambridge University Press.

Mason, C.F. & Macdonald, S.M. (1987). The use of spraints for surveying otter (*Lutra lutra*) populations: an evaluation. *Biological Conservation*, **41**: 167-177.

McLellan, B.N. (1989a). Dynamics of a grizzly bear population during a period of industrial resource extraction. I. Density and age - sex composition. *Canadian Journal of Zoology*, **67**: 1856-1860.

McLellan, B.N. (1989b). Dynamics of a grizzly bear population during a period of industrial resource extraction. II. Mortality rates and causes of death. *Canadian Journal of Zoology*, **67**: 1861-1864.

McLellan, B.N. (1989c). Dynamics of a grizzly bear population during a period of industrial resource extraction. III. Natality rates and rates of increase. *Canadian Journal of Zoology*, **67**: 1865-1868.

Melquist, W.E. & Hornocker, M.G. (1983). Ecology of river otters in west central Idaho. *Wildlife Monographs*, **83**: 1-60.

Moorhouse, A. (1988). *Distribution of holts and their utilisation by the European otter* Lutra lutra *in a marine environment.* MSc thesis. Aberdeen; University of Aberdeen.

Munro, W.T. & Jackson, L. (1979). *Preliminary mustelid management plan for British Columbia*. Victoria (BC); Ministry of the Environment, Fish and Wildlife Branch.

Nicht, M. (1969). Ein Beitrag zum Vorkommen des Steinmarders, *Martes foina* (Erxleben, 1770), in der Großstadt (Magdeburg). *Zeitschrift für Jagdwissenschaft*, **15**: 1-6.

Page, R.J.C. (1981). Dispersal and population of the fox (*Vulpes vulpes*) in an area of London. *Journal of Zoology*, **194**: 485-491.

Rowe-Rowe, D.T. (1992). Survey of South African otters in a freshwater habitat, using sign. *South African Journal of Wildlife Research*, **22**: 49-55.

Ruiz-Olmo, J. & Gosàlbez, J. (1997). Observations on the sprainting behaviour of the otter *Lutra lutra* in the NE Spain. *Acta Theriologica*, **42**: 259-270.

Shannon, J.S. (1989). Social organization and behavioral ontogeny of otters (*Lutra canadensis*) in a coastal habitat in northern California. *IUCN Otter Specialist Group Bulletin*, **4**: 8-13.

Slate, D. (1985). *Movement, activity and home range patterns among members of a high density suburban raccoon population (radio telemetry)*. PhD thesis. New Brunswick (NJ); Rutgers State University.

Stephenson, T.A. & Stephenson, A. (1961). Life between tidemarks in North America. IV A. Vancouver Island I. *Journal of Ecology*, **49**: 1-29.

Stevens, J. (1996). *Applied multivariate statistics for the social sciences*. Mahwah (NJ); Erlbaum.

Stubbe, M., Heidecke, D., Dolch, D., Teubner, J., Labes, R., Ansorge, H., Mau, H. & Blanke, D. (1993). Monitoring Fischotter 1985 - 1991. In: M. Stubbe, D. Heidecke & A. Stubbe (eds.), *Monitoring Fischotter 1985 – 1991 (Tiere im Konflikt 1)*: 11-25. Halle (Saale); Martin Luther Universität Halle-Wittenberg.

Tester, U. (1986). Vergleichende Nahrungsuntersuchung beim Steinmarder *Martes foina* (Erxleben, 1777) in großstädtischem und ländlichem Habitat. *Säugetierkundliche Mitteilungen*, **33**: 37-52.

Toweill, D.E. & Tabor, J.E. (1982). River otter *Lutra canadensis*. In: J.A. Chapman & G.A. Feldhamer (eds.), *Wild mammals of North America*: 688-703. Baltimore (Maryland); Johns Hopkins University Press.

Verwoerd, D.J. (1987). Observations on the food and status of the Cape clawless otter *Aonyx capensis* at Betty's Bay, South Africa. *South African Journal of Zoology*, **22**: 33-39.

Weston, J. & Stirling, D. (1986). *The naturalists' guide to the Victoria area*. Victoria (BC); Victoria Natural History Society.

Wood, D. (1995). Juan de Fuca Marine Trail. *Beautiful British Columbia*, **37** (4): 20-29.

Woolington, J.D. (1984). *Habitat use and movements of river otters at Kelp Bay, Baranof Island, Alaska*. MSc thesis. Fairbanks (Alaska); University of Alaska.

CHAPTER 8

Prehistoric mustelid exploitation: an overview

Ruth Charles

Abstract

This paper examines the way in which archaeological and palaeontological evidence can add information to our perceptions of human-animal interactions. Detailed evidence for mustelid exploitation in north-western Europe during the Late Upper Palaeolithic and Mesolithic is presented, and a
general trend towards the intensification in the exploitation of mammals for their pelts is identified.
A model is developed to explain the underlying causes of this trend, integrating the archaeological
evidence for mustelid exploitation with broader evidence for environmental change and the social
re-organisation of human groups in the temperate zone. In closing it is suggested that mustelids,
alongside other mammals trapped exclusively for their pelts, provided a medium through which
human symbolic behaviour and social identities were negotiated during a period of rapid environmental and social change.

Introduction

When analysing vertebrate assemblages from archaeological sites, the usual prime
concern is to identify the main species present and discuss the ways in which different species contributed to a site's economy. The archaeological objectives are to
reconstruct past human dietary practices, evidence for husbandry and perhaps draw
inferences about the secondary products animals may have provided. Such reports
usually centre on the role of domestic animals – mainly sheep, goats, cattle and pigs
– on sites dating as far back as the Neolithic (about 4,500 years ago in Britain), a
coarse-grained archaeological term linked with the origins and spread of agriculture
itself. Prior to the Neolithic, the Mesolithic and Palaeolithic periods are principally
concerned with the archaeological traces of mobile hunter-gatherer bands, which
occupied sites for relatively short periods of time, often during specific seasons of
the year. In these cases, faunal interpretations again tend to focus on the contribution of large ungulates to a site's economy, as these usually constitute the main
species present. The core aims of archaeological analysis of this material remain the
same – the reconstruction of past human subsistence practices – and in such
instances much emphasis is usually placed on the hunting and trapping of wild animals; studies dating to the Late Pleistocene of western Europe focus on the
exploitation of reindeer, *Rangifer tarandus*, horse, *Equus ferus*, red deer, *Cervus
elephus*, ibex, *Capra ibex*, wild boar, *Sus scrofa*, mammoth, *Elephas primigenius*,
and woolly rhinoceros, *Coelodonta antiquitatis*. Carnivores play a relatively minor

Mustelids in a modern world
Management and conservation aspects of small carnivore: human interactions
edited by Huw I. Griffiths, pp. 127–140
© 2000 Backhuys Publishers, Leiden, The Netherlands

role in such considerations; occasionally the presence or absence of domestic dogs, *Canis familiaris*, from a site is discussed (and the origins of domestic dogs is itself a major research theme), and in some instances the roles that carnivores may have played as predators and agents of faunal accumulation are brought into play.

The seperation of animal bones deposited in archaeological sites *via* human agency from those which are the by-product of carnivore activity is a major research issue within Palaeolithic archaeology. A range of methodologies have been proposed to achive this end, and for the purposes of this paper clear evidence of human butchery practices, usually found in the form of distinctive 'V-shaped' cut marks will be used as the main criterion (*cf.* Potts & Shipman, 1981). When interpreting butchery evidence, it is often possible to suggest which actions (e.g. skinning, meat removal or disarticulation) may have taken place by considering the location and orientation of different marks.

Mustelids rarely figure in the overall picture of human subsistence behaviour, partly due to the relatively low number in which they have been found on archaeological sites, and in part to modern preconceptions regarding potential uses and social significance within human economic practices. However, clear evidence for the past human exploitation of mustelids does exist in faunal collections from a number of well known archaeological sites across Europe. Today there are approximately 53 separate species of mustelid, which are found primarily in the northern temperate zones of north America and Eurasia (Schreiber *et al.*, 1989). These include the badger and the wolverine as well as martens, mink, stoats and weasels. Each member of Mustelidae has its own particular set of environmental preferences and behaviour. This paper will not discuss each species' preferences in detail here. Instead this brief review will centre on evidence drawn principally from a series of later Palaeolithic and Mesolithic sites in north-western Europe, dating between 12,000 and 5,000 years ago. This period spans the final end of the last ice age *c.* 10,000 years ago (*i.e.* the Latest Pleistocene) and the earlier part of the current interglacial (the Holocene). Archaeologically it encompasses groups belonging to the Late Upper Palaeolithic and the Mesolithic. Both pre-date the local emergence of agriculture.

An archaeological (and palaeontological) approach to human-animal interactions differs from those usually employed by zoologists, as it offers a long-term perspective, working in terms of millennia rather than decades. Consequently it offers the opportunity to recognise long-term processes in both animal and human behaviour, and monitor shifting behavioural preferences and tolerances in both groups. The origins of domestication are a good example of such a long term process. The discussion which follows is not intended as a definitive account, but instead an entry point to a relatively under-researched archaeozoological topic dealing with human-mustelid interactions.

In contemporary western European society, carnivores are rarely viewed as a potential food source and only a limited range of mustelids are exploited for their pelts. However, such preferences are not reflected in the European prehistoric archaeological record. Although mustelids do not appear to have been a regular dietary staple at any point, there is evidence that they were sporadically exploited both for their meat and pelts during early prehistory. As part of an exploration into modern dietary perceptions of different mammals, modern poachers and countrymen were questioned in the Oxford region between 1990 and 1994 whilst the author was undertaking doctoral research. When mustelids were discussed (principally relating to badgers) it was strongly suggested that their meat is avoided today because it "tastes bad". However, none of these informants had actually tasted mustelid flesh, believing the nature of the prohibition to be self evident.

The archaeological evidence which exists for the prehistoric exploitation of the three principal mustelid species found in archaeological assemblages spanning the study period – the wolverine, *Gulo gulo*, European badger, *Meles meles*, and pine marten, *Martes martes* – will be summarised in the following pages and the archaeological significance of such data will then be discussed (sites mentioned in the text are shown in Fig. 1). The evidence presented here fits within a broader pattern of the expansion of human subsistence behaviour during the Lateglacial and early Postglacial periods (*cf.* Charles, 1997), in which smaller, mammals attained an increased significance to bands of mobile hunter-gatherers, both as a potential food source and for their pelts.

Wolverine *(Gulo gulo)*

Wolverines are today mainly restricted to the taiga and southern tundra zones of Eurasia, including parts of the old Soviet Union, Norway, Sweden, Finland, Mongolia and northern China; they also extend into the New World across much of Canada, Alaska and possibly the Rocky mountains. This cannot be taken a reflection of their past distribution. They are highly adaptable animals, and records from the earlier parts of this century, as well as the last, suggest that they were found in more southerly regions in the recent past (Schreiber *et al.*, 1989). They have expansive home ranges, approximately 800-900 km^2 in summer, and perhaps even larger in winter (Schreiber *et al.*, 1989). The wolverine is a predator, capable of taking large mammals, although in general it is mainly a scavenger of herbivore carcasses up to the size of reindeer and red deer. Modern wolverines are up to one metre in length, and their pelts are dark brown (sometimes almost black), with a pair of yellowish stripes running from the shoulders to the rump. In general, wolverines tend to avoid human settlements, and to date there is little research available on their ecology and behaviour patterns. It seems unlikely that wolverines came into frequent contact with humans during the Palaeolithic, and their vicious reputation no doubt preceded them. Wolverine remains are rarely found on western European Upper Palaeolithic and Mesolithic sites, and this species is present within only two faunal assemblages studied by the author, the Trou de Chaleux and the Trou des Nutons in north-western Ardennes in Belgium. At both of these sites, only a single specimen shows a direct association with human activity.

In many, if not all, of the regions where it is found today, the wolverine is traditionally hunted for its fur. Like many animals, they often follow set routes and setting traps in 'natural corridors' such as ravines is common practice among recent hunters (Nelson, 1973). As wolverines are among the main scavengers from traplines, wolverine traps are today frequently set towards the ends of trap lines to reduce predation. Similarly, kill sites for other large mammals provide excellent locations in which to trap wolverines (as well as foxes and wolves) as the scent attracts scavenging animals. The wolverine's strength and aggressive nature makes it difficult to confine, and particularly strong traps and snares are used alongside deadfall traps.

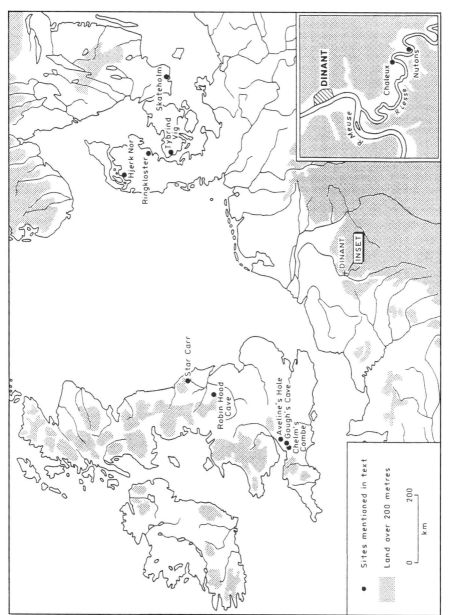

Fig 1. Location map of main sites discussed in the text.

Their fur is especially useful in extremely cold environments, as it does not freeze when damp, and consequently can make an excellent edging for hoods, amongst other uses (R. Jacobi, pers. comm.). The two specimens with good evidence for human exploitation both come from Belgium: the specimen from the Trou de Chaleux is a partial scapula, with numerous marks which appear to have been the result of butchery activities across its posterior surface. The other specimen, a proximal right femur from the Trou des Nutons, has a single, somewhat ambiguous mark, which may also be a cut. Both marks correspond with meat filleting rather than skinning, although the one activity would not preclude the other.

At both sites the faunal spectra, alongside recent radiocarbon dating, indicate that faunal material was accumulated during the Lateglacial and the early Postglacial (Charles, 1996, 1998; R. Orban, pers. comm.). In this instance it is most likely that both specimens are linked to the Late Magdalenian archaeological period, within the Bølling Interstadial phase (*circa* 12,800-12,000 BP) of the Lateglacial. Evidence confirming that wolverines were known to Magdalenian hunter-gatherers exists in the form of late ice age art – the depiction of a wolverine engraved on a perforated *bâton de Commandment* from La Madeleine (Cremades, 1992) is a well known example. Unmodified wolverine bones have also been identified from other Lateglacial contexts in north-western Europe such as Chelm's Coombe at Cheddar, UK (A. Currant, pers. comm.) and Petersfels, Germany (Albrecht *et al.*, 1983) and it appears that viable populations of wolverines inhabited the northern margins of Lateglacial Europe, most probably during the interstadial phases.

Badger *(Meles meles)*

Present knowledge of the temporal and spatial distribution of badgers during the Holocene and Pleistocene in western Europe is patchy. When found in Late Pleistocene faunal assemblages they are usually seen as evidence for more recent contamination. Usually this is interpreted as evidence for Holocene badger setts being excavated into Pleistocene age sediments. Nonetheless, badgers have been found in genuine Late Pleistocene and early Holocene contexts in north-western Europe, including Petersfels (Albrecht *et al.*, 1983) and Kendrick's Cave, UK (which contained two perforated badger teeth used as pendants).

Badgers are denning animals and live in setts; the morphology of these is variable, but they can be extremely large with volumes of many cubic metres. The tunnels tend to be linked, and there are many chambers, often with bedding of vegetation. Badgers also 'like' using caves (H. Kruuk, pers. comm.). Setts are often shared with other carnivores, including foxes, otters and wild cats. These setts are thought to be in long term use, perhaps being used over centuries. Indeed, one near Kirkhead Cavern in Cumbria (UK) is mentioned in the Domesday Book and is still in use. It is unclear whether these setts are used continuously, or episodically by different badger clans. Although in general badgers prefer hilly districts, especially heavily wooded ones (Neal, 1948), they are highly adaptable, and can survive in a range of habitats and soils. Many of the cave sites inhabited by hunter-gatherers during the Upper Palaeolithic and Mesolithic, with steep talus cones and slopes, close to rivers and streams, would also have been ideal locations for badger setts.

It is also possible that badgers played some part in the accumulation of the faunal assemblage found in such cave sites. Although their diet is primarily made up of earthworms (Kruuk, 1989), they have also been observed eating a variety of foodstuffs including salmon, *Salmo* spp., frogs, *Rana temporaria*, toads, *Bufo bufo*, wood pigeon, *Columba palumbus*, passerines, a variety of small mammals including rabbits, *Oryctolagus cuniculus*, and hares, *Lepus* spp., and carrion up to the size of sheep and deer. They have even been observed to kill lambs (see Kruuk, 1989) and to take chunks of food including carrion, back to cubs in the setts. In recent times omnivorous tendencies have been observed amongst badgers in areas away from extensive agriculture, where they take carrion, small mammals and vegetable matter. The cubs are prone to high mortality rates within the setts, but this varies with local ecological conditions (H. Kruuk, pers. comm.). Kruuk has observed corpses of very young badgers well away from setts, which must have been taken there by adults, but thinks that most will be either left inside the sett or eaten by adults. Similarly Kruuk has noted that "small mammal remains can be passed relatively undamaged in the faeces, and their latrines can be inside the sett or, in the cave-based setts in an 'entrance hall'" (H. Kruuk, pers. comm.). One particularly interesting feature is that badgers do not chew or gnaw bones, making it difficult to demonstrate a direct link between badger activity and the accumulation of remains through the study of damage patterns on bones. Given what has been outlined above, badgers could have been responsible for at least part of the accumulation of small mammals and fish bones and even some of the larger mammal bones, more usually attributed to human activity, at many cave sites.

Direct butchery evidence has been observed on badger bones from the Trou de Chaleux and Trou des Nutons in Belgium (Fig. 2), and Gough's Cave and Star Carr in Britain (Charles, 1997, 1998; Fig. 3). In each case only a small number of cut marked bones were present, and the marks indicate different processing activities at different sites.

A minimum number of individuals count (MNI) of four was calculated for the Chaleux badgers, based on the innominate bones, scapulae and femora. No juvenile bones were recorded. In total 66 badger bones were present (1.8% of the assemblage). Although the number of identifiable specimens present (NISP) is too small to formulate any meaningful discussion of significant trends in body part representation, it is interesting to note in passing that the lower portions of the badger limbs were absent. Such body part absence in other species thought to be exclusively taken for their pelts has been used as evidence for prehistoric human use, interpreted as evidence for skinning in which an animal's body has been discarded but the paws removed as part of the pelt (*cf.* Klein, 1973). In this instance, the evidence may suggest the skinning of badgers at Chaleux (and consequently, perhaps, specialist trapping for their pelts).

The only cut marked badger bones from Chaleux are five femora (see Fig. 2). Only longitudinal groups of cuts were present, almost all of which were located towards the proximal ends. The same is true for the five cut bones from Nutons (a right ulna, two left humeri, a right femur and a distal left femur) and for the sole cut specimen from Gough's Cave, a juvenile humerus with longitudinal cuts towards the proximal end of the shaft. In each case these indicate meat removal, suggesting that whilst badgers may have been hunted/trapped for their distinctive pelts, their

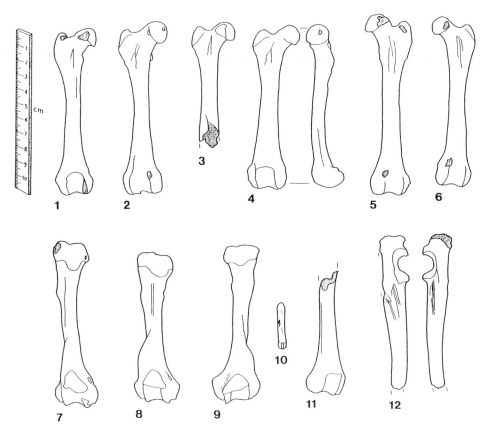

Fig 2. Cut marked badger bones from the Trou des Nutons (Nos 1, 7,8, 11 & 12), Trou de Chaleux (2, 3, 4, 5 & 6) and Star Carr (9 & 10).

meat was also of some interest (Griffiths, 1993). Indeed meat removal is the only activity for which there is any direct evidence at these sites, all radiocarbon dated to between 12,000-13,000 years BP. In contrast, the two cut specimens from Star Carr (an early Mesolithic site dated to *circa* 8,500 years BP) show marks which correspond with skinning, although meat filleting marks are also present on the distal portion of a humerus (Fig. 3). Similarly Rowley-Conwy (in press) has noted a badger skull with cut marks relating to skinning from Ringkloster in Denmark, this time dating to the later part of the European Mesolithic.

Pine martens *(Martes martes)* and other small mustelids

In Mesolithic contexts the contribution of smaller mustelids, alongside other small fur bearing mammals, to the human subsistence economy is becoming apparent. At Star Carr, a well known early Mesolithic site in Britain, the remains of two pine martens show butchery marks consistent with skinning and meat removal. Other evidence for their exploitation comes from Denmark, where Rowley-Conwy (1980)

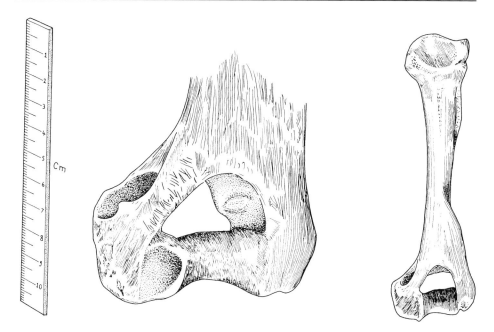

Fig 3. Badger humerus from Star Carr (Yorkshire, UK) with cut marks (detail).

commented on the specialist exploitation of smaller fur bearing mammals within the Ertebølle complex (the final Mesolithic in southern Scandinavia). At Tybrind Vig, Denmark (Trolle-Larson, 1986, 1987) the remains of at least 13 complete pine martens were recovered alongside a polecat and four otters, all apparently processed for their pelts. Similarly some articulated skeletons of pine marten were recovered from Ringkloster (Rowley-Conwy, in press), transverse cuts corresponding with skinning being present on the front of many of the crania; overall at least 18 individuals were recovered from the site, all present as a result of human exploitation.

Prehistoric exploitation of these animals seems to have focused on their pelts. The fact that they do not appear to occur within Lateglacial faunas is probably a function of their distribution and habitat preference during this period, rather than the result of any conscious selection on the part of late ice age trappers. The apparent increased emphasis on the exploitation of such species, linked to the use of specialist trapping camps (cf. Rowley-Conwy, 1980) during the Mesolithic is probably a reflection of the locally available resources. The possibility that an intensification in the trapping of fur bearing mammals during the Ertebølle offered a valuable a commodity for trade with local agricultural communities cannot be discounted, and links between the two groups have been suggested both in terms of lithic technology and pottery (Zvelebil & Rowley-Conwy, 1986).

Discussion

Carnivores and other fur bearing mammals did not form a major dietary staple for western European hunter-gatherers during the Upper Palaeolithic and Mesolithic; however, it is clear that they did contribute to the human economy. Rowley-Conwy (1980) argued that during the Mesolithic the exploitation of fur bearing mammals most probably occurred during the winter, as this is the season when their fur is of the highest quality. Accounts of recent North American hunters and trappers (*cf.* Nelson, 1973) concur with this suggestion, and add that fur trapping primarily for trading purposes is only likely to occur in times of abundance (Winterhalder, 1980). It is unlikely, however, that animals were trapped solely for their furs, and the evidence presented here confirms that meat was removed from many of the mustelids discussed above, alongside a range of other carnivores including lynx, *Lynx lynx*, wild cat, *Felis sylvestris*, fox, *Vulpes* sp., wolf, *Canis lupus* and bear, *Ursus arctos* (Charles, 1997). In addition to providing pelts for clothing and barter, such animals could have provided an occasional alternative to the dietary staples of reindeer, horse, red deer, *Cervus elephus*, and aurochs, *Bos primigenius*, and/or provided meat when such herbivores were rare or absent.

When examining the significance of larger mammals to the subsistence economy of Upper Palaeolithic and Mesolithic populations, a picture of increasing emphasis on the exploitation of fur bearing mammals during these periods emerges alongside the recognition of specialist exploitation camps linked to fur trapping, such as that for the trapping of arctic hares, *Lepus timidus*, at Robin Hood Cave in Britain (Charles & Jacobi, 1994), and wild cat at Hjerk Nor, Denmark (Rowley-Conwy, 1980). This suggests a general broadening of the subsistence base which was mirrored in the use of plant and maritime resources at this time. Rather than arguing for a dramatic shift in the nature of animal exploitation during the Lateglacial and early Postglacial, it is suggested here that the exploitation of fur bearing mammals and other carnivores reflects an expansion in the economic base.

In addition to providing a supplement to dietary staples of locally available plant foods, ungulate and marine resources, the meat from mustelids, alongside other carnivores may have been used as bait to entice further animals into traps. This is certainly possible, although regular use of meat obtained in this way is unlikely due to the low minimum number of individuals counts for each species encountered at each site.

It is probable that an expansion in the subsistence base can be viewed within the broader context of environmental change at the end of the last ice age and the start of the current interglacial, specifically the changes in landscape brought about by extensive marine transgressions during the Holocene, and the development and spread of boreal forests across north-western Europe during this period, bringing with it commensurate changes in regional ecology. The earlier Holocene in Europe is generally characterised by the increase in plant and tree cover leading to the eventual appearance of climax forest. Alongside this eustatic and isostatic changes radically transformed the landscape, including the flooding of the English Channel and the Irish Sea (Simmons *et al.*, 1981). The larger mammals present in north-western Europe throughout this period, such as red deer and horse, are relatively flexible in their behavioural patterns and environmental tolerances, and are known to congregate in large herds in open environments and to lead far more solitary life styles in forested ones. Shifts in exploitation strategies employed by prehistoric hunter-gatherers have been suggested (Jacobi *et al.*, 1976; Simmons *et al.*, 1981) as adaptations to these behavioural and environmental changes.

A model developed to explain the diversity of resource procurement amongst the Cree of North America seems a useful analogy here, in which the vast and widely (but unevenly) distributed resources of boreal forests are recognised by foragers familiar with a large area, but in which it is only feasible to exploit a small portion in any given season or year (Winterhalder, 1983). By applying the general principles of Optimal Foraging Theory (*cf.* Krebs, 1977), a series of different 'patches' within the boreal forest can be recognised in which the available prey occurs in small, dispersed 'packets'. Consequently, the expectation is that foragers spend a considerable amount of time searching for these 'packets', pursue a relatively large proportion of the species encountered on any given trip and so have a fairly broad dietary range and utilise a wide range of 'patches'.

In such a model one would expect the primary dietary focus to be towards the exploitation of larger mammals, further subsidised by the trapping of smaller mammals. This suggestion is certainly borne out at many archaeological sites – the Trou de Chaleux, Trou des Nutons and Trou du Frontal in Belgium (Charles, 1998), Gough's Cave (Currant, 1986, 1991; Currant *et al.*, 1989), Aveline's Hole, Star Carr (Fraser & King, 1954), Ringkloster and Tybrind Vig. These assemblages are dominated by large and medium sized ungulates, all of which show extensive butchery marks relating to skinning, meat removal, disarticulation and subsequent smashing of bones for marrow. Additionally, other smaller fur bearing mammals are present which bear evidence for both skinning and meat extraction. All of these sites can be interpreted as hunting camps, and in most cases the use of these locations by late Pleistocene and early Holocene hunter-gatherers is believed to have been seasonal. It seems most likely that when the opportunity arose for the exploitation of small game this was unlikely to be disregarded. Efficient exploitation of such animals could be greatly enhanced by the use of traps, as the pursuit of larger mammals can be combined with the routine checking of trap lines, thus maximising the potential returns. Such an explanation is proposed here to account for the widening of the dietary selection within north-western European Late Upper Palaeolithic and Mesolithic groups.

Alongside this the possible expansion of symbolic expression *via* clothing and personal adornment might also be invoked as an explanation as to why mustelids, alongside other smaller mammals may have become prized by human groups for their pelts during this period; although its should be noted that this aspect of stone age life remains difficult to quantify. Highly stylised engravings are known from a variety of Lateglacial and early Postglacial locations, including Gönnersdorf in Germany (Bosinski, 1991), Gough's Cave (Charles, 1989) and Kendrick's Cave (Sieveking, 1971) in Britain. Gamble (1991) has suggested that the Magdalenian 'symbolic explosion' of the Lateglacial can be interpreted within the context of social knowledge and communication between pioneer groups re-colonising the north-western European mainland after its abandonment at the height of the Last Glacial Maximum between 20,000 and 16,000 BP (Charles, 1996; Housley *et al.*, 1997), allowing for the maintenance of social contacts over great distances. Gamble noted that this use of symbolism within material culture appears to diminish after the earliest, pioneer phase of this process. However, with the dramatic changes in the north-western European landscape which occurred throughout the early Postglacial caused by isostatic and eustatic changes in sea level, one can again detect the increasing occurrence of symbolic media within the archaeological record. Star Carr in Britain (Clark, 1954), Berlin-Biesdorf (Reinbacher, 1956), Hohen Viecheln (Schuldt, 1961) and Bedburg-Königshoven in Germany (Street, 1991) have all yielded the same, novel, artefact category during the early Postglacial – worked red deer frontlets. The precise use of these objects remains ambiguous, and they are frequently interpreted as head-gear used in hunting equipment and/or ritual. Inspection of the Star Carr frontlets by the author revealed that the antlers on these specimens had been shaved on their medial surfaces, lightening the weight of these objects whilst not diminishing their overall effect when viewed only from below. This adds circumstantial evidence to the suggestions that they were worn, and that they were less likely to be used in a hunting – during which the wearer was unlikely to be viewed exclusively from below by prey.

In addition to the isolated occurrences such as those described above, lithic technology shifted from the pan-European early Mesolithic "broad blade" industries (consisting primarily of obliquely blunted points) to the regionally specific late and later Mesolithic 'narrow blade' industries (made up of a range of microlithic forms) (Jacobi, 1976; Gendel, 1989; Arts, 1989). The redefinition of the landscape by marine transgressions, river development and expansion and forest growth would have had a profound impact on Mesolithic human communities and their communications. If population densities changed (*cf.* Meiklejohn, 1978) and social groups re-structured as an adaptation to different resource availability, then a need for the maintenance of social contact and knowledge between such groups would have become a priority. This social change may be invoked as at least one of the reasons behind an expansion of symbolic behaviour during the European Mesolithic, one aspect of which can be detected in the increased evidence for fur trapping through this period (*cf.* Charles, 1997), which in turn would have led to an increased use of pelts for functional clothing. As a by-product symbolic meanings would also be conveyed, not just by which pelts were used, but also by how they were incorporated within clothing.

Whilst it is unlikely that archaeologists can today reconstruct the precise belief systems associated with the use of such animals, it is perhaps possible to acknowledge that in certain instances a symbolic explanation is the most appropriate. Examples might include the dog burials from the late Mesolithic cemeteries at Skateholm and Bredasten, Sweden (Larsson, 1994) and at Vedbaek, Denmark (Brinch Petersen, 1990) as well as the child burial placed on a swan's wing at the Ertebølle cemetery at Vedbaek, Denmark (Albrethsen & Brinch Petersen, 1976).

Whilst it is true that in many recent and contemporary societies the hunting/trapping and subsequent exploitation of small mammals is often undertaken by women and children, this does not preclude men taking part in such activities (*cf.* Szeuter, 1988). Suggestions that an emphasis on the exploitation of smaller mammals equates with an increased role for women and children in the food quest cannot be supported here. The evidence presented shows a direct link between human activity and the exploitation of small mammals; cut marks (and other forms of butchery evidence) can say little about the gender of the individual who made them – only that such activities took place. Whilst the search for female perspectives and roles within Palaeolithic society remains an important research issue (*cf.* Conkey, 1991), there seems little opportunity to develop it within the framework of this paper, unless the reader wishes to reinforce stereotypes of Palaeolithic and Mesolithic societies in which men hunted big game and women gather plants and occassionally trapped small game. Neither scenario is valid, and the gender of the hunters, trappers and butchers remains unknown.

Conclusions

The evidence presented here relating to the exploitation of mustelids during the late Palaeolithic and early Mesolithic is drawn from the author's personal observations combined with examples known from the published literature. By no means can it be seen as a definitive account. The purpose of this paper has been to document specific instances where such mammals have been exploited, and to draw attention to aspects of Palaeolithic and Mesolithic faunal exploitation beyond the conventional view of these people as big game hunters. This is not to say that large mammals were not hunted – they clearly were, and they dominate many of the vertebrate assemblages discussed here. Instead this paper has highlighted another aspect of prehistoric subsistence, suggesting that mustelids provided occasional variety to Late Pleistocene and early Holocene diets as well as a useful resource for pelts used in clothing manufacture and trade. The symbolic and social implications of this have been briefly raised. It is hoped that evidence reported here will stimulate an awareness of the potential within archaeological and palaeonotological assemblages to add information about the past habitats, environmental preferences and the human exploitation of mammals in the past.

Acknowledgements

I thank Peter Rowley-Conwy for providing access to his unpublished work and Hans Kruuk for commenting widely about badger behaviour. Two anonymous referees raised interesting issues and made insightful comments. Juliet Clutton-Brock and Pat Carter gave access to the Star Carr collections in London and Cambridge, respectively. Much of the material reported here was analysed as part of doctoral and post-doctoral research undertaken by the author between 1990 and 1997, funded respectively by The British Academy and The Queen's College, Oxford. Individual travel grants to inspect faunal collections in Europe were also generously given by the Meyerstein Fund of Oxford University, Christ Church, Oxford, the Excavation & Fieldwork Committee of Newcastle University, the Prehistoric Society and the Society of Antiquaries of London.

References

Albrecht, G., Burke, H. & Poplin, F. (1983). *Naturwissenschaftliche Untersuchungen an Magdalenien-Inventaren vom Petersfels, Grabungen 1974-1976 (Tübingen Monographien zur Urgeschichte, Band 8).* Tübingen; Archaeologica Venatoria.

Albrethsen, S.E. & Brinch Petersen, E. (1976). Excavation of a Mesolithic cemetery at Vedbaek, Denmark. *Acta Archaeologica,* **47:** 1-28.

Arts, N. (1989). Archaeology, environment and the social evolution of later band societies in a lowland area. In: C. Bonsall (ed.), *The Mesolithic in Europe:* 291-312. Edinburgh; John Donald Publishers Ltd.

Brinch Petersen, E. (1990). *Nye grave fra Jaegerstenalderen. Strøby Egede og Vedbaek.* Copenhagen; Nationalmuseets Arbejdsmark (in Danish).

Bosinski, G. (1991). The representation of female figurines in the Rhineland Magdalenian. *Proceedings of the Prehistoric Society,* **57:** 51-64.

Charles, R. (1989). Incised ivory fragments and other Late Palaeolithic finds from Gough's Cave, Cheddar, Somerset. *Proceedings of the University of Bristol Spelaeological Society,* **18:** 400-408.

Charles, R. (1996). Back into the North: the radiocarbon evidence for the human re-colonisation of the north-western Ardennes after the last glacial maximum. *Proceedings of the Prehistoric Society,* **62:** 1-17.

Charles, R. (1997). The exploitation of carnivores and other fur-bearing mammals during the north-western European Late Upper Palaeolithic and Mesolithic. *Oxford Journal of Archaeology,* **16:** 253-278.

Charles, R. (1998). *Late Magdalenian chronology and faunal exploitation in the north-western Ardennes (BAR International Series 737).* Oxford; British Archaeological Reports.

Charles, R. & Jacobi, R.M (1994). Lateglacial faunal exploitation at the Robin Hood Cave, Creswell Crags. *Oxford Journal of Archaeology,* **13:** 1-32.

Clark, J.G.D. (1954). *Excavations at Star Carr an early Mesolithic site at Seamer, near Scarborough, Yorkshire.* Cambridge; Cambridge University Press.

Conkey, M.W. (1991). Contexts of action, contexts for power: material culture and gender in the Magdalenian. In: J.M. Gero & M.W. Conkey (eds.), *Engendering archaeology:* 57-92. Oxford & Cambridge; Basil Blackwell.

Cremades, M. (1992). Analyse et reconstitution technologiques en art mobilier Paléolithique: l'exemple du glouton gravé sur baton perforé de la Madeleine (Dordogne). *L'Anthropologie,* **96:** 319-336.

Currant, A.P. (1986). The Lateglacial mammal fauna of Gough's Cave, Cheddar, Somerset *Proceedings of the University of Bristol Spelaeological Society,* **17:** 286-304.

Currant, A.P. (1991). A Late Glacial Interstadial mammal fauna from Gough's Cave, Somerset, England. In: N. Barton, A.J. Roberts & D.A. Roe (eds.), *The Late Glacial in north-west Europe: human adaptation and environmental change at the end of the Pleistocene (CBA Research Report 77):* 48-50. London; Council for British Archaeology.

Currant, A.P. Jacobi, R.M. & Stringer, C.B. (1989). Excavations at Gough's Cave, Somerset 1986-7. *Antiquity,* **63:** 131-136.

Fraser, F.C. & King, J.E. (1954). Faunal remains. In: J.G.D. Clark (ed.), *Excavations at Star Carr an early Mesolithic site at Seamer, near Scarborough, Yorkshire:* 70-95. Cambridge; Cambridge University Press.

Gamble, C.S. (1991). The social context for European Palaeolithic art. *Proceedings of the Prehistoric Society,* **57:** 3-15.

Gendel, P.A. (1989). The analysis of lithic styles through distributional profiles of variation: examples from the western European Mesolithic. In: C. Bonsall (ed.), *The Mesolithic in Europe:* 40-47. Edinburgh; John Donald Publishers Ltd.

Griffiths, H.I. (1993). The Eurasian badger, *Meles meles* (L., 1758), as a commodity species. *Journal of Zoology,* **230:** 240-242.

Housley, R.A., Gamble, C.S., Street, M.S. & Pettitt, P.B. (1997). The radiocarbon evidence for the Lateglacial human recolonisation of northern Europe. *Proceedings of the Prehistoric Society,* **63:** 25-54.

Jacobi, R.M. (1976). Britain inside and outside Mesolithic Europe. *Proceedings of the Prehistoric Society,* **42:** 67-84.

Jacobi, R.M., Tallis, J.H. & Mellars, P.A. (1976). The southern Pennine Mesolithic and the ecological record. *Journal of Archaeological Science*, **3**: 307-20.

Klein, R.G. (1973). *Ice-Age hunters of the Ukraine*. Chicago; University of Chicago Press.

Krebs, J. (1977). Optimal foraging: theory and experiment. *Nature*, **268**: 583-584.

Kruuk, H. (1989). *The social badger: ecology and behaviour of a group living carnivore (Meles meles)*. Oxford; Oxford University Press.

Larsson, L. (1994). Pratiques mortuaires et sépultures de chiens dans les sociétés Mésolithiques de Scandinavie méridionale. *L'Anthropologie*, **98**: 562-575.

Meiklejohn, C. (1978). Ecological aspects of population size and growth in Lateglacial and early Postglacial north-western Europe. In: P.A. Mellars (ed.), *The early postglacial settlement of north-western Europe*: 65-79. London; Duckworth.

Neal, E. (1948). *The badger*. London; Collins.

Nelson, R.K. (1973). *Hunters of the northern forest: designs for survival among the Alaskan Kutchin*. Chicago; The University of Chicago Press.

Potts, R. & Shipman, P. (1981). Cutmarks made by stone tools on bone from Olduvai Gorge, Tanzania. *Nature*, **291**: 577-580.

Reinbacher, E. (1956). Eine vorgeschichtliche Hirschmaske aus Berlin-Biesdorf. *Ausgrabungen und Funde*, **1**: 147-51.

Rowley-Conwy, P.A. (1980). *Continuity and change in the prehistoric economies of Denmark 3,700 bc to 2,300 bc*. PhD thesis. Cambridge; University of Cambridge.

Rowley-Conwy, P.A. (in press). Meat, furs and skins: Mesolithic animal bones from Ringkloster, a seasonal hunting camp in Jutland. *Journal of Danish Archaeology*.

Schreiber, A., Wirth, R., Riffel, M., & van Rompaey, H. (1989). *Weasels, civets, mongooses, and their relatives. An Action Plan for the conservation of mustelids and viverrids*. Gland; International Union for the Conservation of Nature & Natural Resources.

Schuldt, E. (1961). *Hohen Viecheln. Ein mittel-steinzeitlicher wohnplatz in Mecklenburg (Monographie 10)*. Berlin; Deutsche Akademie der Wissenschaften zu Berlin, Sektion für Vor- und Frühgeschichte.

Sieveking, G. de G. (1971). The Kendrick's Cave mandible. *British Museum Quarterly*, **35**: 230-250.

Simmons, I.G., Dimbleby, G.W. & Grigson, C. (1981). The Mesolithic. In: I. Simmons & M. Tooley (eds.), *The environment in British prehistory*: 82-124. London; Duckworth.

Street, M. (1991). Bedburg-Königshoven: a pre-Boreal Mesolithic site in the lower Rhineland, Germany. In: N. Barton, A.J. Roberts & D.A. Roe (eds.), *The Late Glacial in north-west Europe (CBA Research Report 77)*: 256-270. London; Council for British Archaeology.

Szeuter, C.R. (1988). Small animal exploitation among desert horticulturists in north America. *Archaeozoologica*, **2**: 191-200.

Trolle-Lassen, T. (1986). Human exploitation of the pine marten (*Martes martes* (L.)) at the Late Mesolithic settlement of Tybrind Vig in western Funen. In: L.-K. Königsson (ed.), *Nordic Late Quaternary biology and ecology*: 119-124. Uppsala; Societas Upsaliensis pro Geologia Quaternaria.

Trolle-Lassen, T. (1987). Human exploitation of fur animals in Mesolithic Denmark – a case study. *Archaeozoologia*, **1**: 85-102.

Winterhalder, B. (1980). Canadian fur bearer cycles and Cree-Ojibwa hunting and trapping practices. *American Naturalist*, **115**: 870-879.

Winterhalder, B. (1983). Boreal foraging strategies. In: A.T. Steegmann (ed.), *Boreal forest adaptations*: 201-241. New York; Plenum Press.

Zvelebil, M. & Rowley-Conwy, P.A. (1986). Foragers and farmers in Atlantic Europe. In: M. Zvelebil (ed.), *Hunters in transition: Mesolithic societies of temperate Eurasia and their transition to farming*: 67-93. Cambridge; Cambridge University Press.

CHAPTER 9

The recovery of the polecat, *Mustela putorius*, in Britain

Johnny D.S. Birks

Abstract

The polecat is one of several vertebrate predators in Britain with a restricted range due to past per-secution by humans. Its 20th century recovery from a stronghold in Wales reveals patterns shared with other heavily persecuted species. Polecat recovery has been driven by reduced persecution as gamekeeper numbers declined in the early 20th century, and was boosted subsequently by the recovery of rabbit populations in the 1970s following myxomatosis. Regional variations in other factors will influence the future pattern of recovery, including habitat quality, prey availability, pest control practice, environmental contamination, human population density, road traffic density and opportunities for hybridisation with ferrets. Their geography suggests that a "pressure gradient" exists between the upland core of the polecat's range and the intensively managed, densely populated lowlands at the fringes. Threats to polecat survival increase towards the fringes of its expanding range. Such trends have helped to define and address key conservation issues such as secondary rodenticide poisoning and conflicts with game rearing. This pressure gradient concept could inform conservation action in other carnivores recovering from upland strongholds, such as the wildcat, *Felis silvestris*, and pine marten, *Martes martes*.

Introduction

In most parts of Britain the carnivore community remains depleted as a result of past persecution (Langley & Yalden, 1977; Tapper, 1992) and environmental cont-amination (Strachan & Jefferies, 1996). Of those species which have avoided com-plete extinction, four previously widespread species now have restricted ranges or reduced populations, but all show signs of natural recovery following amelioration of the factors which caused their declines: the wildcat, *Felis silvestris*, is confined to parts of Scotland (Easterbee, 1991); the pine marten, *Martes martes*, is mainly confined to highland Scotland, with small outlier populations in northern England and Wales (Balharry *et al.*, 1996; Strachan *et al.*, 1996); the Eurasian otter, *Lutra lutra*, is in the early stages of a population recovery following a severe decline (Strachan & Jefferies, 1996); the polecat, *Mustela putorius*, is restricted mainly to Wales and the west of England (Birks, 1997; Birks & Kitchener, 1999).

Interest in promoting the recovery of British mammals has been growing (Jefferies & Mitchell-Jones, 1993), especially since the 1992 Convention on Biological Diversity at Rio de Janeiro which encouraged governments to commit themselves to action on biodiversity restoration (e.g. Anon., 1995). However, the restoration of carnivore populations, whether through natural recovery, reintroduc-

Mustelids in a modern world
Management and conservation aspects of small carnivore: human interactions
edited by Huw I. Griffiths, pp. 141–152
© *2000 Backhuys Publishers, Leiden, The Netherlands*

tion or translocation, presents particular difficulties arising from the species' social organisation, trophic status and the human antipathy they generate (Yalden, 1993). Problems arising from negative human attitudes, revealed in the context of large carnivore conservation in central Europe by Breitenmoser (1998), emphasise the need to address the cultural, as well as physical, rehabilitation of carnivores.

The patterns of several carnivores' declines (and subsequent recovery) have many common themes arising from a commonality of causal factors, notably persecution. The conservation issues generated by carnivore recovery are explored in this paper through case studies of the polecat, a species currently extending its range in Britain from an upland stronghold into the more densely-populated, intensively-managed lowlands (Blandford, 1987; Birks, 1993, 1997).

The polecat's recovery

The polecat's decline in Britain was halted in the second decade of the 20th century, when the First World War led to a sudden reduction in intense predator persecution. By this time the species had been trapped to extinction over most of Britain (see Fig.1) and survived mainly in a small, 70-km radius core range in mid-Wales (Langley & Yalden, 1977; Harris *et al.*, 1995). Early evidence of recovery was reported in the 1920s (Blandford, 1987). Persecution continued to diminish in line with the decline in numbers of gamekeepers (Tapper, 1992), although commercial rabbit-trapping remained a significant constraint on polecat numbers until the 1950s (Walton, 1970). Organised distribution-mapping from the late 1950s (e.g. Walton, 1968; Arnold, 1978) revealed the pattern of range expansion from the species' Welsh stronghold (and see Fig.1).

A new phase of distribution mapping in the 1990s confirmed that the polecat's range expansion had continued eastwards into the English Midlands, augmented by covert reintroductions elsewhere (Birks, 1993). In order to monitor this recovery and to identify important conservation issues arising from it, a suite of collaborative studies was established and co-ordinated by the Vincent Wildlife Trust (Birks & Kitchener, 1999).

In seeking to understand the factors which might promote or hinder the polecat's recovery, the markedly contrasting physical and socio-economic characteristics at the core and fringe of the species' range emerge as potential key influences. As a consequence of its persecution-induced decline, the polecat survived only in a rugged, upland landscape supporting a very low human population, an extensive, pastoral-dominated agriculture and limited economic development. From this historical stronghold in the far west of Britain, the polecat has now expanded its range eastwards into lowland landscapes characterised, at the fringe, by relatively high human populations, intensive, arable-dominated agriculture and considerable economic development. It is reasonable to envisage a gradient between these two extremes which can help to predict and define the pressures affecting polecat recovery. This 'pressure gradient' concept can be applied to other recovering carnivores with similarly restricted distributions, including the wildcat and pine marten which are also largely confined to upland strongholds (Langley & Yalden, 1977).

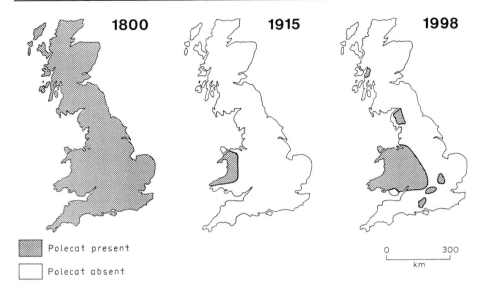

Fig. 1. The changing distribution of the polecat in Britain since 1800, redrawn from Langley & Yalden (1977) and Birks & Kitchener (1999). The species' main range is shaded. The 1998 map shows the current extent of range expansion, including new outlier populations arising from covert reintroductions.

Factors affecting recovery

Many anthropogenic factors impinge upon carnivore populations, especially in densely populated, industrialised countries where pressure upon land is intense. Morris (1993) identifies three particular threats which might affect polecat populations in Britain: road kills, persecution and hybridisation with feral ferrets. Other authors have identified further issues which might have a bearing on the species' recovery, including habitat constraints (Yalden, 1986), rodenticide contamination (Shore *et al.*, 1996), intraguild competition (Strachan & Jefferies 1996) and the polecat's poor cultural image (Birks, 1993). These recovery issues are discussed below in the context of the geographical pressure gradient concept identified above (see also Table 1).

Habitat and prey availability

The successful restoration of carnivore populations depends heavily upon the availability of stocks of suitable prey (Yalden, 1993). These, in turn, are dictated by the availability of suitable habitat. In this respect, both spatial and temporal trends are relevant to the polecat's recovery. The landcover map of Great Britain (Barr *et al.*, 1993) shows the west to east transition of landscape types, from upland grass/shrub heath and marsh/rough grassland in the Welsh hills, to arable-dominated landscapes with urban development in the lowlands of eastern England. This pattern influences the availability of wildlife habitats, which tend to be more extensive in the upland north and west of Britain than in the lowland south-east (Anon., 1989; DETR,

1997a). For example, 44.2% of Wales is covered by rough grassland, bracken, woodland, moorland, marsh and bog; in the arable landscapes which dominate the east of England these habitats cover just 12.2% (Barr *et al.*, 1993).

The ways in which polecat prey populations are affected by these trends are not well understood. Although wildlife habitats are clearly more extensive in the core of the polecat's range, upland landscapes tend to be less productive. In Wales studies of red kite, *Milvus milvus*, revealed a poorer reproductive rate than elsewhere in Europe, leading its authors to suggest that this reflected the lower productivity of the hill land in its Welsh stronghold (Davis & Newton, 1981). Yalden (1986) suggests that this argument might equally apply to the polecat, which occupied an almost identical stronghold. However, assumptions regarding greater prey diversity and biomass in the more productive lowlands than in the uplands might be countered to a degree by the limiting effects of reduced habitat availability in intensive, lowland farmland.

Agricultural intensification since the 1950s has had profoundly negative impacts upon semi-natural habitats and biodiversity in Britain, especially in the lowlands (Anon., 1984, 1993, 1995; Marchant *et al.*, 1990; Donald, 1998). Thus, the polecat is currently recolonising landscapes which have changed substantially since its disappearance. Moreover, these lowland landscapes, at the fringe of the species' range, have been modified by agriculture and development much more than those characterising its stronghold. This change is continuing: for example, 236,000 km of field boundaries (14% of the total available), an important habitat for polecats in lowland farmland (Birks, 1998; Birks & Kitchener, 1999), was lost between 1984 and 1990 – most of this occurring in arable landscapes (Barr *et al.*, 1993).

Habitat change due to agricultural intensification has been implicated in the decline of polecats in a number of European countries (e.g. Jensen & Jensen, 1972; Libois, 1984; Weber, 1988) so some effect on the recovery of the species in Britain might be expected. Lower polecat population densities are apparent in the English lowlands than in Wales, from both game bag records (Tapper, 1992) and from a monitoring exercise based upon live-trapping (Birks, 1997; Birks & Kitchener, 1999). However, it is not clear whether this pattern reflects reduced carrying capacity near the fringe of the polecat's range or the lag in population growth inherent in natural population recovery.

There is one element of the polecat's generalist feeding ecology which is likely to facilitate its successful occupation of modern farmland. Recent studies have shown that rabbits, *Oryctolagus cuniculus*, are an especially important prey item (Blandford, 1986; Birks & Kitchener, 1999). Britain's rabbit population has been recovering following the effects of myxomatosis (Tapper, 1992) and it has been suggested that the predicted effects of global warming might enhance the species' productivity and capacity to increase in future (Bell & Webb, 1991; Harris *et al.*, 1995). Significantly, rabbits are able to maintain strong populations on intensive farmland and, compared with Wales, their numbers are higher in east and south-east England (Trout *et al.*, 1986). Thus, in contrast to the pattern of most other influences, the biomass of a key prey species apparently increases from the core towards the fringe of the polecat's range.

Environmental contamination

Through their status as top predators, carnivores recovering in industrialised countries are prone to contamination through the bioaccumulation of persistent toxins.

Species with an aquatic dietary component, such as the otter, are especially vulnerable to chemicals magnified by the aquatic food chain (Chanin & Jefferies, 1978). In parts of its European range, where predation upon wetland species is common, the polecat has been described as vulnerable to pollutant biomagnification (Mason & Weber, 1990) though there is little evidence of such contamination in Britain (Jefferies, 1992). The prevailing westerly winds in Britain, and the concentration of economic activity in the lowland south and east, combine to produce higher levels of pollutants at the fringe of the polecat's range than in its core. For example, concentrations of poly-chlorinated biphenyls (PCBs), a group of chemicals implicated in mustelid poisoning, are two or three times higher in the south-east of England than in South Wales (DETR, 1997a).

In addition to this pattern of general environmental contamination, accidental poisoning with rodenticides has emerged as a more specific issue of conservation concern. Predation by polecats upon rodents in farmyards leads to exposure to the anticoagulant poisons used to control such infestations. Radio-tracking revealed that nearly half the polecats studied on lowland farmland in winter were vulnerable to such poisoning because they made heavy use (>40% of recorded time) of farmyards where rodenticides were regularly used (Birks, 1998). This leads to mortality which is believed to be common, but is difficult to record because animals die out of sight, often on private property (Walton, 1970; Birks, 1998). There are no data on mortality rates or sub-lethal effects, though 31% of road casualty polecats from the west of England showed evidence of rodenticide contamination (Shore *et al.*, 1996). Rodenticide use by farmers has been recorded more frequently on farms near the fringe of the species' range than in the core (Packer & Birks, 1999). Furthermore, rodenticide use is increasing in Britain, and is greatest in the east (Thomas & Wild, 1996). Moreover, Birks (1998) suggests that the reduced habitat quality and prey diversity of intensively farmed land are likely to make the polecat more dependent upon common agricultural pests such as (potentially contaminated) farmyard rodents at the fringe of its range. Thus, a gradient of increasing risk of rodenticide contamination can be envisaged between the pastoral core and the arable-dominated fringe of the polecat's range.

In order to clarify the significance of rodenticide poisoning to polecat conservation, the Vincent Wildlife Trust and Institute of Terrestrial Ecology are currently collaborating in a study of geographical variation in the pattern of rodenticide exposure in British polecats (Shore *et al.*, in press). This will involve assessing the rodenticide burden of road casualties collected during the 1990s on a broad transect across the polecat's current range in southern Britain. Geographical variations in the frequency and level of contamination will be interpreted in the light of data on regional variations in rodenticide use on farms.

Current government monitoring of rodenticide contamination in carnivores is regarded as inadequate (Birks, 1998; McDonald *et al.*, 1998). Therefore, it is important that an effective programme of ecotoxicological monitoring is established, ideally through the systematic screening of road casualty animals which are known to have lived through the winter period (when most rodenticide is applied). Additionally, prior to any rodenticide being licensed for use, full ecotoxicological risk assessments should be undertaken for a range of predators likely to suffer secondary exposure.

Other agricultural pest control practices are thought to affect polecats adversely. As a consequence of increasing economic damage to crops by Britain's growing rabbit population, a range of control measures is in common use (Trout *et al.*, 1986; Trout, 1994). 80% of farmers employ rabbit control and management techniques to limit rabbit damage, and one of the most effective recommended methods (used by 27% of farmers in England and Wales) is the fumigation or 'gassing' of rabbit burrows (Trout, 1994). The polecat's frequent use of rabbit burrows as daytime resting sites (Birks & Kitchener, 1999) makes the species vulnerable to such methods of rabbit control. Burrow fumigation is used on significantly more farms near the fringe of the polecat's range than in the core (Packer & Birks, 1999).

Persecution

Given the causes of the polecat's decline, it would be surprising if a 'persecution gradient' did not persist as a potential influence on recovery. Indeed Blandford (1987) predicted that the polecat's eastward spread from Wales would be slowed by increasing persecution associated with game shooting in England. The same point has been made in connection with the pine marten in Scotland, where predator control is viewed as a potential hindrance to recolonisation (Balharry *et al.*, 1996). Tapper's (1992) data show that the density of gamekeepers increases from <0.1/1000 ha in mid-Wales to 0.4-0.8/1000 ha in parts of south and eastern England. Questionnaire surveys conducted by Packer & Birks (1999) confirm that 91% of gamekeepers throughout the polecat's main range routinely trap the species; a much lower proportion of farmers reported killing polecats, but intolerant attitudes and the likelihood of persecution were more prevalent towards the fringe of the species' range. Thus, a persecution gradient exists between the core and fringe as a function of changes in the number of gamekeepers and proportion of farmers willing to kill polecats.

The conservation implications of this issue are considered by Packer & Birks (1999) who recommend measures to reduce the conflict between polecat predation and game management. In particular, they propose improvements to the husbandry of penned game so as to minimise easy polecat access opportunities. They also suggest the development of measures to prevent the non-target capture of polecats in lethal spring traps set for other species.

Table 1. The pressure gradient concept: a summary of trends influencing polecat recovery in Britain.

Recovery pressure	Trend from core to fringe of polecat range
Habitat availability	Declining
Prey biomass	Increasing
Rodenticide use	Increasing
Persecution	Increasing
Traffic density	Increasing
Human awareness/tolerance	Declining
Hybridisation opportunities	Increasing
Intraguild pressures	Increasing

Accidental anthropogenic mortality

The polecat has long been regarded as being unusually vulnerable to road traffic accident (RTA) mortality (Walton, 1970). This is such a common cause of death that most distribution surveys of the species in Britain have relied heavily upon RTAs as a source of records (e.g. Walton, 1968; Arnold, 1993; Birks & Kitchener, 1999). The most recent survey revealed that the areas of highest road density in south Wales and the west Midlands appear as significant gaps in the species' expanding range (Birks & Kitchener, 1999). This led the authors to speculate that traffic density might be a key factor operating upon the pattern of polecat recovery. Furthermore, a live-trapping study revealed evidence of a negative relationship between polecat numbers and the density of main roads near the fringe of the species' range (Birks, 1997).

A road atlas of Great Britain reveals striking variations in road density between sparsely-populated mid-Wales (where at least eight 10 x 10 km squares contain no stretches of 'A' class roads at all) and the densely-populated south-east of England (where every square contains a substantial length of such roads, and many contain lengths of >30 km). This road density gradient is reflected in the volume of cars licensed for use, with Wales supporting approximately half as many as the three adjacent English regions, and only 15% of the figure licensed in south-east England (DETR, 1997b). Through RTA mortality, this gradient of traffic density is likely to influence the pattern of polecat recovery, even to the extent of preventing viable populations establishing in the areas of highest road density. Such an effect has been suggested for badgers, *Meles meles*, in Essex, where a reduced density of setts was found near busy roads (Skinner *et al.*, 1991). Many parts of south-east England have road densities comparable with the valleys of south Wales, where polecats remain absent from at least 17 of the 10 x 10 km squares, despite ample time for recolonisation (Birks & Kitchener, 1999). Given the evidence of continuing growth in the volume of vehicles licensed for use in Britain (DETR, 1997b) the area of land currently unfavourable for polecats due to RTA mortality may grow in future.

Cultural identity

There are many examples of charismatic wildlife species which have benefited considerably, in terms of legal protection and positive conservation action, from the political support they enjoy. For example, in Britain the badger is a common, much-loved species which is championed by a nationally co-ordinated network of *c.* 85 Badger Groups with a total membership of approximately 20,000 (National Federation of Badger Groups, pers. comm.). As a result of this constituency of support, the badger is more heavily protected, in both practical and legal terms, than most other species. In contrast, the polecat is unfamiliar to most people in Britain: only 3.8% of schoolchildren within the species' range in England could name it correctly when shown a photograph, compared to 83.7% for the otter (Birks, 1993). Moreover, there is frequent confusion with another scarce mustelid – the pine marten – and with feral ferrets (Birks & Kitchener, 1999). This unfamiliarity is understandable given the polecat's widespread extinction beyond living memory, and its very limited representation in popular art and literature.

The polecat is so little known that it can be said to have no clear cultural identity in Britain today. Paradoxically, this might be a beneficial position when one considers the species' appalling historical reputation as a foul-smelling chicken-predator. The animal was so despised that, in the 16th and 17th centuries, the name 'polecat' was applied contemptuously to "vile persons and prostitutes"; frequent reference was also made to the polecat's powerful defensive 'stink' - implanted deep in the nation's collective memory by injured or terrified animals over centuries of persecution (Birks & Kitchener, 1999). Faint echoes of this unpleasant image linger on in the contemporary saying "to stink like a polecat", and in a memorable political insult cast in the mid-1980s by one party leader, who said of a prominent opponent: "He has tried and failed to turn himself into a responsible statesman and has reverted to type – a semi-housetrained polecat" (*Daily Mail*, 16.12.1985). With these rare exceptions, it seems that the polecat's near-extinction has erased its earlier terrible reputation. The current recolonisation, therefore, presents an opportunity to establish a new identity for the species which sustains, rather than threatens, its conservation status.

Since negative attitudes towards carnivores among minority interests may seriously threaten recovery plans (e.g. Reading & Kellert, 1993; Bright & Harris, 1994; Breitenmoser *et al.*, 1994) there are grounds for establishing counter measures in carnivore conservation programmes. In Britain, intolerance among landowners is greater towards the fringe of the polecat's range (Packer & Birks, 1999) so there is a case for promoting change in this sector of the rural community, and among the public generally. Great care needs to be taken in such education efforts, not least because of the tendency for uninformed publicity to hark back to old-fashioned attitudes: in a sample of 25 newspaper and magazine articles about the polecat's recovery in Britain in the 1990s and written by professional journalists rather than ecologists, the animal's unpleasant smell was referred to in the text of 60% and in the title of 32% of articles; likewise fierceness or pest status was referred to in 40% of texts and 36% of titles (Birks, unpubl.). The perpetuation of such negative attitudes will not help to generate a constituency of support for the polecat.

A viable route to greater awareness of, and a more favourable image for, the polecat is through popular art and literature. Many wild mammals are familiar to Britain's urban population mainly because of their roles in children's story books and television programmes, or through their position as prominently-displayed conservation icons. The polecat is absent from the huge array of greetings cards, stickers, tea towels and place mats which are dominated by appealing images of otters, badgers, rabbits and squirrels. Such exposure, combined with the cachet of rarity, can radically change the popular view of a species. For example, within a generation the otter has been transformed, in the eyes of the British public, from pest to nation's favourite (Serpell, 1991; Strachan & Jefferies, 1996).

Hybridisation

Hybridisation between native wild mammals and introduced or feral species is a potential conservation issue (Balharry *et al.*, 1994). Several authors have identified the presence of escaped or feral ferrets as a threat to the genetic integrity of the polecat (e.g. Morris, 1993; Harris *et al.*, 1995). In Britain, introgression between wild polecats and feral ferrets has been the subject of phenotypic and genetic studies (Lynch, 1995; Davison *et al.*, 1998, this volume; Birks & Kitchener, 1999). These have tended to conclude that, despite widespread evidence of genetic introgression, the close relationship between the two 'species' and the probable selective advantage of the native polecat phenotype alleviate conservation concern surrounding this issue (Davison *et al.*, 1998). Nevertheless, a gradient of hybridisation opportunity exists as a consequence of expansion of the polecat population into areas of increasing human and rabbit population density (both of which can be expected directly to influence the number of ferrets likely to be lost and surviving in the wild state): Packer & Birks (1999) found that ferreting to control rabbits occurred more near the fringe (67% of farms) than in the core (18% of farms) of the polecat's range. It is also likely that introgression is more likely to occur where polecat population densities are so low that animals fail to find wild mates; such situations may arise in sparse, isolated populations, and where dispersing males travel beyond the advancing front of the species' range. Predictably, therefore, the occurrence of phenotypic evidence of introgression in British polecats increases in frequency in a west to east direction towards the fringe of their range (Pratt, 1995; Birks & Kitchener, 1999).

Intraguild pressures

There is growing evidence of the influence of intraguild interference, competition and predation on the structure of carnivore communities, including marked effects upon mustelids (e.g. Mulder, 1990). Given that carnivore populations tend to be denser in more productive, lowland habitats (Harris *et al.*, 1995), one can envisage a gradient in intraguild pressure between the polecat's upland core and the rest of its range.

The negative impact of otters upon populations of feral mink, *Mustela vison*, in Britain, involving the larger predator killing or driving out the smaller, has led to suggestions that the polecat might be similarly affected (Strachan & Jefferies, 1996). Indeed Jefferies (1992) has suggested that the increasing rate of polecat spread in the late 1950s might be explained partly by the otter's sharp decline in Britain at that time. If there is truth in this suggestion, then the otter's current recovery (Strachan & Jefferies, 1996) would be expected to have a negative impact upon the polecat's spread.

The polecat and feral mink are physically and ecologically similar, leading to suggestions that competition between them might be unusually intense (Birks, 1993). Dietary studies have shown that subtle differences in resource utilisation allow coexistence (Lodé, 1993; Sidorovich, 1992), but interference competition is likely to be a factor in the relationship between these two species (folklore among Swedish trappers suggests that mink and polecats hate each other so much that both die of fury if placed in a cage together!). The current decline of the feral mink in Britain is best explained by the otter's recovery (Strachan & Jefferies, 1996); but the polecat's recovery might be an additional contributory factor in Wales and the English Midlands.

Conclusions

The 'pressure gradient' concept is of value in understanding the recovery of species, such as the polecat, which are expanding their ranges from upland landscapes into more intensively managed lowlands. In particular, quantifiable trends in conservation threats along the pressure gradient can contribute to predictive modelling of future spread. Finally, potential conservation issues, such as rodenticide contamination, persecution and RTA mortality, can be defined and addressed in the context of identifiable pressure gradients.

The tendency for negative pressures to increase, as the polecat spreads from its western stronghold, raises doubts about the species' ability to reoccupy all of its former range. Ideally, regular monitoring of the polecat's distribution and abundance should be carried out in order to determine patterns of recovery and test predictions. However, the lack of abundant and distinctive field signs makes the species difficult to monitor systematically (Birks & Kitchener, 1999). Further assessment and monitoring of the key threats identified above will also be important. In particular:

Knowledge of the influence of rodenticide poisoning and road traffic accident mortality remains inadequate and must be improved.

Efforts to generate popular interest in the polecat as a recovering native species will help to counter unreasonable negative attitudes.

Organisations representing keepers of game and poultry have an important role to play in the conservation of an age-old enemy: promotion of improvements to game and poultry husbandry will defuse the conflicts and intolerance likely to lead to persecution; the promotion of changes in trapping practice will reduce non-target mortality.

References

Anon. (1984). *Nature conservation in Great Britain*. Peterborough; Nature Conservancy Council.
Anon. (1989). *Guidelines for the selection of biological SSSIs*. Peterborough; Nature Conservancy Council.
Anon. (1993). *Biodiversity challenge – an agenda for conservation in the UK*. Sandy; Royal Society for the Protection of Birds.
Anon. (1995). *Biodiversity: the UK Steering Group Report*. London; HMSO.
Arnold, H.R. (1978). *Provisional atlas of the mammals of the British Isles*. Abbots Ripton; Institute of Terrestrial Ecology.
Arnold, H.R. (1993). *Atlas of mammals in Britain*. Abbots Ripton; Institute of Terrestrial Ecology.
Balharry, E., Staines, B.W., Marquiss, M. & Kruuk, H. (1994) *Hybridisation in British mammals (JNCC Report No. 154)*. Peterborough; Joint Nature Conservation Committee.
Balharry, E.A., McGowan, G.M., Kruuk, H. & Halliwell, E. (1996). *Distribution of pine martens in Scotland as determined by field survey and questionnaire (SNH Research Report No. 48)*. Battleby; Scottish Natural Heritage.
Barr, C.J., Bunce, R.G.H., Clarke, R.T., Fuller, R.M., Furse, M.T., Gillespie, M.K., Groom, G.B., Hallam, C.J., Hornung, M., Howard, D.C. & Ness, M.J. (1993). *Countryside survey 1990 - Main Report*. London; Department of the Environment.
Bell, D.J. & Webb, N.J. (1991). Effects of climate on reproduction in the European wild rabbit (*Oryctolagus cuniculus*). *Journal of Zoology*, **224**: 639-648.
Birks, J. (1993). The return of the polecat. *British Wildlife*, **5**: 16-25.
Birks, J.D.S. (1997). A volunteer-based system for sampling variations in the abundance of polecats (*Mustela putorius*). *Journal of Zoology*, **243**: 857-863.

Birks, J.D.S. (1998). Secondary rodenticide poisoning risk arising from winter farmyard use by the European polecat *Mustela putorius*. *Biological Conservation*, **85**: 233-240.

Birks, J.D.S. & Kitchener, A.C. (Eds.) (1999). *The distribution and status of the polecat Mustela putorius in Britain in the 1990s*. London; The Vincent Wildlife Trust.

Blandford, P.R.S. (1986). *Behavioural ecology of the polecat in Wales*. PhD thesis. Exeter; University of Exeter.

Blandford, P.R.S. (1987). Biology of the polecat *Mustela putorius*: a literature review. *Mammal Review*, **17**: 155-198.

Breitenmoser, U., Breitenmoser-Würsten, C., Capt, S. & Bernhart, F. (1994). Population dynamics of a reintroduced lynx population in Switzerland: are human-caused losses a threat? In: *Seminar on the management of small populations of threatened mammals*: 70-72. Strasbourg; Council of Europe Press.

Brietenmoser, U. (1998). Large predators in the Alps: the fall and rise of Man's competitors. *Biological Conservation*, **83**: 279-289.

Bright, P.W. & Harris, S. (1994). *Reintroduction of the pine marten: feasibility study* (*Unpublished English Nature Contract Report F72-11-10*). Bristol; Bristol University.

Chanin, P.R.F. & Jefferies, D.J. (1978). The decline of the otter *Lutra lutra* L. in Britain: an analysis of hunting records and discussion of causes. *Biological Journal of the Linnean Society*, **10**: 305-328.

Davis, P.E. & Newton, I. (1981). Population and breeding of red kites in Wales over a 30-year period. *Journal of Animal Ecology*, **50**: 759-772.

Davison, A., Birks, J.D.S., Griffiths, H.I., Kitchener, A.C., Biggins, D. & Butlin, R.K. (1998). Hybridization and the phylogenetic relationship between polecats and domestic ferrets in Britain. *Biological Conservation*, **87**: 1155-11161.

DETR (1997a). *Digest of environmental statistics No. 19*. London; Department of the Environment, Transport and the Regions.

DETR (1997b). *Transport statistics Great Britain*. London; Department of the Environment, Transport and the Regions.

Donald, P.F. (1998). Changes in the abundance of invertebrates and plants on British farmland. *British Wildlife*, **9**: 279-289.

Easterbee, N. (1991). Wildcat. In: G.B Corbett & S. Harris (eds.), *The handbook of British mammals*: 431-437. Oxford; Blackwell Scientific Publications.

Harris, S., Morris, P., Wray, S. & Yalden, D. (1995). *A review of British mammals: population estimates and conservation status of British mammals other than cetaceans*. Peterborough; Joint Nature Conservation Committee.

Jefferies, D.J. (1992). Polecats *Mustela putorius* and pollutants in Wales. *Lutra*, **35**: 28-39.

Jefferies. D.J. & Mitchell-Jones, A.J. (1993). Recovery plans for British mammals of conservation importance, their design and value. *Mammal Review*, **23**: 155-166.

Jensen, A. & Jensen, B. (1972). The polecat (*Putorius putorius*) in Denmark. *Dansk Vildtundersøgelser*, **18**: 1-32.

Langley, P.J.W. & Yalden, D.W. (1977). The decline of the rarer carnivores in Great Britain during the nineteenth century. *Mammal Review*, **7**: 95-116.

Libois, R. (1984). Atlas des mammifères de Wallonie, le genre *Mustela* en Belgique. *Cahiers d'Ethologie Appliquée*, **4**: 281-287.

Lodé, T. (1993). Diet composition and habitat use of sympatric polecat and American mink in western France. *Acta Theriologica*, **38**: 161-166.

Lynch, J. M. (1995). Conservation implications of hybridisation between mustelids and their domesticated counterparts: the example of polecats and feral ferrets in Britain. *Small Carnivore Conservation*, **13**: 17-18.

Mason, C.F. & Weber, D. (1990). Organochlorine residues and heavy metals in kidneys of polecats (*Mustela putorius*) from Switzerland. *Bulletin of Environmental Contamination and Toxicology*, **45**: 689-696.

Marchant, J.H., Hudson, R., Carter, S.P. & Whittington, P. (1990). *Population trends in British breeding birds*. Tring; British Trust for Ornithology.

McDonald, R.A., Harris, S., Turnbull, G., Brown, P. & Fletcher, M. (1998). Anticoagulant rodenticides in stoats (*Mustela erminea* L.) and weasels (*M. nivalis* L.) in England. *Environmental Pollution*. **103**: 17-23.

Morris, P.A. (1993). *A Red Data Book for British mammals*. London; Mammal Society.

Mulder, J.L. (1990). The stoat _Mustela erminea_ in the Dutch dune region, its local extinction, and a possible cause: the arrival of the fox _Vulpes vulpes_. _Lutra_, **33:** 1-21.

Packer, J.J. & Birks, J.D.S. (1999) An assessment of British farmers' and gamekeepers' experiences, attitudes and practices in relation to the European polecat _Mustela putorius_. _Mammal Review,_ **29:** 75-92.

Pratt, V.J. (1995). _Are there any polecats in England?_ BSc thesis. Edinburgh; University of Edinburgh, Department of Zoology.

Reading, R.P. & Kellert, S.R.(1993). Attitudes toward a proposed reintroduction of black-footed ferrets (_Mustela nigripes_). _Conservation Biology_, **7:** 569-580.

Serpell, J. (1991). It's the elephant by a nose. _BBC Wildlife_, **9:** 849-851.

Shore, R.F., Birks, J.D.S., Freestone, P & Kitchener, A.C. (1996). Second-generation rodenticides and polecats (_Mustela putorius_) in Britain. _Environmental Pollution_, **91:** 279-282.

Shore R.F., Birks J.D.S. & Freestone P. (in press). Exposure of non-target vertebrates to second-generation rodenticides in Britain, with particular reference to the polecat _Mustela putorius_. _New Zealand Journal of Ecology._

Sidorovich, V. (1992). Comparative analysis of the diets of European mink (_Mustela lutreola_), American mink (_M. vison_), and polecat (_M. putorius_) in Byelorussia. _Small Carnivore Conservation_, **6:** 2-4.

Skinner, C., Skinner, P. and Harris, S. (1991). An analysis of some of the factors affecting the current distribution of badger _Meles meles_ setts in Essex. _Mammal Review_, **21:** 51-66.

Strachan, R. & Jefferies, D.J. (1996). _Otter survey of England 1991-1994_. London; The Vincent Wildlife Trust.

Strachan, R., Jefferies, D.J. & Chanin, P.R.F. (1996). _Pine marten survey of England and Wales 1987-1988._ Peterborough; Joint Nature Conservation Committee.

Tapper, S. (1992). _Game heritage_. Fordingbridge; The Game Conservancy Ltd.

Thomas, M.R. & Wild, S. (1996). _Rodenticide usage on farms in Great Britain growing arable crops, 1994 (Pesticide Usage Survey Report 130)._ London; Ministry of Agriculture, Fisheries & Food.

Trout, R.C. (1994). Don't let rabbits beet your profits down to the ground. _British Sugar Beet Review_, **62:** 30-33.

Trout, R.C., Tapper, S.C. & Harradine, J. (1986). Recent trends in the rabbit population in Britain. _Mammal Review_, **16:** 117-123.

Walton, K.C. (1968). The distribution of the polecat, _Putorius putorius_, in Great Britain, 1963-67. _Journal of Zoology_, **155:** 237-240.

Walton, K.C. (1970). The polecat in Wales. In: W.S. Lacey (ed.), _Welsh wildlife in trust_: 98-108. Bangor; North Wales Wildlife Trust.

Weber, D. (1988). Die aktuelle Verbreitung des Iltisses (_Mustela putorius_ L.) in der Schweiz. _Revue Suisse de Zoologie_, **95:** 1041-1056.

Yalden, D.W. (1986). Opportunities for reintroducing British mammals. _Mammal Review_, **16:** 53-63.

Yalden, D.W. (1993). The problems of reintroducing carnivores. _Symposia of the Zoological Society of London_, **65:** 289-306.

CHAPTER 10

Conservation implications of hybridisation between polecats, ferrets and European mink (*Mustela* spp.)

Angus Davison*, Johnny D.S. Birks, Tiit Maran, David W. Macdonald, Vadim E. Sidorovich & Huw I. Griffiths

Abstract

Hybridisation is defined as the interbreeding of individuals from distinct populations. In extreme cases, it may result in the functional loss or extinction of a native species. In this chapter, we review briefly some examples of hybridisation in mammals, and discuss the potential impact of legislation that was originally introduced to protect groups of organisms in discrete units, *i.e.* species. The remainder of the chapter describes two cases of mustelid hybridisation in detail: between polecats and introduced domestic ferrets in Britain, and between polecats and endangered European mink in Eastern Europe. In particular, we concentrate on the implications of hybridisation for the conservation of these species.

Introduction

Hybridisation is generally defined as the interbreeding of individuals from distinct populations, whether they are from the same species or are more distantly related. Subsequent genetic introgression may occur when the hybrids mate (backcross) to one or both of the parental populations (Rhymer & Symberloff, 1996). Although usually viewed in a negative manner, hybridisation is a natural process whereby groups of organisms may exchange genetic material. It follows that hybridisation may be constructive: many plant species have arisen as a result of hybridisation (Rieseberg, 1997), and it has been estimated that as many as 10% of all bird species may exchange genes through hybridisation in the wild (Grant & Grant, 1992; Grant, 1993).

Hybridisation may become a cause for conservation concern when human mediated actions such as habitat loss and pollution cause a population to crash. If the population density of one group is sufficiently diminished, the endangered taxon is then unlikely to find a mate of the same type. In extreme cases the process may lead to the functional loss or extinction of the native species (Rhymer & Symberloff, 1996). Increasingly, non-native animals that were introduced by humans also may threaten the integrity of native species by hybridisation (Rhymer & Symberloff, 1996). In this chapter we briefly review some examples of hybridisation in mam-

---

* Corresponding author.

Mustelids in a modern world
Management and conservation aspects of small carnivore: human interactions
edited by Huw I. Griffiths, pp. 153–162
© *2000 Backhuys Publishers, Leiden, The Netherlands*

mals, then discuss the possible implications of hybridisation between two related groups of mustelid species.

Hybridisation in mammals

Endangered mammals may be vulnerable to hybridisation because complete reproductive isolation rarely is present between congeners. For example, wolves have been particularly prone to hybridisation because interbreeding with other wolf species and domestic/feral dogs has been compounded by human persecution and fragmentation of historic species, ranges (Wayne & Gittleman, 1995; Brownlow, 1996). In the USA, captive bred red wolves, *Canis rufus*, have now been reintroduced to parts of their former range, despite on-going arguments as to whether they are an extant species/subspecies, or originated as a modern hybrid between the grey wolf, *Canis lupus*, and the coyote, *Canis latrans* (Roy *et al.*, 1996; Nowak & Federoff, 1998; Payne *et al.*, 1998). Similarly, extensive hybridisation between coyotes and grey wolves has occurred in other localities in the USA. In Europe, morphological and genetic evidence suggest that many wolf populations are composed mainly of hybrids between local feral dogs and what remains of native wolf populations.

As implied above, separate species, races, or distinct populations of the same species may hybridise. This has meant that legislation that was designed to protect species, such as the Endangered Species Act in the USA and the Wildlife and Countryside Act in the UK, may be ineffective because the defining criterion of an 'uncontaminated' species is satisfied no longer. In the USA, the alleged hybrid status of the red wolf has led to attempts to remove its protected status, as well as to withdraw funding for further reintroductions. The most recent interpretation of the United States' Endangered Species Act suggests that red wolves could be protected irrespective of their putative hybrid origin, providing that "they have developed outside of confinement, are self-sustaining, naturally occurring taxonomic species and meet the criteria for threatened or endangered species" (Frampton & Foster, 1996; Wayne *et al.*, 1998). With improved methods for detecting genetic introgression, it is inevitable that more examples of prior hybridisation will be uncovered. In particular, modern molecular methods often have revealed previously unsuspected introgression into apparently 'uncontaminated' groups of organisms.

In Britain, several of the larger mammal species are at risk from hybridisation. Scottish wildcats, *Felis silvestris*, have hybridised with introduced domestic cats, *Felis catus*, perhaps for hundreds of generations. Current molecular genetic work aims to determine the degree of differentiation that remains, if any, between the two taxa (E. Barrett, pers. comm.). Similarly, Japanese sika deer, *Cervus nippon*, that were introduced to Britain relatively recently (approximately 20 generations ago) have escaped or been released from deer parks, and have hybridised extensively with native red deer, *Cervus elaphus*. Although introgression occurs in both directions, the sika type may be at a selective advantage (Abernethy, 1994). Amongst the small carnivores of Britain, two mustelids – polecats, *Mustela putorius* (Davison *et al.*, 1998) and pine martens, *Martes martes* (Davison, unpubl.) – are at risk from hybridisation. The remainder of this chapter describes two examples of hybridisation between mustelid species whose status is of both local and European-wide conservation concern: (1) polecats and the introduced domestic ferret in Britain, and (2) polecats and European mink in Eastern Europe.

Hybridisation between polecats and introduced domestic ferrets in Britain

Domestic ferrets were probably introduced to Britain by the Normans for hunting rabbits, *Oryctolagus cuniculus* – possibly as early as the 11th century (Thomson, 1951). The true date of introduction is unknown, however, the first documentary evidence of ferrets in Britain dates to the 14th century (Yalden, 1999). Since it is unknown whether ferrets were domesticated from the European polecat, *Mustela putorius*, or their eastern European congener, the steppe polecat, *Mustela eversmannii*, they are usually given species (rather than subspecies) status as *Mustela furo*. Inevitably, some ferrets escaped into the wild and hybridised with native polecats, *M. putorius*, which were widespread and common at the time. Polecats began to decline around 1850, becoming extinct throughout much of England and Scotland, and reaching a nadir in the years prior to World War I. Along with a number of other British carnivores which survived in relict populations (wildcats and pine martens, *Martes martes*; Strachan *et al.*, 1996), the near extinction of the polecat was a direct result of persecution by gamekeepers (Langley & Yalden, 1977).

Fortunately, a small population of polecats survived in a Welsh refugium, and also in two of the English Border Counties (Langley & Yalden, 1977; Harris *et al.*, 1995). In the post-war era, sporting estates fell into decline so that polecats were soon reported to be increasing in numbers (Langley & Yalden, 1977). The relaxation from persecution, the banning of the gin trap in the 1950s, and the post-myxomatosis increase in rabbit numbers, apparently have allowed polecats to expand their range. This expansion continues to the present day, where polecats have been found as far east as Oxfordshire and Northamptonshire (Birks, 1993, 1995, 1997, this volume). In addition, polecats have been re-introduced unofficially to parts of Scotland (e.g. Argyll), Cumbria, and southern England. Concern has arisen as to the extent of polecat/domestic ferret introgression in Britain, and particularly, whether the eastern edge of the expanding population and re-introduced populations are of mainly hybrid (or ferret) origin.

The principle aim of this study was to question whether any British polecat/ferret populations remain genetically distinct, despite up to a millennium of hybridisation (Davison *et al.*, 1998). Mitochondrial DNA (mtDNA) sequence variation was first used to investigate whether any population-specific mtDNA sequences (haplotypes) exist in supposed pure, hybrid and introduced populations (cf. Avise, 1994). MtDNA has the advantage that it is passed on from the mother only (*i.e.* is maternally inherited) so that the haplotype detected in hybrid offspring will be from the mother of that mating. If introgression is predominantly one way, mtDNA analysis combined with morphological study is able to reveal the direction of hybridisation. More sophisticated analyses typically involve biparentally-inherited markers such as DNA microsatellites, which can help to identify the degree to which any individual is a hybrid.

In samples of road-killed animals collected between 1994-96, two distinct British polecat haplotypes were found: their distribution is mapped in Fig. 1. One haplotype was centred on Wales and the English Border Counties, whilst the other was found throughout Britain. Since the primarily Welsh and English border county haplotype maps onto the refugial distribution of polecats in Britain, and the other haplotype is identical to that found in pure-bred feral ferrets from the Scottish islands and to two previously reported domestic ferret DNA sequences (Lento *et al.*, 1995; Ledje & Arnason, 1996a), it is likely that they derive from the polecat and the domestic ferret, respectively. Although morphological studies show hybridisation

Fig. 1. Map showing approximate distribution of the two distinct polecat mtDNA haplotypes found in Britain (grey = polecat lineage, black = ferret lineage). The extent to which the geographic distribution of each type overlaps in England/Wales is not known. Further sampling will be required to more accurately determine their full ranges, and any changes which may occur with time.

between polecat and ferrets, the mtDNA haplotypes appear to have remained large-ly distinct geographically. This pattern may reflect an historical distribution of pole-cats and domestic ferrets that has persisted even beyond the World War I population bottleneck, because polecats have always been more abundant in mid-Wales, and the reverse was true elsewhere following local polecat extinctions.

However, wild polecats are surprisingly tolerant of human activity and, like ferrets, may inhabit the vicinity of settlements or rabbit burrows (Birks & Kitchener, 1999; Blandford, 1987; Weber, 1989). Since domestic ferrets have been bred selectively in captivity for hundreds of years (McKay, 1995), the resulting qualities of docility and tameness may limit the capacity of ferrets to survive and breed in the feral state (Poole, 1972). These circumstances will result in strong selection for a polecat phe-notype, and may explain why the enduring feral ferret colonies are found on offshore islands where native predators are scarce or absent (Blandford & Walton, 1991).

Wild polecats are easily distinguished from pure bred domestic ferrets by mor-phology (Birks & Kitchener, 1999). Thus, phenotypic polecats were found further eastwards than the polecat haplotype, consistent with a primary population expansion mediated by dispersing male polecats, and selection favouring a polecat phenotype. Also, the practise of using ferrets to control rabbits (ferreting) occurs more frequent-ly towards the east of the British polecat's range (Packer & Birks, 1999). Therefore, it is consistent that the ferret haplotype was found more often near the fringe of the range, and that morphological evidence of introgression increases in frequency in a west to east direction. The stock that was introduced to Argyll, Cumbria and southern England may not have been pure-bred polecat, since the polecat haplotype was not discovered in these locations (although sample sizes were small). Microsatellite DNA fingerprinting may help to resolve the extent of hybridisation and the degree of dis-tinctness that remains between the British polecat and the ferret.

In Britain, native polecats are partially protected under the Wildlife and Countryside Act (1981). What consequence does hybridisation with ferrets have to the protection of the native species? Preliminary results suggest that, in Britain, two parental populations may be present which have hybridised to varying degrees depending upon the local release and survival of feral ferrets (Davison *et al.*, 1998). Further DNA sequence analysis was unable to demonstrate whether ferrets were domesticated from *M. putorius*, *M. eversmannii*, or conceivably from both species, only that speciation was recent or that a history of introgression through hybridisa-tion had obscured the species' phylogeny (Davison *et al.*, 1998). Therefore, whilst it may be possible to declare uncontroversially whether an individual animal with ferret characters (both phenotypic and mtDNA) is a ferret or a hybrid (and is thus unprotected), the reverse procedure of identifying a pure polecat is not as simple since it is difficult to exclude any introgression. Further molecular work could reveal whether the introgression is predominantly one way; given the likely selec-tive advantage of polecats over ferrets, perhaps polecat alleles are more likely to introgress into feral ferrets.

Balharry *et al.* (1994) suggest that polecats and even polecat/domestic ferret hybrids (if they are considered as *M. putorius* rather than *M. furo* or *M. eversmannii*) may receive some protection under Schedule 6 of Britain's Wildlife and Countryside Act (Anon., 1981). The probable selective advantage of the native polecat phenotype may result in polecats out-competing ferrets, in contrast to other instances of hybridisation between taxa of conservation concern such as stiff-tail ducks (Balharry *et al.*, 1994) or red deer (Abernethy, 1994). The spread of the native British polecat is more likely to be limited by other factors such as suitability of habitat, persecution pressure, pesticide poisoning and road traffic density (Birks, this volume).

Hybridisation between native European mink and polecats in eastern Europe

European mink, *Mustela lutreola*, are one of Europe's most endangered carnivores (Maran *et al.*, 1998; Rozhnov, 1993). Recent population censuses estimate that the species now exists in isolated populations covering only one fifth of its former range (Maran, 1992; Sidorovich *et al.*, 1995). European mink therefore are included in the IUCN Global Red Data Book (Groombridge, 1993). In the Western Palaearctic, vulnerable populations exist still in Spain (Palomares, 1991; Ruiz-Olmo & Palazon, 1991), France (Chanudet & Saint-Girons, 1981) and Romania (Youngman, 1982). The territories of the former Soviet Union, specifically the regions of Tver and Pskov (both in Russia) and Vitebsk (in Belarus), were regarded as the remaining stronghold of the European mink in the 1980s, but recent surveys have revealed drastic population declines and local extinctions (Maran, 1992; Sidorovich *et al.*, 1995). No single satisfactory explanation has been discovered, despite two recent syntheses on the course and causes of the decline (Maran & Henttonen, 1995; Maran *et al.*, 1998).

Aggression between recently introduced American mink, *Mustela vison*, and native European mink has been proposed as one of the main explanations for the mink's decline (Maran *et al.*, 1998; Sidorovich, this volume). Hybridisation between *M. vison* and *M. lutreola* has not been implicated in the normal sense, since even with successful captive matings the hybrid embryo is reabsorbed (Ternosvkii, 1977). However, it has been suggested that mate covering of female European mink by male American mink may result in European mink reproductive failure – once the female has mated it is unreceptive to further mating and this results in no cub production for that year. Recent evidence does not support this hypothesis: radiotracking studies of the two species in Belarus recorded aggressive attitudes from male American mink towards female European mink, both during and after the mating season of the American mink (Sidorovich, this volume).

Interactions with polecats (*M. putorius*, *M. eversmannii*) also have been implicated in mink decline in two ways: indirectly, through their better adaptation to an intensively farmed landscape (Maran *et al.*, 1998), and directly, by hybridisation (Ognev, 1931; Novikov, 1939; Heptner *et al.*, 1967; Youngman, 1982; Tumanov & Zverjev, 1986). However, elucidation of the conservation implications of hybridisation has been hindered by a poor understanding of mustelid evolutionary relationships and, until relatively recently, the literature surrounding the taxonomy of genus *Mustela* has been confused. Specifically, the convergent morphology of European and American mink (probably a result of similar habitat utilisation) has meant that in the past they have been distinguished only as subspecies (Ognev, 1931). More recent morphological and molecular phylogenetic analyses place the American mink as the most distantly-related member of *Mustela* (Youngman, 1982; Masuda & Yoshida,

1994; Davison *et al.*, 1999). Karyotyping results confirm that *M. lutreola* (2n = 38), *M. sibirica* (2n = 38), *M. putorius* (2n = 40; Frykman, 1972; Grafodatskii *et al.*, 1982) and *M. eversmannii* (2n = 36 or 38; Grafodatskii *et al.*, 1982; Wang *et al.*, 1984; Xu & Gao, 1986) are closely related congeners. However, either relatively recent speciation of European mink from polecats and black-footed ferrets, *M. nigripes*, and/or hybridisation resulted in a mitochondrial phylogenetic tree in which eastern European *M. lutreola* are more closely related to polecats and black-footed ferrets than are the previously identified sister taxa (Fig. 2; Youngman, 1982; Davison *et al.*, 1998; Davison, unpubl.).

Hybridisation between mink and polecats may be detrimental because hybrids are poorly adapted to either habitat, or else disruption of coadapted gene complexes may result in outbreeding depression (Lynch, 1991). For a species that is vulnerable to extinction, any detrimental factor may have a catastrophic effect (Maran *et al.*, 1998). As mentioned, hybrids between European mink and polecats have been reported sporadically (Maran *et al.*, 1998 and references therein), and it has been suggested that as European mink decline, the likelihood of hybridisation will increase. Prior to the probable extinction of European mink in Estonia, almost all recovered animals were suspected hybrids (Maran & Raudsepp, 1994). In relatively undisturbed habitats in Belarus, polecats and European mink co-existed both before and after the arrival of American mink.

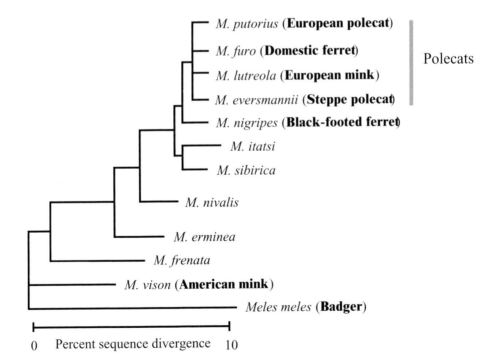

Fig. 2. Phylogenetic tree showing putative relationships between members of the genus *Mustela*, reconstructed using cytochrome b sequence data (adapted from Davison *et al.*, 1998). Note that *M. lutreola* from eastern Europe falls within the polecat group.

To attempt to confirm hybridisation between European mink and polecats, and also to test whether there is any predominant direction to the matings, European mink were sampled from Russia (Tver, Pskov), Belarus (Vitebsk) and Estonia by members of the *M. lutreola* Captive Breeding Programme. Six animals were identified as polecat-European mink hybrids by phenotype. Of these, four Estonian animals had mitochondrial haplotypes which were otherwise not found in morphologically-pure European mink (n = 35) but which were present in polecats (Davison, unpubl.). If these animals were F1 hybrids, this suggests that the mating was between a female polecat and a male mink.

The hybridisations with polecats detected are probably a symptom of dangerously low population levels, rather than an explanation for the local extinction of European mink. Past and current levels of hybridisation have not been compared or quantified, but throughout this century low numbers of hybrids regularly have been recorded (Ognev, 1931; Heptner *et al.*, 1967). If hybridisation results in fertile offspring, and the selection against them is weak, a relatively greater fraction will hybridise each generation. This may result in a hybrid swarm, with a population of individuals introgressed to various extents. Thus, the key factors that threaten European mink survival, such as interactions with American mink and habitat degradation, are increasing and may act synergistically with hybridisation.

Whilst it is unknown whether hybrids are maladapted to either or both ecological niches, or whether outbreeding depression operates (Lynch, 1991), hybridisation with polecats is almost certainly not the key factor operating on the extinction of the European mink. However, hybridisation may complicate attempts to save vulnerable species populations.

Acknowledgements

We are grateful to the Vincent Wildlife Trust for funding the polecat project. Thanks also to numerous persons who donated specimens, particularly R. Allgower, D. Biggins, C. Craik, A. Gergar, V. Katchanovsky, A. Kitchener, H. Kruuk, B. Kryštufek, V. Rozhnov and H. Schofield. Thanks to Roger Butlin, Rosie Sharpe and two anonymous reviewers for commenting on the manuscript.

References

Abernethy, K. (1994). The establishment of a hybrid zone between red and sika deer (genus *Cervus*). *Molecular Ecology*, **3**: 551-562.
Anon (1981). *Wildlife and Countryside Act.* London; Her Majesty's Stationery Office.
Avise, J.C. (1994). *Molecular markers, natural history and evolution.* New York; Chapman & Hall.
Balharry, E., Staines B.W., Marquiss, M. & Kruuk H. (1994). *Hybridisation in British mammals* (*JNCC Report No. 154*). Peterborough; Joint Nature Conservation Committee.
Birks, J.D.S. (1993). The return of the polecat. *British Wildlife*, **5**: 16-25.
Birks, J.D.S. (1995). Recovery of the European polecat (*Mustela putorius*) in Britain. *Small Carnivore Conservation*, **12**: 9.
Birks, J.D.S. (1997). A volunteer-based system for sampling variations in the abundance of polecat (*Mustela putorius*). *Journal of Zoology*, **243**: 857-863.
Birks, J.D.S. & Kitchener, A.C. (Eds.) (1999). *The distribution and status of the polecat Mustela putorius in Britain in the 1990s.* London; The Vincent Wildlife Trust.

Blandford, P.R.S. (1987). Biology of the polecat *Mustela putorius*: a literature review. *Mammal Review*, **17**: 155-198.

Blandford, P.R.S. & Walton, K.C. (1991). Feral ferret *Mustela furo*. In: G. Corbett & S. Harris (eds.), *The handbook of British mammals*: 405-406. Oxford; Blackwell Scientific Publications.

Brownlow, C.A. (1996). Molecular taxonomy and the conservation of the red wolf and other endangered carnivores. *Conservation Biology*, **10**: 390-396.

Chanudet, F. & Saint-Girons, M.-C. (1981). La répartition du vison européen dans la Sud-Oest de la France. *Annales de la Société des Sciences Naturelles de Charante-Maritime*, **6**: 851-858.

Davison, A., Birks, J.D.S., Griffiths, H.I., Kitchener, A.C., Biggins, D. & Butlin, R.K. (1998). Hybridization and the phylogenetic relationship between polecats and domestic ferrets in Britain. *Biological Conservation*, **87**: 155-161.

Frampton, G.T. & Foster, N. (1996). Proposed policy and proposed rule on the treatment of intercrosses and intercross progeny (the issue of 'hybridization'); request for public comment. *Federal Register*, **61**: 4710-4713.

Frykman, I. (1972). Chromosome studies of *Mustela putorius* in tissue culture. *Hereditas*, **70**: 59-68.

Grafodatskii, A., Ternovskaya, Y. & Ternovskii, D. (1982). [Distribution of structural heterochromatin and the nucleolar organizer regions in the chromosomes of Siberian polecat, mink, and their hybrids.] *Doklady Akademiya Nauk SSSR*, **262**: 34-36 (in Russian with English abstract).

Grant, P.R. & Grant, B.R. (1992). Hybridization of bird species. *Science*, **256**: 193-197.

Grant, P.R. (1993). Hybridisation of Darwin finches on Isla-Daphne-Major, Galapagos. *Philosophical Transactions of the Royal Society of London (Series B)*, **340**: 127-139.

Groombridge, B. (Ed.) (1993). *1994 IUCN Red List of threatened animals*. Gland; International Union for the Conservation of Nature & Natural Resources.

Harris, S., Morris, P., Wray, S. & Yalden, D. (1995). *A review of British mammals: population estimates and conservation status of British mammals other than cetaceans*. Peterborough; Joint Nature Conservation Committee.

Heptner, V.G., Naumov, N.P., Yurgenson, P.B., Sludsky, A.A., Chirkova, A.F. & Bannikov, A.G. (1967). [*Mammals of the USSR. Part 2. Vol. 1.*] Moscow; Akademiya Nauk SSSR (in Russian).

Langley, P.J.W. & Yalden, D.W. (1977). The decline of the rarer carnivores in Great Britain during the Nineteenth Century. *Mammal Review*, **7**: 95-116.

Ledje, C. & Arnason, U. (1996). Phylogenetic analyses of complete cytochrome b genes of the order Carnivora with particular emphasis on the Canifornia. *Journal of Molecular Evolution*, **42**: 135-144.

Lento, G.M., Hickson, R.E., Chambers, G.K. & Penny, D. (1995). Use of spectral analysis to test hypotheses on the origin of pinnipeds. *Molecular Biology and Evolution*, **12**: 28-52.

Lynch, M. (1991). The genetic interpretation of inbreeding depression and outbreeding depression. *Evolution*, **45**: 622-629.

MacKay, J. (1995). *Complete guide to ferrets*. Shrewsbury; Swan Hill Press.

Maran, T. (1992). The European mink, *Mustela lutreola*, in protected areas in the former Soviet Union. *Small Carnivore Conservation*, **7**: 10-12.

Maran, T. & Henttonen, H. (1995). Why is the European mink, *Mustela lutreola*, disappearing? – a review of the process and hypotheses. *Annales Zoologici Fennici*, **32**: 47-54.

Maran, T. & Raudsep, T. (1994). Hybrid between the European mink and the polecat in the wild – is it a phenomena concurring with the European mink decline? In: *2nd North European Symposium on the Ecology of the Small and Medium Sized Carnivores*: Abstract 42.

Maran, T., Macdonald, D.W., Kruuk, H., Sidorovich, V. & Rozhnov, V.V. (1998). The continuing decline of the European mink, *Mustela lutreola*: evidence for the intraguild aggression hypothesis. *Symposia of the Zoological Society of London*, **71**: 297-324.

Masuda, R. & Yoshida, M.C. (1994). A molecular phylogeny of the family Mustelidae (Mammalia, Carnivora), based on comparison of mitochondrial cytochrome b nucleotide sequences. *Zoological Science*, **11**: 605-612.

Novikov, G.A. (1939). [*The European Mink.*] Leningrad; Akademiya Nauk SSSR (in Russian).

Nowak, R.M. & Federoff, N.E. (1998). Validity of the red wolf: response to Roy *et al. Conservation Biology*, **12**: 722-725.

Ognev, S.I. (1931). [*Animals of the Eastern Europe and the northern Asia. Carnivores. II.*] Moscow-Leningrad; Akademiya Nauk SSSR (in Russian).

Packer, J.J. & Birks, J.D.S (1999). An assessment of British farmers' and gamekeepers' experiences, attitudes and practices in relation to the European polecat *Mustela putorius. Mammal Review*, **29**: 75-92.

Palomares, F. (1991). Situation of the European and American mink populations in the Iberian peninsula. *Mustelid and Viverrid Conservation*, **4:** 16.

Poole, T.B. (1972). Some behavioural differences between the European polecat, *Mustela putorius*, the ferret, *M. furo*, and their hybrids. *Journal of Zoology*, **166:** 25-35.

Rhymer, J.M. & Simberloff, D. (1996). Extinction by hybridization and introgression. *Annual Review of Ecology and Systematics*, **27:** 83-109.

Rieseberg, L.H. (1997). Hybrid origins of plant species. *Annual Review of Ecology and Systematics*, **28:** 359-389.

Roy, M.S., Geffen, E., Smith, D. & Wayne, R.K. (1996). Molecular genetics of pre-1940 red wolves. *Conservation Biology*, **10:** 1413-1424.

Rozhnov, V.V. (1993). Extinction of the European mink: ecological catastrophe or a natural process? *Lutreola*, **1:** 10-16.

Ruiz-Olmo, J. & Palazon, S. (1991). New information on the European and American mink in the Iberian Peninsula. *Mustelid and Viverrid Conservation*, **5:** 13.

Sidorovich, V.E., Savchenko, V.V. & Budny, V.B. (1995). Some data about the European mink *Mustela lutreola* distribution in the Lovat River Basin in Russia and Belarus: current status and retrospective analysis. *Small Carnivore Conservation*, **12:** 14-18.

Strachan,, R., Jefferies, D.J. & Chanin, P.R.F. (1996). *Pine marten survey of England and Wales 1987-1988.* Peterborough; Joint Nature Conservation Committee.

Ternovskii, D.V. (1977). [*Biology of mustelids (Mustelidae).*] Novosibirsk; Akademiya Nauk SSSR (in Russian).

Thomson, A.P.D. (1951). A history of the ferret. *Journal of the History of Medicine*, **6:** 471-480.

Tumanov, I.L. & Zverjev, E.L. (1986). [Present distribution and number of the European mink (*Mustela lutreola*) in the USSR.] *Zoologichesky Zhurnal*, **65:** 426-435 (in Russian with English summary).

Wang, Z., Quan, G., Yie, Z. & Wang, S. (1984). Karyotypes of three species of Carnivora. *Acta Zoologica Sinica*, **30:** 188-194.

Wayne, R.K. & Gittleman, J.L. (1995). The problematic red wolf. *Scientific American*, **1995** (July): 26-31.

Wayne, R.K., Roy, M.S. & Gittleman, J.L. (1998). Origin of the red wolf: response to Nowak and Federoff and Gardener. *Conservation Biology*, **12:** 726-729.

Weber, D. (1989). The ecological significance of resting sites and the seasonal habitat change in polecats (*Mustela putorius*). *Journal of Zoology*, **217:** 629-638.

Xu, K. & Gao, X. (1986). Karyotype analysis of the Tibetan fox, the tiger weasel, and the musked polecat. *Acta Theriologica Sinica*, **6:** 1-11.

Yalden, D.W. (1999). *The history of British mammals.* London; T & AD Poyser Ltd.

Youngman, P.M. (1982). Distribution and systematics of the European mink *Mustela lutreola* Linnaeus 1761. *Acta Zoologica Fennica*, **166:** 1-48.

CHAPTER 11

Otters recovering in man-made habitats in central Europe

Andreas Kranz* & Aleš Toman

Abstract

Central Europe is amongst those regions of the world that are most influenced by man, and the Eurasian otter, *Lutra lutra*, is amongst those mammal species that suffered most from habitat destruction, pollution and direct persecution. However, over the last decade, otter populations have been recovering and even recolonising areas from which they had become extinct. Against this background of increasing otter numbers we address the following questions: (1) how does man influence the abundance and availability of the otter's prey? (2) how does man destroy and create new otter habitats? and (3) how do otters respond to the presence of humans? The presented data derive from seven years intensive otter research in the Czech Republic and Austria, with additional observations made in Germany and Slovakia.

In central Europe traditional fish farms can provide food for otters that may result in an up to eight-fold increase in otter densities. In addition, human activities, such as those that lead to changes in natural water levels and temperatures, can alleviate the effects of ice cover. As ice cover restricts winter fish availability, this is believed to favour the otter's survival. The recovery of the otter population indicates that man does not only destroy otter habitats, but also creates new ones such as reservoirs, fish farms and flooded former quarries and open-cast mines. Such man-made habitats may even be preferred by otters. Similarly, although natural day resting sites were lost due to human activities, artificial cavities also were created. Overall, both habitat use (e.g. the permanent presence of otters in cities) and otter behaviour when directly encountering man, indicate that otters generally do no not consider humans to be a danger. This may change, however, if the illegal persecution of otters in fish farming areas continues.

Introduction

In Europe the activities of humans have become one of the most important habitat factors for wildlife. For a mustelid such as the Eurasian otter, *Lutra lutra*, humans influence habitat, prey populations and also the animals themselves. Mason & Macdonald (1986) and Foster-Turley *et al.* (1990) consider habitat destruction and pollution to be the main human-related threats to otters. This view is rooted in the overall decline of the species during this century, which coincided with areas densely populated with humans, and in which habitat destruction is more advanced and environmental pollution generally more intensive. Otters became totally extirpated in Switzerland (Weber, 1990), the Netherlands and Luxembourg (Foster-Turley *et*

---

* Corresponding author.

Mustelids in a modern world
Management and conservation aspects of small carnivore: human interactions
edited by Huw I. Griffiths, pp. 163–183

al.,1990). Otters also disappeared from much of their former range in Italy, western Germany, Austria, France and the Czech Republic (see review by Foster-Turley *et al.*, 1990). Fortunately, in the last decade or so, otter numbers have increased again throughout Europe (Macdonald,1994) and notably in central Europe (Stubbe & Stubbe, 1994; Kranz, 1995; Romanowski *et al.*, 1997).

Against a background of an increase in otter numbers which we demonstrate for a small area in central Europe, we here address the following questions: (1) how do humans influence the populations of the prey of otters in terms of both their abundance and availability? (2) how do unintentional human activities act to create new otter habitats and destroy old ones and, (3) is the presence of humanity itself a cause of disturbance to otters, and what is the situation facing otters at fish farms today?

Study areas, material and methods

All the data presented here were collected between 1990-1998 (the locations of the study areas are shown in Fig. 1). Most data originate from the Czech Moravian Highlands close to the Austrian border and from the Waldviertel region in northern Lower Austria. Additional study areas are located in the Oberlausitz region of Saxony (Germany) close to the Polish border (to study large-scale "new" otter habitat), in the Jeseniky Mountains in north-eastern Moravia, Czech Republic (to study reintroduced, radio-tagged otters living at a reservoir) and in the Beskidy Mountains in eastern Moravia, Czech Republic (to study the effects of disturbance and pollution). One more set of observations comes from a reservoir in central Slovakia.

The otter survey in northern Austria was conducted according the IUCN's method, and some additional survey points were checked in order to identify the population's actual borders as precisely as possible (Kranz, 1995). In addition to this large-scale approach, 36 km² of a fish pond area in northern Lower Austria and comprising 115 ponds, was selected in order to identify changes in pond utilisation.

The abundance of fish in ponds was quantified in a 100 km² study area in the southern Czech Moravian Highlands. Data on the stocking of the ponds were obtained from fish farmers, and fish in streams were quantified by electro-fishing using the De Lury Method (Bagenal, 1978).

Within the same 100 km² sample area, snow tracking surveys were conducted to estimate the number of otters present. This was done by up to eight experienced people, who walked along all the streams and ponds in a given area right after a previous night's snow, so that only one night's tracks would be found.

Seven otters (one [sub-] adult male, two adult, non-breeding females and four sub-adult females) in the Czech Moravian Highlands and the Waldviertel region, and three further otters from the Jeseniky Mountains were radio implanted (König & König, in press), otters generally being located by the use of an H-antenna. Day resting sites were approached from several different directions as close as was necessary for a reliable location (usually to <10 m). Under certain conditions, e.g. on crusted snow or when the animal was sleeping in large reed beds, the distances were greater. Tracking throughout the night was carried out in order to quantify habitat use and home range size and shape. In general, day resting sites reflected the area in which animals foraged during the night. The home ranges of these animals were

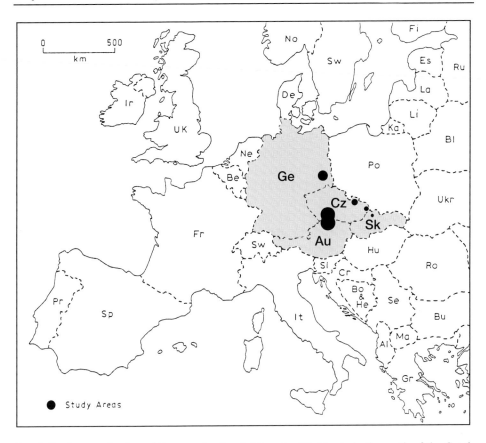

Fig. 1. Study areas in Central Europe: the Czech Moravian Highlands in the south of the Czech Republic, the north of Austria, the Oberlausitz region of Saxony (Germany), the Jeseniky Mountains and the Beskidy Mountains in north-eastern and eastern Moravia (Czech Republic) and central Slovakia.

derived by compiling their day resting sites and the areas at which they were located during at least three different nights. Resting sites which would increase an otter's range, but which were used only once, were treated as outliers and were not included in the home range.

The three animals in the Jeseniky Mountains were located each day for the first two months after release, and twice a week on average. In addition, these otters were tracked during the night on an irregular basis.

Regular use of a given habitat, as indicated by the presence of spraints, was defined from places where several spraints were found in at least three independent observations separated by at least one month.

Results and discussion

Population Development

In Austria, otters living north of the River Danube expanded their range considerably from 1990 to 1994 and 1996. In fact, west of the River Kamp there is no water course remaining to be recolonised by otters since the decline in the population in the 1970s and early 1980s (Fig. 2). This range expansion is obviously the result of an increase of otter numbers. This contention is supported by the small scale survey in the fish pond area which showed an increase in the number of ponds used by otters: during six surveys in 1992, 63% of 115 ponds were used at least once by otters, but in 1996 this had increased to 80% (Fig. 3). The area where this small scale survey was conducted is located in northernmost Lower Austria, an area which was already completely inhabited (according to the IUCN large-scale survey) by otters in 1975 (Kraus, 1980) and in 1990 (Fig. 2). The more detailed small-scale survey showed that mainly small ponds, far away from the main stream and often completely surrounded by agricultural land, are used only by otters under conditions of increasing population pressure.

Human influence on fish abundance

In central and eastern Europe carp, *Cyprinus carpio*, are farmed for human consumption in artificial ponds. Due to their age, size and bank-side vegetation, many of these ponds are rather similar to very shallow natural lakes, although pond sizes, distribution and numbers may differ considerably (Kranz *et al.*, in press). In a 100 km^2 study area in the southern Czech Moravian Highlands, 96 ponds (average size = 1.3 ha) were counted. 75% of the total pond area was used for fish production and stocked mainly with carp (92%, numerically). The average stocking density in spring was 680 kg/ha, and 1,200 kg/ha in autumn. The remaining 25% were identified as angling ponds. Here stocking levels were highly variable, but exact data are not available as the ponds are drained only once every five to ten years. Taking only the fish production farms into account, the ponds in the 100 km^2 sample area provide 85 tonnes of fish in excess of those living in streams.

Rivers and streams frequently are canalised so that their natural productivity is lower than prior to human interference. However, streams in central Europe tend also to be stocked artificially with fish. In the Czech Moravian Highlands annual stocking levels vary between 34-95 kg/ha (J. Basant, pers. comm.). The main stream in the 100 km^2 study area was stocked with 50 kg/ha of rainbow trout, *Oncorhyncus mykiss*. From electro-fishing data the biomass of this stream varied between 32-209 kg/ha (average = 105 kg/ha), which appears very low for this mesotrophic five metre-wide stream. Besides the effect of angling, the abundance of fish in streams is influenced by the electro-fishing activities of the angling association, who try to remove "undesirable" species such as perch, *Perca fluviatilis*, whenever possible.

The significance of ponds is reflected by the size and shape of the ranges of all seven radio-tagged otters (Kranz, unpubl.). Here we would like to highlight the significance of ponds from the habitat use of a subadult otter (designated OF2) that was tracked permanently for 14 consecutive nights (Tab. 1, Fig. 4).

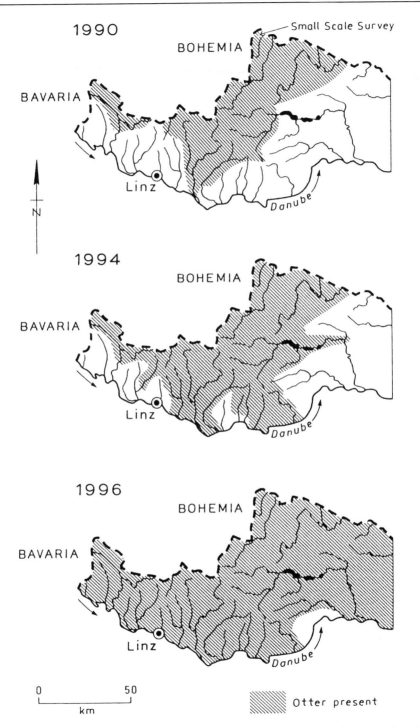

Fig. 2. The increase of the otter population in the Waldviertel and Mühlviertel regions of northern Austria from 1990 to 1996 (the arrow indicates the location of the small-scale survey area in Fig. 3).

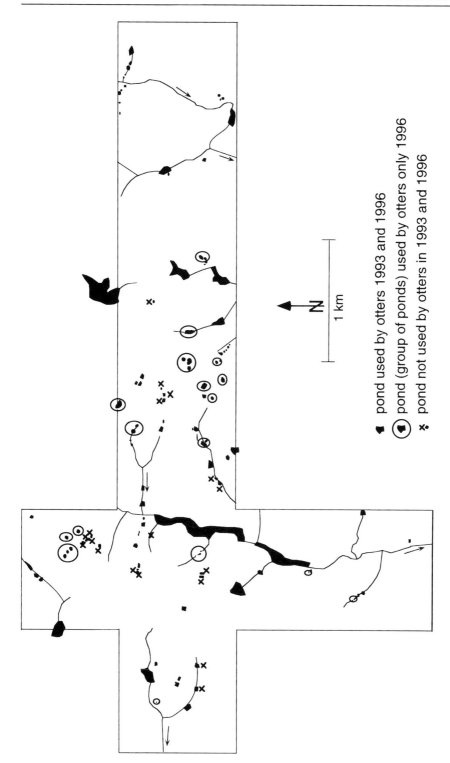

■ pond used by otters 1993 and 1996

⊕ pond (group of ponds) used by otters only 1996

✗ pond not used by otters in 1993 and 1996

1 km

N

Fig. 3. The 17% increase in the number of fish ponds used by otters in a 36 km² study area in northern Austria from 1993 to 1996.

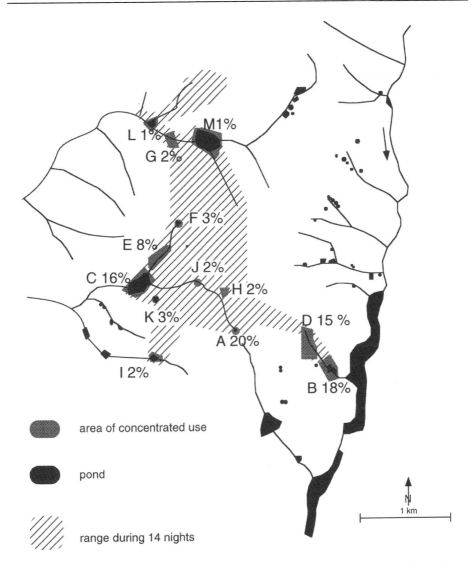

Fig. 4. Areas of concentrated use (A-M) by a subadult female during 14 consecutive nights of permanent radio tracking (n = 82.6 hours) in Litschau (Austria). The otter spent 88% within 13 well-defined areas, mainly ponds and forests (cf. also Table 1) and 12% in-between these areas.

Otter numbers in a fish pond area

The largest snow tracking survey conducted so far covered the entirety of the 100 km², 96 pond study area. At least 16 individual otters could be identified, three of which were still-dependent juveniles. In our opinion, and from our experience of snow tracking surveys in a similar landscape (but without ponds), the numbers identified indicate otter densities at least eight times higher than the landscape would support without the presence of man-made fish ponds.

Table 1. Thirteen areas of concentrated use by a subadult female otter in northern Austria during 14 nights (82.6 hours activity) ranked according to intensity of use. Areas in capitals are identical with those in Fig. 4.

Area	Presence %	Habitat	Size (ha)
A	20	1 pond (Fig. 14)	0.12
B	18	4 ponds & spruce forest (12 m high)	0.25 + 1.00
C	16	1 pond (Fig. 15)	2.94
D	15	derelict grassland, spring, trickle (Fig. 15)	3.00
E	8	spruce forest (7 m high), ditch	2.50
F	3	2 ponds	0.15
G	2	1 pond	0.26
H	2	spruce forest (10 m high)	0.50
I	2	1 pond	0.15
J	2	spruce forest (20 m high), trickle	0.05
K	3	spruce & alder forest, stream <1m	1.50
L	1	1 pond	0.43
M	1	1 pond (Fig. 15)	3.74

Persecution of otters

Although otters are fully legally protected in all central and western European countries, illegal persecution of otters does occur. This is particularly true in areas around fish farms. Fish farmers do not believe in the use of deterrent devices (A. Kranz, unpubl.) – most fish ponds are too large and have too natural a bank for the installation of fences to be useful. Much of the traditional knowledge on how to kill otters effectively may have been lost because otter numbers have been very low in recent decades, so that persecution was unnecessary. Today the traps that we find are quite often set inappropriately. However, leghold traps and other special otter traps have been found in Austria (Kranz, 1994), and in the Czech Republic and Hungary (G. Nechay, pers. comm.). The illegal shooting of otters also occurs (Gutleb *et al.*, 1995; Kranz, 1995). In the last few years, farmers have tried to kill otters with poisoned baits made up from fish and rodenticide. These poisoned fish have been found on the banks of ponds in the Czech Republic and Austria (U. König, pers. comm.). The true impact of this persecution remains unknown, however, in our south Bohemian fish pond area three out of nine of the radio-tagged otters either were killed in traps, or shot (Kranz *et al.*, in press).

Human influences on the availability of fish

In central Europe ice is considered to have a major effect on the availability of fish to otters. Hence, all human activities which reduce the effects of ice favour otters. Three radio-tagged otters survived very cold periods (temperatures <-10°C) in the winters of 1992/93 and 1996/97 by living in villages. Due to human activities or the presence of special infrastructural features (e.g. drainage pipes; see also Table 2) the otters had access to water in ponds. A radio-tagged adult female used four geographically separate areas from May to December until all the ponds in her home range were totally frozen. She then moved into the village of Stare Mesto, where, due to the presence of pipes and relatively warm waste water, she had access to fish in a small stream and two garden ponds (Fig. 5). We argue that this part of her all-year home range was essential for her survival, although only accounting for 6% of all days of the entire radio-tracking period. Another radio-tagged female otter survived extremely cold periods in three villages (Fig. 6), in two of these villages she did not show her presence by tracks. Here the ponds were covered with a thick layer of ice and there was no layer of air between the water and the ice, but the otter entered the ponds using an underwater entrance to an underground den.

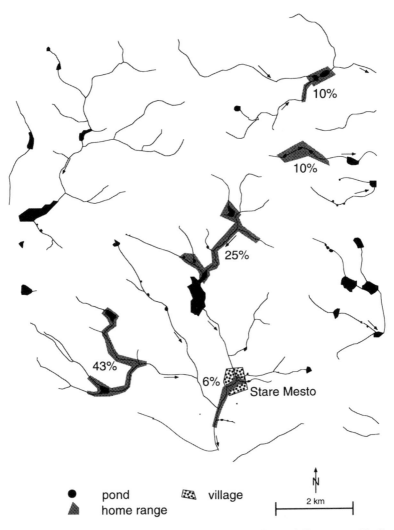

Fig. 5. The nine-month home range of an adult female otter. She used five geographically separate areas. During a severe frost period, she shifted her home range towards the village Stare Mesto, where she had still access to fish in ornamental ponds (% indicates how many days the otter spent in each part of her home range according to the locations of day resting sites; during the remaining 6% she was either not located or found outside the area).

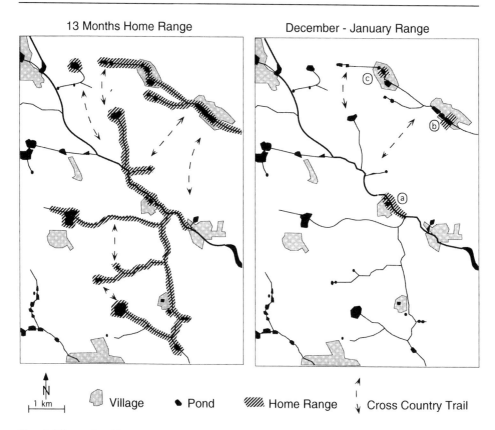

Fig. 6. The entire 13-month home range of an adult female otter radio tracked in the Czech Moravian Highlands during 1996/97, contrasted with her range during December and January of that winter, when severe frost made access to the water difficult. In that period, the otter used streams and ponds in three villages (a, b, c) where still she had access to the water due to human infrastructures such as drainage pipes.

Reservoirs used for hydro-electric power stations and for supplying drinking water have changing water levels. In winter this causes bank-edge breaks in the ice cover. In three reservoirs, one in Lower Austria, one in the Czech Republic and one in Slovakia, otters were observed to make regular use of these crevices in the ice in order to reach the water (Fig. 7). Otherwise, these water bodies would have been unattractive to otters when compared to natural lakes in winter (Erlinge, 1967).

Destruction of habitats and the creation of new habitats

Foraging areas

The destruction of otter habitat is well-known and has been documented throughout most of Europe (Mason & Macdonald, 1986). Frequently it is not destruction of

Fig. 7. A reservoir in winter: due to human-induced changing water levels the ice layer breaks at the edge of the bank. In severe frost periods, this provides the only access to the water for otters (photo: A. Kranz).

the entire habitat, but a reduction in overall habitat quality, e.g. streams become canalised and this decreases prey populations and may destroy resting sites. Hence, on a larger scale, otters occur in lower numbers in such habitats; on a smaller scale, they spend less time in degenerated habitats.

The creation of new habitat is frequently preceded by the destruction of old ones. Reservoirs for hydro-electric power plants or drinking water supply are generally built by destroying rivers, streams and adjacent wetlands. Even fish ponds are quite often constructed in wet patches of the landscape which are unsuitable for other land-use types, and so may destroy wet meadows, moors or streams.

In Hungary between 1950 and 1998, the area of fish ponds increased from 10,800 ha to 27,000 ha (G. Nechay, pers. comm.). This may be considered as a major large-scale habitat improvement for Hungarian otters. These new ponds are

Fig. 8. (a) a regularly used otter trail and *(b)* tracks crossing a road in a kaolin mine in Saxony. These show that otters are able to quickly colonise new habitats (photos: A. Kranz).

rapidly colonised by otters, as is evidenced by well-worn otter paths and regularly used sprainting sites just four years after pond construction (Kranz, unpubl. data from several localities south-east of Lake Balaton).

In the Oberlausitz fish pond area of Saxony (Germany) the open-cast mining of brown coal and kaolin destroy centuries-old fish ponds and their adjacent wetlands on a large scale. However, after a few decades, these ponds are refilled with water and communities of fish, amphibians and birds quickly build up new populations. Human access is generally prohibited to these areas because of the danger to life posed by underground erosion. Otters quickly make use of such habitats, even in the immediate vicinity of mines that still are working (Fig. 8).

Former quarries are frequently filled with water and often used for sport angling. The radio-tagged male otter used such a quarry for 24 days during a cold period in December 1996. During 18 of these days, he used no other habitat than the quarry. This quarry had no inlet or outlet, and was stocked with fish for angling. Due to some subterranean warm-water springs, there were two spots on the bank which were not frozen as hard as the surrounding area. Here the otter slept underground in a crevice, had access to the water under the surface of the ice, and kept 10 x 10 cm holes open where the ice was thinner because of the influence of the springs. Such quarries are quite common in the Czech Moravian Highlands and the Lower Austrian Waldviertel region. They mainly provide granite and frequently are located somewhere uphill, often on the tops of hills. After the experience with the radio-tagged otter, we monitored a sample of 14 quarries four times per year. Eight of these were used in two seasons at least (according to spraints and tracks), and two were positive in every season. The remaining four quarries did not provide any evidence of the presence of otters, although this does not necessarily mean that they are not used at all. For instance, the quarry used by the radio-tagged otter in December 1996 was one of the quarries monitored over the following year, but no evidence of otter presence was found (the actual radio-tagged male was killed by a poacher in March 1997; Kranz *et al.*, in press).

As in the case of the radio-tagged male from the quarry, other radio-tracked otters also used unexpected habitats which usually are not considered to be suitable as otter habitat and, as a result, are not checked during surveys. A subadult female made regular use of a tiny fire-water reservoir in the middle of a village (Fig. 9). This reservoir could only be reached through pipes and all banks were built of concrete. Another radio-tagged otter was repeatedly tracked in an ornamental pond on a golf course (Fig. 10). Both the reservoir and the ornamental pond were also used by other otters, as shown by direct observations and, later on, when the radio-tracked otters had left the area, from spraints and food remains.

In 1997, three radio-tagged otters were reintroduced to the Moravice catchment of the Jeseniky Mountains. They were released at the upper end of an *c.* 14 km-long reservoir (area = *c.* 830 ha). There were no otters present prior to the release (Toman, unpubl.) and, as they were released at the upper end of the reservoir, this reintoduction provided an experiment: where would the otters establish their home ranges? The adult and the subadult male were released in May 1997. From May-October 1997, the adult male used both the river, plus tributary streams, and the upper part of the reservoir (Fig. 11a). However, with the beginning of winter this otter reduced its range along the river, and used only the upper end of the reservoir

Fig. 9. This fire-water reservoir in a village in northern Austria was repeatedly used for foraging by a subadult radio-tagged otter and by untagged individuals (photo: A. Kranz).

Fig. 10. An ornamental pond on a golf course was used by a radio-tagged otter (other than that in Fig. 9) for foraging, as well as by others (photo: A. Kranz).

and one tributary. During the first two months after its release the subadult male was found only on the river upstream of the reservoir and along one tributary. This range overlapped completely with that of the adult male. In July, radio contact with the subadult was lost. This coincided with disastrous floods which caused massive damage throughout Moravia, Poland and eastern Germany in the summer of 1997. However, in October this animal was located again, and was followed until March 1997 when the battery of the radio-transmitter failed. During the months from October to March he used only the upper third of the reservoir, and almost no streams at all (Fig. 11b). In autumn 1997 an adult female was released at the same site as the two males. From November until March, her home range comprised the upper third of the reservoir plus the mouths of four streams, including the main river. From April to June 1996, she shifted her range to the centre of the reservoir (Fig. 11c). We do not have a straight-forward explanation for why these otters did not make more use of the streams, or for why they generally preferred the reservoir to the streams in winter. No electro-fishing data are available from the streams but, from our visual observations, there is no doubt that the river and the stream held large fish populations. In its lower sections live mainly nase, *Chondrostoma nasus*, and greyling, *Thymallus thymallus*, and further upstream are mainly trout, *Salmo trutta*, and bullhead, *Cottus gobio*. In contrast, the reservoir was mainly inhabited by roach, *Rutilus rutilus*, bream, *Abramis brama*, perch, pike, *Esox lucius*, and zander (also known as pike-perch), *Stizostedion lucioperca*. The ice cover on the reservoir was permanently broken along the banks (Fig. 7) - this was because of a constant increase in water level (the reservoir had been constructed just recently, and was still filling with water).

Day resting sites

Habitat loss also may occur in terms of loss of shelter for day resting sites. Macdonald & Mason (1983) argued that old trees with their extensive root systems might be an important prerequisite for underground dens. Our own observations based on seven radio-tagged otters point in the same direction. However, otters do not necessarily need natural holts. Of a total of 491 underground holt locations, 27 (5.5%) were located in drainage pipes (Table 2, Fig. 12). Above-ground resting sites (555 locations) quite frequently were associated either with man-made piles of sticks (6.3%) or broken trees (7.2%). Stick piles are the result of modern forestry (*i.e.* a "clean" forest). Broken trees, in contrast, are considered undesirable and are removed as quickly as possible. In terms of otter day resting sites, this means habitat destruction. Nevertheless, otters again appear to be flexible and use the man-made stick piles (Table 2).

The distance of day resting sites from water may elucidate another aspect of the lives of otters in a modern world. In 50% of all observations (Table 3), resting sites were in the close vicinity (<10 m) of water bodies (ponds or streams greater than one metre wide) which could serve as a safe means of escape. It is argued that such a behaviour can only develop in areas where natural predators such as wolves, *Canis lupus*, are absent. Indeed, according to V. Sidorovich (pers. comm.) in Belarus (where wolves are still common) otters do not leave the close vicinity of water bodies to travel overland or to rest somewhere off-bank.

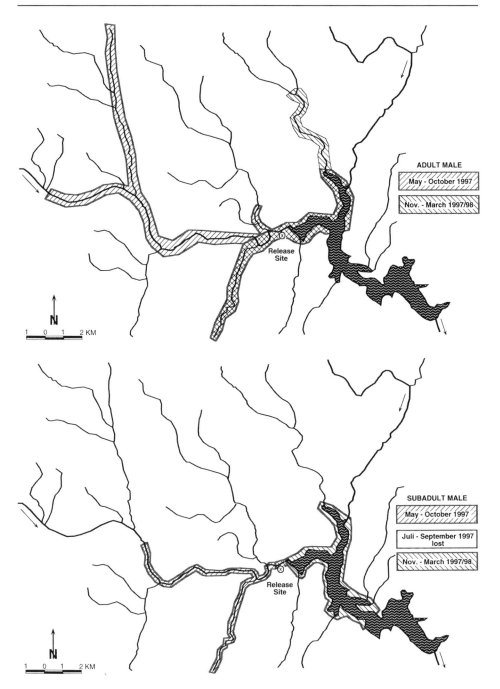

Fig. 11a–b.

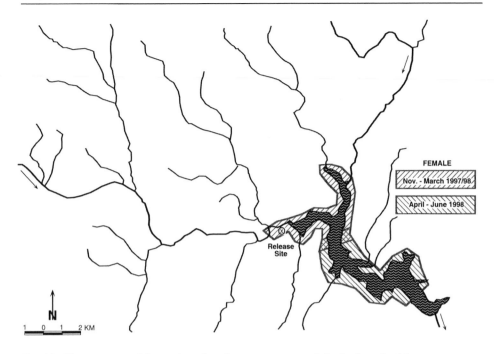

Fig. 11c. Home ranges of three reintroduced otters at a reservoir in the Jeseniky Mnts.

Table 2. Day resting site locations of seven radio-tagged otters in drainage pipes, in man-made stick piles or under broken trees. In total, these otters were located 555 times above ground and 491 below ground.

Otter	FO1	FO2	FO3	FO4	FO5	FO6	MO1
Pipe	0	13	2	0	0	1	11
Stick-pile	14	17	0	0	1	0	3
Broken tree	10	20	2	1	1	2	4

Table 3. Distance of day resting sites to the nearest water (n = seven radio-tagged otters, 1331 locations). Half of the resting sites were located more than 10 m from water bodies (*i.e.* streams more than one metre wide), which would be hazardous if natural predators such as wolves or feral dogs existed in the study area.

	Distance to the nearest water		
	< 10 m	10 – 50 m	> 50 m
pond	25.7%	2.5%	2.5%
>3 m wide stream	10.5%	0	0
1 – 3 m wide stream	12.7%	1.7%	0.9%
<1 m wide stream	31.4%	8.4%	3.7%
	SAFE	RISKY	

Fig. 12. Day resting site of a radio-tagged male otter in a drainage pipe (photo: A. Kranz).

Fig. 13. Regularly used otter habitat along a river within the steel factory of Trinec in eastern Moravia (Czech Republic) (photo: A. Kranz).

Disturbance by humans

Otters have been persecuted as a pest and hunted as a fur bearer for centuries (Festetics, 1980) and, as a result, have become extremely shy. In other words, encounters with man were considered as a source of disturbance to otters. However, otters are no longer hunted in most European countries, and this may well have an effect on their behaviour towards man, as is the case with many species occurring either in national parks or in cities and towns.

During our field work we had several encounters with protected otters, but also some with the still-persecuted fox, *Vulpes vulpes*; the behaviours of the two species were strikingly different (Kranz, unpubl.). Foxes almost always responded with rapid flight. In contrast, otters mostly ignored our presence (continuing with their activities) or snorted and moved slowly out of sight - this may be seen as a sign of discomfort or anger.

Besides these direct observations, information from radio tracking and field signs (tracks and scats) indicate that nowadays otters may live very close to humans, although frequently this remains unnoticed by the latter (Figs. 9 & 10). An extreme example is provided by the otters living along the River Olse in eastern Moravia. The river flows over 8 km and through the huge steel factory of Trinec (Fig. 13). Thus there is a tremendous level of noise along the river, as well as permanent artificial light, and people moving around the river and along gangways above it. Air pollution levels are considerable, and waste water reaches the stream. However, upstream as well as within the factory, fish are abundant and otters regularly forage in the river and one of its tributaries. Nevertheless, it should be kept in mind that our observations originate from subadult animals or non-breeding females. The sensitivity of females with cubs is thought to be much greater (Jefferies, 1987). In addition, spraint data must be interpreted with caution as well, as they mainly originate from males (Strachan & Jefferies, 1996).

Conclusions

At the end of the 20th century, recovering otter populations face a remarkable set of circumstances in central Europe (although many of the observations may hold true for most of Europe). Human activities lead to increased fish populations by stocking rivers, ponds and reservoirs. In addition, many new habitats are created, but habitat destruction has ceased in most regions. This is particularly true for those rivers which have not been canalised in the past. In addition, human activities and infrastructures (e.g. reservoirs, drainage pipes) reduce the impact of ice which otherwise restricts otter access to water. Otters do benefit from this situation, and particularly so in villages and towns, which they use despite the immediate proximity of humans. Similar behaviour patterns have been observed for stone martens, *Martes foina* (e.g. Hermann, 1994) and urban foxes (e.g. Harris & Rayner, 1986). Both species make increasing use of villages, towns and even cities, and are apparently thriving there. In the case of the otter, it remains unclear whether this is a behavioural response to a modern lack of hunting pressure, because otters were observed in cities (e.g. Berlin) in the last century (Festetics, 1980). It is also unclear whether these urban habitats are optimal for otters or not. Their colonisation in recent years (a result of increasing otter population pressure) actually may indicate rather suboptimal conditions. On the other hand, towns like Trinec with its steel factory, were inhabited by otters even when populations were shrinking elsewhere (Poledník, 1991). However, at fish farms (Kranz *et al.*, 1998) increasing otter numbers mean that otters again are perceived as a pest and illegally persecuted. This situation is new, insofar as the traditional ecological knowledge of how to kill pest otters effectively has been lost, and fish farmers are also becoming increasingly worried about radio-tagged otters which, if killed, would reveal their illegal activities. However, given that persecution does not happen in excess, that some threats have become neutralised (e.g. road traffic mortality by building tunnels and fences) and new threats are not appearing, the future of the otter may be more secure than appeared in the recent past.

Acknowledgements

We are grateful to several people assisting in the field work, in particular S. Appel, M. Bodesínsky, K. Förster, P. Kacer and M. Knollseisen. All activities were possible only with the support and supervision of Prof. H. Gossow in Vienna and Ing. V. Hlavac in Havlícuv Brod (Czech Republic). Most of the work was financed by the Austrian Science Foundation (P8742-Bio and P10626-Bio), additional money was received from the Austrian Hunters' Association and the Lower Austrian Nature Conservancy (Niederösterreichischer Naturschutzbund). The reintroduction project in the Jeseniky Mountains also received financial support from the Government of Luxembourg through the Třebon Otter Foundation.

References

Bagenal, T. (1978). *Methods for assessment of fish productivity in fresh waters* (3rd ed.). Oxford; Blackwell Scientific Publications Ltd.
Erlinge, S. (1967). Home range of the otter *Lutra lutra* L. in Southern Sweden. *Oikos*, **18**: 186-209.
Festetics, A. (1980). Der Fischotter - Naturgeschichte und Tier-Mensch-Beziehung. In: C. Reuther & A. Festetics (eds.), *Der Fischotter in Europa - Verbreitung, Bedrohung, Erhaltung*: 9-65. Oderhaus u. Göttingen; privately published.
Foster-Turley, P., Macdonald, S.M. & Mason, C.F. (1990). *Otters, an Action Plan for conservation.* Gland; International Union for the Conservation of Nature and Natural Resources.
Gutleb, A.C., Henninger, W., Loupal, G. & Kranz, A. (1995). Evidence for illegal attempts to kill otters (*Lutra lutra*) in Austria. *IUCN Otter Specialist Group Bulletin*, **11**: 13-15.
Harris, S. & Rayner J.M.V. (1986). Urban fox (*Vulpes vulpes*) population estimates and habitat requirements in several British cities. *Journal of Animal Ecology*, **55**: 575-591.
Herrmann, M. (1994). Habitat use and spatial organisation by the stone marten. In: S.W. Buskirk, A.S. Harestad, M.G. Raphael & R.A. Powell (eds.), *Martens, sables and fishers: biology and conservation*: 122-136. Ithaca (NY); Cornell University Press.
Jefferies, D.J. (1987). The effects of angling interests on otters with particular reference to disturbance. In: P.S. Maitland & A.K. Turner (eds.), *Angling and wildlife in freshwaters* (*ITE Symposium No. 19*): 23-30. Grange-over-Sands; Institute for Terrestrial Ecology.
König, C. & König, U. (in press). Surgical intraperitoneal implantation - a practicable method to fit Eurasian otters with radio transmitters. In: R. Dulfer, J. Nel, A.C. Gutleb & A. Toman (eds.), *Proceedings of the VII International Otter Colloquium, Třebon, Czech Republic, 1998.*
Kranz, A. (1994). Otters increasing - threats increasing. *IUCN Otter Specialist Group Bulletin*, **10**: 28-30.

Kranz, A. (1995). Verbreitung der bayerisch-böhmisch-österreichischen Otterpopulation (*Lutra lutra*) 1994 in Österreich. *BOKU-Reports on Wildlife Research and Game Management*, **9**: 1-25.

Kranz, A., Toman, A. & Roche, K. (1998). Otters and fisheries in central Europe - what is the problem? In: H. Gossow & A. Kranz (eds.), *Otters and fish farms. BOKU-Reports on Wildlife Research and Game Management*, **14**: 142-144.

Kranz A., Toman A., Knollseisen, M. & Prasek, V. (in press). Fish ponds in Central Europe: a rich but risky habitat for otters. In R. Dulfer, J. Nel, A.C. Gutleb & A. Toman (eds.), *Proceedings of the VII International Otter Colloquium, Třebon, Czech Republic, 1998*.

Kraus, E. (1980). Probleme des Fischotterschutzes in Niederösterreich (Österreich). In: C. Reuther & A. Festetics (eds.), *Der Fischotter in Europa - Verbreitung, Bedrohung, Erhaltung*: 205-210. Oderhaus u. Göttingen; privately published.

Macdonald, S.M. & Mason, C.F. (1983). Some factors influencing the distribution of otters (*Lutra lutra*). *Mammal Review*, **13**: 1-10.

Macdonald, S. (1994). Meeting of European Section OSG. *IUCN Otter Specialist Group Bulletin*, **10**: 10-14.

Mason, C.F. & Macdonald, S.M. (1986). *Otters: ecology and conservation*. Cambridge; Cambridge University Press.

Poledník, L. (1991). The occurrence of the otter (*Lutra lutra*) in the northern Moravia. *Vydra*, **1991** (2): 14-16.

Romanowski, J., Gruber, B. & Brzezinski, M. (1997). The recovering otter population of central Poland. *IUCN Otter Specialist Group Bulletin*, **14** (1): 24-25.

Strachan, R. & Jefferies, D.J. (1996). *Otter survey of England 1991-1994*. London; The Vincent Wildlife Trust.

Stubbe, M. & Stubbe, A. (Eds.) (1994). *Säugetierarten und deren feldökologische Erforschung im östlichen Deutschland (Tiere im Konflikt 3)*. Halle (Saale); Martin-Luther-Universität Halle-Wittenberg.

Weber, D. (1990). *Das Ende des Fischotters in der Schweiz (Schriftenreihe Umwelt Nr. 128)*. Bern; BUWAL.

CHAPTER 12

The application of Geographic Information Systems and computer modelling to mustelid research

Mary C. Gough* & Steve P. Rushton

Abstract

Geographic Information Systems (GIS) and modelling are currently very fashionable in applied ecological research. These computer-based systems provide a means of extrapolating in space and time that is not feasible with traditional methods of data collection and analysis alone. Due to the increasing pressures faced by many mustelid species there is a pressing need to increase our understanding of the factors influencing mustelid populations at landscape scales if we are to manage them effectively. In this paper we provide examples of how GIS and modelling approaches can be used to facilitate this area of mustelid research.

Introduction

A discussion of mustelids in a modern world would be incomplete without considering the application of new computer-based technologies to aid mustelid research. Many authors have stressed the need to utilise Geographic Information Systems (GIS) and predictive models for the development of Decision Support Systems (DSS) to create a more holistic and integrated approach to wildlife management (Bissonette *et al.*, 1989; Norton & Possingham, 1993; Thompson & Welsh, 1993; Ellis & Seal, 1995; Naesset, 1997; Starfield, 1997; MacDonald *et al.*, 1998). Although these technologies have received considerable academic and practitioner attention in the last ten years (Lombard, 1993; Worrall & Bond, 1997), many wildlife professionals and conservationists are still unaware of their potential application, partly because these tools have a large amount of technical overhead (Blinn *et al.*, 1994). There are also many misconceptions surrounding modelling and GIS techniques and their ability to meet our demands (Starfield, 1997). The aim of this work is to illustrate how GIS and modelling approaches can be used to facilitate ecological research on mustelids.

---

* Corresponding author.

Mustelids in a modern world
Management and conservation aspects of small carnivore: human interactions
edited by Huw I. Griffiths, pp. 185–199
© 2000 Backhuys Publishers, Leiden, The Netherlands

Why use GIS or modelling?

Early work on mustelids was necessarily descriptive as information on the natural history of these species was required. Having obtained a basic understanding of the ecology of some species, attempts have been made to quantify the influence of changes in life history processes (e.g. mortality), on population size, structure and persistence. This work has mainly focused on the furbearing species and others where there was a strong economic interest. There has also been considerable interest in quantifying relationships between mustelids and their habitats, particularly as habitat loss and fragmentation are thought to be responsible for the declines of some species in parts of their range (Gibilisco, 1994; Mason & MacDonald, 1994; Griffiths & Thomas, 1997). Wildlife managers want to know the likely impacts of habitat manipulation and culling on mustelid populations and their distributions before operations are carried out, so that appropriate decisions can be made. Studying mustelids in the field, however, is notoriously difficult because these species are so elusive. Most studies have involved only a few individuals and have been conducted at small temporal and spatial scales. If mustelid research is to move from a descriptive to a predictive science, techniques are required to extrapolate up to the landscape scale.

Modelling provides a means of investigating species-landscape interactions through time. Several models have been created to investigate mustelid population dynamics (e.g. Harris *et al.*, 1988; Lacy & Clark, 1988, 1993; Strickland, 1994; Ansorge *et al.*, 1997; Bright & Smithson, 1997) and the dynamics of disease within mustelid populations (e.g. White & Harris, 1995; Smith *et al.*, 1995, 1997; Swinton *et al.*, 1997), but none of this research has focused on the interaction between the animal and the landscape. Analysis of species-landscape interactions clearly requires large amounts of spatial information. Storage and manipulation of these data on conventional map-based media is often very laborious.

GIS are computer-based systems designed to provide efficient methods for the storage, manipulation and analysis of large quantities of spatial data. Data obtained from maps, remote sensing (e.g. satellite imagery) and/or field surveys that relate to different ecological and socio-economic features of landscapes can be stored in different layers within a GIS. For example, one layer may hold land cover data whilst other layers may contain species distributions, culling regimes, potential habitat alterations and land values. GIS enable data from any combination of these layers to be manipulated to solve a particular problem. Typical GIS procedures include overlay, where maps can be simply overlaid, or any other mathematical function such as multiplication, subtraction or division may be performed. Data manipulated in spatial overlay procedures are most often stored in raster (grid cell) maps, but vector formats based on the storage of boundaries and nodes can also be used. The technical background to GIS, with particular relevance to ecologists, can be found in introductory texts such as Burrough (1986), Johnson (1990), Maguire *et al.* (1991), Haines-Young (1991) and Wadsworth & Treweek (1999).

The use of GIS in conservation biology ranges from simple static analyses of land cover and species distributions through to complex dynamic simulation modelling. GIS are now routinely used for relatively straightforward mapping of species distributions and evaluation of habitats for conservation purposes from local

(Veitch *et al.*, 1995) to international scales (Vanlatesteijn, 1995). Habitats considered most important to the species of interest are identified and spatial data are outputted as maps or summary statistics. This technique was used by Yonzon & Hunter (1991) to quantify the specialist habitat available for the red panda, *Ailurus fulgens*, within a Himalayan national park; they found only 6% of the park included the habitat types required by this endangered species. These approaches have also been used to investigate multi-species and biodiversity issues (Conroy & Noon, 1996). For example, A. Smith *et al.*, (1997) overlaid lemur abundance, microhabitat variables, land use data and a map of disturbance risk within a GIS to identify conservation priority areas in Madagascar. For large scale biodiversity assessment, GAP analysis has been used (Scott *et al.*, 1993; Menon & Bawa, 1997; Debinski & Humphrey, 1997). This technique combines regional scale distribution data for indicator species of plants and animals and their habitats and allows identification of gaps in the representation of habitats and centres of species richness in management plans. Areas requiring protection can thus be identified (Merrill *et al.*, 1995) and the most appropriate location of buffer zones decided (Nepal & Weber, 1994).

Whilst overlay analyses are commonly undertaken, GIS offer more advanced data manipulation facilities and functions to determine distances between features, or to locate the shortest path between points in terms of time or cost. These capabilities allow complex structural queries of spatial data and can be used for investigating the relationships between species and their environment. Clifford *et al.* (1995) used a GIS to evaluate ecological risks to species at a dieldrin contaminated site. Here the GIS was used to create a 3-D "risk surface" which was superimposed on site specific maps to provide an effective risk-management decision-making tool by facilitating evaluation of the effects of various potential remediation scenarios.

GIS have been widely used to analyse habitat use and requirements of mammal species, particularly herbivores (Aspinall, 1993; Chang *et al.* 1995; Knick & Dyer, 1997; van Deelen *et al.*, 1997; Kernohan *et al.*, 1998), but also carnivores e.g. panthers, *Felis concolor* (Maehr & Cox, 1995), grizzly bears, *Ursus arctos horribilis* (Mace *et al.*, 1996), grey wolves, *Canis lupus* (Mladenoff & Sickley, 1998), and mustelids and their prey. Reading & Matchett (1997) used a GIS to examine characteristics of black-tailed prairie dog, *Cynomys ludovicianus*, colonies including slope, aspect, soils, land tenure, and distance from roads. The results were to be used to develop a model of preferred black-tailed prairie dog habitat for prairie dog monitoring and management, which could also facilitate the identification of potential black-footed ferret, *Mustela nigripes*, re-introduction sites (see Vargas *et al.*, this volume). Paragi *et al.* (1996) used a GIS to determine habitat availability for American marten, *Martes americana*. This information was used to test whether martens selectively used post-fire successional stages in the Alaskan taiga, and whether selection could be explained by differences in marten hunting behaviour, habitat, prey abundance, or demography.

Habitat Suitability Indices (HSIs) which attempt to characterise habitat quality for selected wildlife species (Garcia & Armbruster, 1997; Brooks, 1997) also have been developed within GIS. Such models have been developed for many mammals, particularly herbivores including black-tailed deer, *Odocoilus hemionus* (Boroski *et al.*, 1996), moose, *Alces alces* (Hepinstall *et al.*, 1996; Rempel *et al.*, 1997), beaver, *Castor canadensis* (Robel *et al.*, 1993), grey squirrel, *Sciurus carolinensis* (Bender *et al.*, 1996) and American marten (Bowman *et al.*, 1996; Robitaille, 1998). Allen (1983) developed an HSI model for the fisher, *Martes pennanti*, which was subsequently validated by Thomasma *et al.*(1991) after testing to determine whether the model accurately represented habitat suitability for the species.

Data analysis within a GIS is not restricted to simple rule-based approaches, but can be extended to incorporate more formal statistical modelling procedures to create mathematical links between a species' observed distribution and habitat characteristics. Once species-habitat relations have been elucidated and quantified, models can be generated which enable temporal and spatial extrapolation of data, thus enabling the prediction of species distributions in the future or in areas not surveyed.

Modelling approaches can be broadly classified as "associative" or "process-based" depending on their underlying philosophy. Associative approaches attempt to determine relationships between the distribution of a species and environmental features, without explicitly modelling the mechanisms involved. Such models can be thought of as a "top down" approach, as existing animal distribution data are overlaid on landscape information and attempts made to identify relationships between the incidence or abundance of the species and measured landscape characteristics. Process-based models offer an alternative, "bottom-up" approach, whereby the life history and behavioural processes of the species within the landscape are simulated and the distribution of the species emerges as the model is run (Rushton *et al.*, 1997; Macdonald *et al.*, 1998). A wide range of associative approaches have been used to investigate mustelid-habitat relationships. Of these approaches, regression modelling has probably been the technique most commonly employed. Regression models attempt to relate the incidence or abundance of a species to a suite of explanatory variables (McCullagh & Nelder, 1983; Tabachnick & Fidell, 1996). Once such a relationship has been derived the model can be used to predict the incidence or abundance of the species elsewhere using the predictor variables. This can be done relatively easily within a GIS, although it has not been widely applied to mustelids.

We used an associative approach within the GIS GRASS (Westervelt *et al.*, 1990) to predict badger, *Meles meles*, densities in north-east England. Badger population density has been related to the availability of their main food resource, earthworms (Kruuk & Parish, 1982). The biomass of earthworms present in a landscape is dependent on the habitat and the soil type, with the surface-active lumbricid species that predominate in the diet of badgers being absent from acidic soils (Edwards & Lofty, 1977). Using a formalin extraction method, we sampled earthworm populations at 23 sites throughout the Tyne catchment, and derived a relationship between biomass per unit area and soil pH (Rushton, unpubl.). A GIS map of soil pH was then overlaid with woodland and grassland to identify areas of suitable earthworm foraging habitat for badgers. The relationship between earthworm biomass and soil pH was then used to create a new map layer of predicted food availability for badgers in each one km square in the catchment. The correlation between badger population density and earthworm biomass derived by linear regression by Kruuk & Parish (1982) was then was used to produce a map of predicted badger density (Fig. 1). The most obvious feature of this map is the higher predicted density of badgers in the river valleys where soils are more mineral and of higher pH than in the surrounding upland areas. This predicted distribution compares favourably with the map of estimated badger sett density produced by Neal (1986).

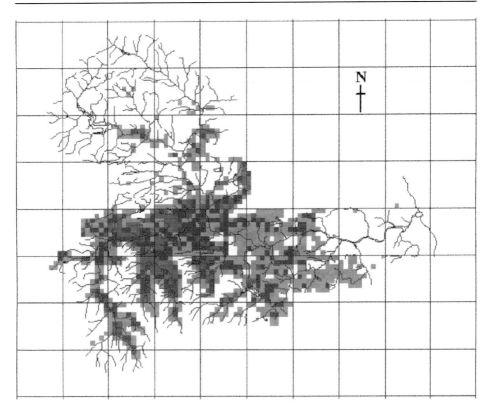

Fig. 1. Map showing the predicted density of badgers (*Meles meles*) within of the River Tyne catchment, north-east England. Darker colours indicate higher predicted badger densities. Grid square size = 10 x 10 km.

The major weakness of associative models is their reliance on correlation. Explanatory variables may not be causal at all, merely correlated with other, unmeasured causal factors. In addition, these simple regression models do not consider spatial autocorrelation. This occurs when the value of a variable at a given site is dependent upon its value at neighbouring sites (Cliff & Ord, 1981). Regression models can be modified to incorporate spatial autocorrelation (see Upton & Fingleton, 1985) but, because of the mathematical complexity and larger data requirements, this has rarely been carried out. Notable exceptions are the models of Pereira & Itami (1991), Augustin *et al.* (1996) and Li *et al.* (1997) developed for squirrels, deer and cranes, respectively. Another drawback of associative models is that they are static, usually being based on "snapshots" of a species' distribution at a given time and place. There are many reasons why the relationship between a species and the landscape may change with time and, in addition, individuals within one area of the species' range may not use the landscape in the same way as individuals in another area. This is particularly likely in highly adaptable mustelid species such as polecats, *Mustela putorius*, which show great plasticity in their habitat requirements. Associative models therefore are less likely to be successful for these species. Furthermore, these models often do not contribute to our understanding of the mechanisms determining the observed densities of species (Wiens *et al.*, 1993; Grimm, 1994).

A dynamic approach

These problems can be overcome by developing mechanistic process-based models which simulate the dynamics of animals in the landscape. GIS can be linked to these models to store the animal input and output data and provide the habitat information which forms the template on which the behavioural and life-history processes of the species are simulated. Process-based models may represent life history processes at the level of populations or individuals. Models developed for wildlife management have been mainly population-orientated (e.g. Starfield & Bleloch, 1986; Lurz *et al.*, 1995; Bascompte & Sole, 1996; Hof & Raphael, 1997; McArdle *et al.*, 1997; Rushton *et al.*, 1997; Wu & Levin, 1997; Root, 1998; Weiss & Weiss, 1998), but there has been a growing interest in development of individual-based models (De Angelis & Gross, 1992; Judson, 1994; Liu *et al.*, 1995; Andersen, 1996; Wu *et al.*, 1996; Moen, 1997; Tischendorf, 1997; Letcher *et al.*, 1998). Individual-based models, also known as i-space configuration models (Metz & Diekmann, 1986), simulate the births and deaths of individual animals and the overall effects on the population are derived from summation of the life histories of each individual. It has been argued that these models are more suitable than population-based models for describing small populations which are subject to a high degree of temporal stochasticity in the environment, and also populations in which environmental exposure and encounters with other individuals are likely to vary greatly (De Angelis & Rose, 1992).

These characteristics are typical of many mustelid populations, including that of the polecat in England. This species currently is expanding its range eastwards from its stronghold in Wales and recolonising England - mainly in response to a reduction in human persecution (Blandford, 1987; Birks, 1993, this volume). In an attempt to facilitate the recovery of the species, conservationists have reintroduced polecats into the Lake District in north-west England. We utilised the GIS GRASS (Westervelt *et al.*, 1990) to assess the potential suitability of the landscape (in different seasons) within the Lake District National Park for polecats. In common with the badger the polecat is a generalist species taking as wide a variety of prey as available (Lodé, 1997). In contrast with the badger, however, the abundance of polecat prey (rodents, lagomorphs and amphibians) cannot be quantified or predicted easily at the landscape scale. Our assessment of landscape suitability was therefore based upon habitat preferences of polecats available in the literature. Land cover data for the National Park (derived from aerial photographs) were divided into three main categories: (1) cover types never utilised by polecats, (2) types traversed by polecats but not utilised for foraging, and (3) cover types providing foraging habitat. The individual cover types in the foraging habitat were weighted on the basis of polecat habitat preferences determined by Birks (1998). A map showing the overall habitat suitability of each grid square was then produced in the GIS (Fig. 2). The darker areas on the map indicate potentially higher suitability for polecats. Not all of these areas will be utilised by polecats however because the species is still re-colonising and an associative model based on this habitat map would therefore over-predict the distribution of the species in this landscape.

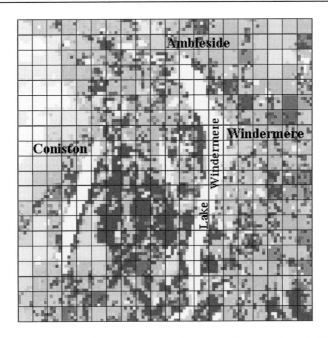

Fig. 2. Landscape suitability map for polecats, *Mustela putorius*. Darker colours indicate those areas of the Lake District National Park offering the greatest amount of habitats preferred by polecats. Grid square size = 1 x 1 km. Each pixel = 200 x 200 m.

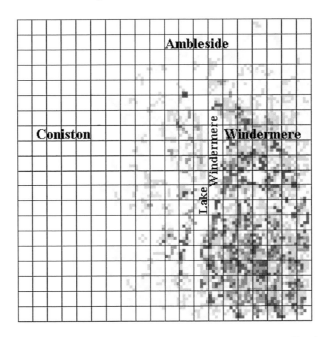

Fig. 3. Map showing those areas within the Lake District National Park predicted to be utilised by polecats, 10 years after the release of 20 individuals at the southern end of Lake Windermere. Darker colours indicate those areas most likely to be utilised. Grid square size = 1 x 1 km.

To investigate the spread of the polecat population through time, we linked the habitat suitability map to an individual-based model simulating polecat population dynamics. In this model twenty polecats were "released" at the southern end of Lake Windermere. Formation of seasonal home ranges by individual polecats was simulated by assuming that polecats pre-empt space. Male and female polecats were allowed to overlap areas of home range not within the core area of another animal. Juvenile polecats dispersed up to a maximum distance of 10 km from their natal range. The reproduction and mortality of individuals in the landscape was simulated stochastically using information derived from field data (Blandford, 1987; Weber, 1989). The model was set to simulate polecat population dynamics and space use over a 10 year period. The model was run repeatedly for a time-span of 10 years and maps were generated within the GIS to show those parts of the study area incorporated into polecat home ranges each year. These maps were combined to create a single map showing the probability that different areas of the map were being utilised by polecats (Fig. 3) in the final year. This map shows that after ten years polecats were predicted to be present mainly in the south-east of the study area.

Habitat loss has been suggested as a factor contributing to the decline in polecats in other parts of Europe (Blandford, 1987). Moreover, linear features such as hedgerows, dry stone walls and ditches provide an important habitat for the polecat (Birks, 1998), however, there has been a considerable loss of these features in many parts of Britain (Pollard *et al.*, 1974; Barr *et al.*, 1993). To investigate the possible consequences of further removal of linear features on polecat space use we reduced the coverage of linear features by 50% and ran the model again. Comparison of outputs from the two sets of simulations revealed a significant increase of 6% (p <0.01) in mean individual home range size in response to the reduction in linear features. Home range overlap also increased by 3% (p <0.05). There was no significant difference in population size. These results suggest that polecats would be able to compensate for the reduction in linear features by increasing home range size and overlap, without any negative impact on population size. Evaluating the impacts of large-scale landscape and environmental change, as undertaken in this example, is clearly difficult to investigate experimentally in the field. This is one reason why spatially explicit population models are considered powerful tools for investigating animal population changes at large spatial scales (Pulliam *et al.*, 1992; Dunning *et al.*, 1995; Conroy *et al.*, 1995; Turner *et al.*, 1995).

Population Viability Analysis

By enabling extrapolation in time, simulation models can also be used to evaluate the probability that a population will persist or go extinct under different conditions or management scenarios within a given time frame. This procedure, known as Population Viability Analysis (PVA) has been increasingly used in the last decade to aid the management of threatened species (Caughley & Gunn, 1996). There are many commercial computer packages available, each with strengths and weaknesses (Boyce, 1992; Lindenmayer *et al.*, 1995; Witteman & Gilpin, 1995; Brook *et al.*, 1997). Most PVA models, including the extensively used package VORTEX (Lacy, 1993) are non-spatial. The Conservation Breeding Specialist Group of the World

Conservation Union (IUCN) has conducted more than 80 PVAs using VORTEX (Miller, 1995). VORTEX is an individual-based model incorporating genetic variation in the population, thus enabling assessment of possible inbreeding depression. The model includes both demographic and environmental stochasticity. VORTEX was used by Lacy & Clark (1993) to estimate extinction probabilities for American marten populations under different fur trapping and timber harvesting scenarios. The authors concluded that such population modelling is invaluable to adaptive management of martens as well as other species. Van Ewijk *et al*. (1996) used VORTEX to assess the feasibility of several potential otter reintroduction scenarios prior to release. Schneider & Yodzis (1994) developed a custom-built, individual-based model to examine extinction processes in American martens. Although this model was not linked to a GIS, it was spatially explicit and could easily be modified to operate in a GIS environment. The spatial distribution of resources and individuals can affect species persistence (Levin, 1992), yet only one commercially available PVA package, RAMAS-space (Akcakaya & Ferson, 1992), is spatially explicit. PVA models utilising GIS-held habitat data have been developed for some species. Akcakaya *et al*. (1995) linked GIS generated spatial data directly to a metapopulation model to assess extinction risks of the helmeted honeyeater, *Lichenostomus melanops cassidix*. Spatially explicit models such as this have much larger data requirements than other models, and require more time, equipment and technical expertise to develop (Kareiva *et al*., 1997). Beissenger & Westphal (1998) stress that all demographic population models, spatial or not, should be used with caution for PVA due to the uncertainties surrounding their predictions caused by lack of data for parameterising and testing these models (Jeffers & North, 1991; Wennergren *et al*., 1995; Lima & Zollner, 1996). Prediction is not the only reason for building models however, often the most beneficial aspect of model development is forcing us to think clearly about what we know about a species, enabling hypotheses to be generated, and highlighting those areas where more information is required to test these hypotheses (Starfield, 1997). Models can also be used to design the most effective strategy for collecting data in the field (e.g. Zielinski & Stauffer, 1996). Modelling should therefore be considered as an approach that provides a strong conceptual framework for future research.

Concluding remarks

Although modelling and GIS are currently very much in vogue in ecological research, they are not a panacea offering perfect solutions to every problem. Neither are they a substitute for good natural history skills, field research, or other more traditional ecological techniques. These new technologies should be regarded as one of the many tools available to wildlife managers and therefore complimentary to other research methods. Scientists and wildlife managers need to become comfortable with models and GIS by gaining an understanding of their potential application to solving different problems and learning how to work within their limitations (Starfield, 1997).

Acknowledgements

We are extremely grateful to the Lake District National Park Authority for providing us with land cover data utilised in the polecat model. Our thanks also go to an anonymous referee for her helpful comments on earlier drafts of this manuscript. The badger modelling was undertaken as part of the NERC/ESRI funded North East Land Use Programme (NELUP).

References

Akcakaya, H.R. & Ferson, S. (1992). *RAMAS/space: spatially structured population models for conservation biology, Version 1.3*. New York; Applied Biomathematics.

Akcakaya, H.R., McCarthy, M.A. & Pearce, J.L. (1995). Linking landscape data with population viability analysis - management options for the Helmeted Honeyeater *Lichenostomus melanops cassidix*. *Biological Conservation*, **73:** 169-176.

Allen, A.W. (1983). *Habitat suitability index models: fisher (FWS/OBS-82/10.45)*. Washington (DC); US Department of the Interior, Fish & Wildlife Service.

Andersen, D.C. (1996). A spatially-explicit model of search path and soil disturbance by a fossorial herbivore. *Ecological Modelling*, **89:** 99-108.

Ansorge, H., Schipke, R. & Zinke, O. (1997). Population structure of the otter, *Lutra lutra*. Parameters and model for a central European region. *Zeitschrift für Säugetierekunde*, **62** (Suppl 2): 143-151.

Aspinall, R. (1993). Modelling habitat suitability for red deer. Use of geographic systems for interpreting land-use policy and modelling effects of land-use change. In: R. Haines-Young, D.R. Green & S.H. Cousins (eds.), *Landscape ecology and GIS*: 223-236. London; Taylor & Francis.

Augustin, N.H., Mugglestone, M.A. & Buckland, S.T. (1996). An autologistic model for the spatial distribution of wildlife. *Journal of Applied Ecology*, **33:** 339-348

Barr, C.J., Bunce, R.G.H., Clarke, R.T., Fuller, R.T., Furse, M.T., Gillespie, M.K., Groom, G.B., Hallam, C.J., Hornung, M., Howard, D.C. & Ness, M.J. (1993).*Countryside survey 1990 (Main Report)*. London; Department of the Environment.

Bascompte, J. & Sole, R.V. (1996). Habitat fragmentation and extinction thresholds in spatially explicit models. *Journal of Animal Ecology*, **65:** 465-473.

Beissinger, S.R. & Westphal, M.I. (1998). On the usefulness of demographic models of population viability in endangered species management. *Journal of Wildlife Management*, **62:** 821-841

Bender, L.C., Roloff, G.J., Haufler, J.B. (1996). Evaluating confidence-intervals for habitat suitability models. *Wildlife Society Bulletin*, **24:** 347-352.

Birks, J.D.S. (1993). The return of the polecat. *British Wildlife*, **5:** 16-25.

Birks, J.D.S. (1998). Secondary rodenticide poisoning risk arising from winter farmyard use by the European polecat *Mustela putorius*. *Biological Conservation*, **85:** 233-240.

Bissonette, J.A., Fredrickson, R.J. & Tucker, B.J. (1989). American marten: a case for landscape-level management. *Transactions of the North American Wildlife and Natural Resources Conference*, **54:** 89-101.

Blandford, P.R.S. (1987). Biology of the Polecat *Mustela putorius*: a literature review. *Mammal Review*, **17:** 155-198

Blinn, C.R., Martodam, D.J. & Queen, L.P. (1994). Enhancing access for natural resource professionals to Geographic Information Systems - an example application. *Forestry Chronicle*, **70:** 75-79.

Boroski, B.B, Barrett, R.H., Timossi, I.C. & Kie, J.G. (1996). Modelling habitat suitability for black-tailed deer (*Odocoileus hemionus columbianus*) in heterogeneous landscapes. *Forest Ecology and Management*, **88:** 157-165.

Bowman, J.C., Robitaille, J.F. & Watt, W.R. (1996). Northeastern Ontario Forest Ecosystem Classification as a tool for managing Marten habitat. *Forestry Chronicle*, **72:** 529-533.

Boyce, M.S. (1992). Population Viability Analysis. *Annual Review of Ecology and Systematics*, **23:** 481-506

Bright, P.W., Mitchell, P. & Morris, P.A. (1994). Dormouse distribution - survey techniques, insular ecology and selection of sites for conservation. *Journal of Applied Ecology*, **31**: 329-339.

Bright, P.W. & Smithson, T.J. (1997). *Species recovery programme for the pine marten in England: 1995-96 (English Nature Research Reports No. 240)*. Peterborough; English Nature.

Brook, B.W., Lim, L., Harden, R. & Frankham, R. (1997). Does population viability analysis software predict the behaviour of real populations? A retrospective study on the Lord Howe Island woodhen *Tricholimnas sylvestris* (Sclater). *Biological Conservation*, **82**: 119-128

Brooks, R.P. (1997). Improving habitat suitability index models. *Wildlife Society Bulletin*, **25**: 163-167.

Burrough, P. (1986). *Principles of Geographic Information Systems* (2nd ed.). Oxford; Oxford University Press.

Caughley, G. & Gunn, A. (1996). *Conservation biology in theory and practice*. Oxford; Blackwell Scientific Publications.

Chang, K.T., Verbyla, D.L. & Yeo, J.J. (1995). Spatial-analysis of habitat selection by Sitka blacktailed deer in southeast Alaska, USA. *Environmental Management*, **19**: 579-589.

Cliff, A.D. & Ord, J.K. (1981). *Spatial processes: models and applications*. London; Pion.

Clifford, P.A., Barchers, D.E., Ludwig, D.F., Sielkin, R.L., Klingensmith, J.S., Graham, R.V. & Banton, M.I. (1995). An approach to quantifying spatial components of exposure for ecological risk assessment. *Environmental Toxicology and Chemistry*, **14**: 895-906.

Conroy, M.J., Cohen, Y., James, F.C., Matsinos, Y.G. & Maurer, B.A. (1995). Parameter-estimation, reliability, and model improvement for spatially explicit models of animal populations. *Ecological Applications*, **5**: 17-19.

Conroy, M.J. & Noon, B.R. (1996). Mapping of species richness for conservation of biological diversity: conceptual and methodological issues. *Ecological Applications*, **6**: 763-773.

De Angelis, D.L. & Gross, L.J. (Eds.) (1992). *Individual-based models and approaches in ecology: populations, communities and ecosystems*. New York; Chapman & Hall.

De Angelis, D.L. & Rose, K.A. (1992). Which individual-based approach is most appropriate for a given problem? In: D.L. De Angelis & L.J. Gross (eds.), *Individual-based models and approaches in ecology: populations, communities and ecosystems*: 67-87. New York; Chapman & Hall.

Debinski, D.M. & Humphrey, P.S. (1997). An integrated approach to biological diversity assessment. *Natural Areas Journal*, **17**: 355-365.

Dunning, J.B., Sewart, D.J., Danielson, B.J., Noon, B.R., Root, T.L, Lamberson, R.H. & Stevens, E.E. (1995). Spatially explicit population-models - current forms and future uses. *Ecological Applications*, **5**: 3-11.

Edwards, C.A. & Lofty, J.R. (1977). *The biology of earthworms*. London; Chapman & Hall.

Ellis, S. & Seal, U.S. (1995). Tools of the trade to aid decision-making for species survival. *Biodiversity and Conservation*, **4**: 553-572.

Garcia, L.A. & Armbruster, M. (1997). A decision support system for evaluation of wildlife habitat. *Ecological Modelling*, **102**: 287-300.

Gibilisco, C.J. (1994). Distributional dynamics of modern *Martes* in North America. In: S.W. Buskirk, A.S. Harestad, M.G. Raphael & R.A. Powell (eds.), *Martens, sables and fisher: biology and conservation*: 59-71. Ithaca (NY); Cornell University Press.

Griffiths, H.I. & Thomas, D.H. (1997). *The conservation and management of the European badger (Meles meles) (Nature and Environment No. 90)*. Strasbourg; Council of Europe Press.

Grimm, V. (1994). Mathematical models and understanding in ecology. *Ecological Modelling*, **75**: 641-651.

Haines-Young, R.H., Green, D.R. & Cousins, S. (Eds.) (1993). *Landscape ecology and Geographic Information Systems*. London; Taylor & Francis.

Harris, R.B. & Clark, T.W. & Shaffer, M.L. (1988). Extinction probabilities for isolated black-footed ferret populations. In: U.S. Seal, E.T. Thorne, M.A. Bogan & S.H. Anderson (eds.), *Conservation biology and the black-footed ferret*: 69-82. New Haven (Connecticut); Yale University Press.

Hepinstall, J.A., Queen, L.P. & Jordon, P.A. (1996). Application of a modified habitat-suitability-index model for moose. *Photogrammetric Engineering and Remote Sensing*, **62**: 1281-1286.

Hof, J. & Raphael, M.G. (1997). Optimization of habitat placement: A case study of the Northern Spotted Owl in the Olympic Peninsula. *Ecological Applications*, **7**: 1160-1169.

Jeffers, J.N.R. & North, P.M. (1991). Modelling: a basis for management or an illusion? In: I.F. Spellerberg, F.B. Goldsmith & M.G. Morris (eds.), *The scientific management of temperate communities for conservation*: 523-541. Oxford; Blackwell Scientific.

Johnson, L.B. (1990). Analysing spatial and temporal phenomena using geographical information systems - a review of ecological applications. *Landscape Ecology*, **4:** 31-44.

Judson, O. (1994). The rise of the individual-based model in ecology. *Trends in Ecology and Evolution*, **9:** 9-15.

Kareiva, P., Skelly, D. & Ruckleshaus, M. (1997). Re-evaluating the use of models to predict the consequences of habitat loss and fragmentation. In: S.T.A. Pickett, R.S. Ostfield, M. Shachak & G.E. Likens (eds.), *The ecological basis of conservation*: 156-166. New York; Chapman & Hall.

Kernohan, B.J., Millspaugh, J.J., Jenks, J.A. & Naugle, D.E. (1998). Use of an adaptive kernel home-range estimator in a GIS environment to calculate habitat use. *Journal of Environmental Management*, **53:** 83-89.

Knick, S.T. & Dyer, D.L. (1997). Distribution of black-tailed jackrabbit habitat determined by GIS in southwestern Idaho. *Journal of Wildlife Management*, **61:** 75-85.

Kruuk, H. & Parish, T. (1982). Factors affecting population density, group size and territory size of the European badger *Meles meles. Journal of Zoology*, **196:** 31-39

Lacy, R.C. (1993). VORTEX - a computer-simulation model for population viability analysis. *Wildlife Research*, **20:** 45-65

Lacy, R.C. & Clark, T.W. (1988). Genetic variability in black-footed ferret populations: past, present and future. In: U.S. Seal, E.T. Thorne, M.A. Bogan & S.H. Anderson (eds.), *Conservation biology and the black-footed ferret*: 83-103. New Haven (Connecticut); Yale University Press.

Lacy, R.C. & Clark, T.W. (1993). Simulation modelling of American marten (*Martes americana*) populations - vulnerability to extinction. *Great Basin Naturalist*, **53:** 282-292.

Letcher, B.H., Priddy, J.A., Walters, J.R. & Crowder, L.B. (1998). An individual-based, spatially-explicit simulation model of the population dynamics of the endangered red-cockaded woodpecker, *Picoides borealis. Biological Conservation*, **86:** 1-14.

Levin, S.A. (1992). The problem of pattern and scale in ecology. *Ecology*, **73:** 1943-1967.

Li, W.J., Wang, W.J., Ma, Z.J. & Tang, H.X. (1997). A regression model for the spatial distribution of the Red-crowned Crane in Yancheng Biosphere Reserve, China. *Ecological Modelling*, **103:** 115-121.

Lima, S.L. & Zollner, P.A. (1996). Towards a behavioural ecology of ecological landscapes. *Trends in Ecology and Evolution*, **11:** 131-135.

Lindenmayer, D.B., Clark, T.W., Lacy, R.C., Thomas, V.C. (1993). Population viability analysis as a tool in wildlife conservation policy - with reference to Australia. *Environmental Management*, **17:** 745-758.

Lindenmayer, D.B., Burgman, M.A., Akcakaya, H.R, Lacy, R.C. & Possingham, H.P (1995). A review of the generic computer-programs ALEX, RAMAS/SPACE and VORTEX for modelling the viability of wildlife metapopulations. *Ecological Modelling*, **82:** 161-174.

Liu, J.G., Dunning, J.B & Pulliam, H.R. (1995). Potential effects of a forest management plan on Bachman sparrows *Aimophila aestivalis* - linking a spatially explicit model with GIS. *Conservation Biology*, **9:** 62-65.

Lodé, T. (1997). Trophic status and feeding habits of the European polecat *Mustela putorius* L. 1758. *Mammal Review*, **27:** 177-184.

Lombard, A.T. (1993). Multispecies conservation, advanced computer architecture and GIS - where are we today? *South African Journal of Science*, **89:** 415-418.

Lurz, P.W.W., Garson, P.J. & Rushton, S.P. (1995). The ecology of squirrels in spruce dominated plantations: implications for forest management. *Forest Ecology and Management*, **79:** 79-90.

MacDonald, D.W., Mace, G. & Rushton, S.P. (1998). *Proposals for the future monitoring of British mammals.* London; Joint Nature Conservation Committee & Department of the Environment, Transport & the Regions.

Mace, R.D., Waller, J.S., Manley, T.L., Lyon, L.J. & Zuuring, H. (1996). Relationships among grizzly bears, roads and habitat in the Swan Mountains, Montana. *Journal of Applied Ecology*, **33:** 1395-1404.

Maehr, D.S. & Cox J.A. (1995). Landscape features and panthers in Florida. *Conservation Biology*, **9:** 1008-1019.

Maguire, D.J., Goodchild, M.F. & Rhind, D.W. (1991). *Geographical Information Systems.* London; Longman Scientific & Technical.

Mason, C.F. & MacDonald, S.M. (1994). *Status and conservation needs of the otter* (*Lutra lutra*) *in the western Palaearctic* (*Nature and Environment, No. 67*). Strasbourg; Council of Europe Press.

McArdle, B.H., Hewitt, J.E. & Thrush, S.F. (1997). Pattern from process: it is not as easy as it looks. *Journal of Experimental Marine Biology and Ecology*, **216:** 229-242.

McCullagh, P. & Nelder, J.A. (1983). *Generalised linear models*. London; Chapman & Hall.

Menon, S. & Bawa, K.S. (1997). Applications of geographic information systems, remote-sensing, and a landscape ecology approach to biodiversity conservation in the Western Ghats. *Current Science*, **73**: 134-145.

Merrill, T, Wright, R.G. & Scott, J.M. (1995). Using ecological criteria to evaluate wilderness planning options in Idaho. *Environmental Management*, **19**: 815-825.

Metz, J.A.J. & Diekmann, O. (Eds.) (1986). *The dynamics of physiological structured populations* (*Lecture Notes in Biomathematics 68*). Berlin; Springer-Verlag.

Miller, P.S. (1995). The PHVA process: linking small population management with wildlife conservation. *Proceedings of the International Conference and Workshop on Conservation Biology, Kuching, Sarawak, Malaysia*: unpaginated abstract.

Mladenoff, D.J. & Sickley, T.A. (1998). Assessing potential grey wolf restoration in the northeastern United States: a spatial prediction of favorable habitat and potential population levels. *Journal of Wildlife Management*, **62**: 1-10.

Moen, R., Pastor, J. & Cohen, Y. (1997). A spatially explicit model of moose foraging and energetics. *Ecology*, **78**: 505-521.

Naesset, E. (1997). Geographical Information Systems in long-term forest management and planning with special reference to preservation of biological diversity: a review. *Forest Ecology and Management*, **93**: 121-136.

Neal, E. (1986). *The natural history of badgers*. Beckenham; Croom Helm.

Nepal, S.K. & Weber, K.E. (1994). A buffer zone for biodiversity conservation - viability of the concept in Nepal Royal Chitwan National Park. *Environmental Conservation*, **21**: 333-341.

Norton, T.W. & Possingham, H.P. (1993). Wildlife modelling for biodiversity conservation. In: A.J. Jakeman, M.B. Beck & M.J. McAleer (eds.), *Modelling change in environmental systems*: 243-266. Chichester; John Wiley & Sons.

Paragi, T.F., Johnson. W.N., Katnik, D.D. & Magoun, A.J. (1996). Marten selection of post-fire seres in the Alaskan taiga. *Canadian Journal of Zoology*, **74**: 2226-2237.

Pereira, J.M.C. & Itami, R.M. (1991). GIS-based habitat modeling using logistic multiple regression: a case study of the Mt Graham red squirrel. *Photogrammetric Engineering and Remote Sensing*, **57**: 1475-1486.

Pollard, E., Hooper, M.D. & Moore, N.W. (1974). *Hedges*. London; Collins.

Pulliam, H.R., Dunning, J.B. & Liu, J.G. (1992). Population dynamics in complex landscapes. *Ecological Applications*, **2**: 165-177.

Reading, R.P & Matchett, R. (1997). Attributes of black-tailed prairie dog colonies in north central Montana. *Journal of Wildlife Management*, **61**: 664-673.

Rempel, R.S., Elkie, P.C., Rodgers, A.R. & Gluck, M.J. (1997). Timber-management and natural-disturbance effects on moose habitat: landscape evaluation. *Journal of Wildlife Management*, **61**: 517-524.

Robel, J., Fox, L.B. & Kemp, K.E. (1993). Relationship between habitat suitability index values and ground counts of beaver colonies in Kansas. *Wildlife Society Bulletin*, **21**: 415-421.

Robitaille, J. (1998). American marten, *Martes americana*, winter habitat studies in Ontario, Canada. In: S. Reig (ed.), *Abstracts of the Euro-American Mammal Congress, Santiago de Compostela, Spain*: 170 (abstract).

Root, K.V. (1998). Evaluating the effects of habitat quality, connectivity, and catastrophes on a threatened species. *Ecological Applications*, **8**: 854-865.

Rushton, S.P., Lurz, P.W.W., Fuller, R. & Garson, P.J. (1997). Modelling the distribution of the red squirrel at the landscape scale: a combined GIS and population dynamics approach. *Journal of Applied Ecology*, **34**: 1137-1154.

Schneider, R.R & Yodzis, P. (1994). Extinction dynamics in the American marten (*Martes americana*). *Conservation Biology*, **8**: 1058-1068.

Scott, J.M., Davis, F., Csuti, B., Noss, R., Butterfield, B., Groves, C., Anderson, H., Caicco, S., Derchia, F., Edwards, T.C., Ulliman, J. & Wright, R.G. (1993). GAP Analysis - a geographic approach to protection of ecological diversity. *Wildlife Monographs*, **123**: 1-41.

Smith, A.P., Horning, N. & Moore, D. (1997). Regional biodiversity planning and lemur conservation with GIS in western Madagascar. *Conservation Biology*, **11**: 498-512.

Smith, G.C., Richards, M.S., Clifton-Hadley, R.S. & Cheeseman, C.L. (1995). Modeling bovine tuberculosis in badgers in England: preliminary results. *Mammalia*, **59**: 639-650.

Smith, G.C., Cheeseman, C.L. & Clifton-Hadley, R.S. (1997). Modelling the control of bovine tuberculosis in badgers in England: culling and the release of lactating females. *Journal of Applied Ecology*, **34:** 1375-1386.

Starfield, A.M. & Bleloch, L. (1986). *Building models for conservation and wildlife management* (2nd ed.). New York; MacMillan Press.

Starfield, A.M. (1997). A pragmatic approach to modelling for wildlife management. *Journal of Wildlife Management*, **61:** 261-270.

Strickland, M.A. (1994). Harvest management of fishers and American martens. In: S.W. Buskirk, A.S. Harestad, M.G. Raphael & R.A. Powell (eds.), *Martens, sables and fishers: biology and conservation*: 149-164. Ithaca (NY): Cornell University Press.

Swinton, J., Tuyttens, F., Macdonald, D. Nokes, D.J., Cheeseman, C.L. & Clifton-Hadley, R.S. (1997). A comparison of fertility control of bovine tuberculosis in badgers: the impact of perturbation induced transmission. *Philosophical Transactions of the Royal Society of London (Series B)*, **352:** 619-631.

Tabachnick, B.G. & Fidell, L.S. (1996). *Using multivariate statistics* (3rd ed.). New York; Harper Collins.

Thomasma, L.E., Drummer, T.D. & Peterson, R.O. (1991). Testing the habitat suitability index model for the fisher. *Wildlife Society Bulletin*, **19:** 291-297.

Thompson, I.D. & Welsh, D.A. (1993). Integrated resource management in boreal forest ecosystems - impediments and solutions. *Forestry Chronicle*, **69:** 32-39.

Tischendorf, L. (1997). Modelling individual movements in heterogeneous landscapes: potentials of a new approach. *Ecological Modelling*, **103:** 33-42.

Turner, M.G., Arthaud, G.J., Engstrom, R.T., Hejl, S.J., Liu, J.G., Loeb, S. & McKelvey, K. (1995). Usefulness of spatially explicit population models in land management. *Ecological Applications*, **5:** 12-16.

Upton, G. & Fingleton, B. (1985). *Spatial data analysis by example, Vol. 1*. Chichester; John Wiley & Sons.

van Deelen, T.R., McKinney, L.B., Joselyn, M.G. & Buhnerkempe, J.E. (1997). Can we restore elk to southern Illinois? The use of existing digital land-cover data to evaluate potential habitat. *Wildlife Society Bulletin*, **25:** 886-894.

van Ewijk, K. Y., Knol, A.P. & de Jong, R.C.C.M. (1997). An otter PVA as a preparation of a reintroduction experiment in The Netherlands. *Zeitschrift für Säugetierkunde*, **62** (Suppl 2)**:** 238-242.

Vanlatesteijn, H.C. (1995). Assessment of future options for land use in the European Community. *Ecological Engineering*, **4:** 211-222.

Veitch, N., Webb N.R.& Wyatt, B.K. (1995). The application of geographic information-systems and remotely-sensed data to the conservation of heathland fragments. *Biological Conservation*, **72:** 91-97.

Wadsworth, R. & Treweek, J. (1999). *Geographical Information Systems for ecology: an introduction.* Essex; Longman Scientific & Technical.

Weber, D. (1989). Zur Populationsbiologie Schweizerischer Iltisse (*Mustela putorius* L.). *Zeitschrift für Jagdwissenschaft*, **35:** 86-89.

Weiss, S.B & Weiss, A.D. (1998). Landscape-level phenology of a threatened butterfly: a GIS-based modeling approach. *Ecosystems*, **1:** 299-309.

Wennergren, U., Ruckelshaus, M. & Kareiva, P. (1995). The promise and limitations of spatial models in conservation biology. *Oikos*, **74:** 349-356

Westervelt, J.M., Shapiro, M., Goran, W. & Geredes, D. (1990). *Geographic Resource Analysis Support System. Version 4.0 - Users Reference Manual* (*USACERL Report N-87/22*). Washington (DC); United States Army Construction Engineering Research Laboratory.

White, P.C.L. & Harris, S. (1995). Bovine tuberculosis in badger (*Meles meles*) populations in southwest England: the use of a spatial stochastic simulation model to understand the dynamics of the disease. *Philosophical Transactions of the Royal Society of London (Series B)*, **349:** 391-413.

Wiens, J.A., Stenseth, N., Van Horne, B. & Ims, R.A. (1993). Ecological mechanisms and landscape ecology. *Oikos*, **66:** 369-380.

Witteman, G.J. & Gilpin, M. (1995). RAMAS METAPOP - Viability analysis for stage-structured metapopulations. *Quarterly Review of Biology*, **70:** 381-382.

Worrall, L. & Bond, D. (1997). Geographical Information Systems, spatial analysis and public policy: the British experience. *International Statistical Review*, **65:** 365-379.

Wu, J.G. & Levin, S.A. (1997). A patch-based spatial modeling approach: conceptual framework and simulation scheme. *Ecological Modelling*, **101:** 325-346.

Wu, Y.P, Turner, M.G, Wallace, L.L, Romme, W.H. (1996). Elk survival following the 1988 Yellowstone fires: a simulation experiment. *Natural Areas Journal*, **16:** 198-207.

Yonzon, P.B. & Hunter, M.L. (1991). Conservation of red panda *Ailurus fulgens. Biological Conservation*, **57:** 1-11.

Zielinski, W.J. & Stauffer, H.B. (1996). Monitoring *Martes* populations in California: survey design and power analysis. *Ecological Applications*, **6:** 1254-1267.

CHAPTER 13

A spatial analysis of mustelid distributions in northern Italy

Lorenzo Fornasari*, Luciano Bani, Ivan Bonfanti, Elisabetta de Carli & Renato Massa

Abstract

We performed a pilot survey of carnivores in the north-western section of Lombardy, northern Italy (area = c. 4,000 km^2). The study area ranges from the densely populated, agricultural and industrial Po Valley to the broad-leaved woodlands of the central Alps. Seven carnivorous mammal species can be found here, including six mustelids (stoat, *Mustela erminea*, weasel, *Mustela nivalis*, European polecat, *Mustela putorius*, pine marten, *Martes martes*, stone marten, *Martes foina*, and Eurasian badger, *Meles meles*) plus one canid, the red fox, *Vulpes vulpes*. Our survey was conducted in 1997 using one kilometre-long line transects, with censuses performed within 375 one km^2 grid squares, chosen by a random sampling design. Red fox was the most widespread species, martens and European badger were common, weasel was moderately rare and stoat and European polecat were very rare. Distributional data were analysed at three different scales: habitat, ecomosaic and landscape. Among the mustelids, only the martens and stoat were found in different natural habitats in alpine landscapes, while the polecat was found only in wooded habitats (and woodland-dominated ecomosaics) close to certain lakes. Weasel and badger selected for woodland at each level, but they appeared to be associated with the woods fractal dimension or woods interconnection, respectively. Non-alpine marten records (mainly interpreted as representing stone marten) appeared associated with red fox in landscape and ecomosaic selection (agricultural areas) but showed different habitat selection (small woods *vs.* open habitats). All species (including red fox) were negatively affected by the proximity of urban areas. We suggest that the distribution of key species such as badger may be used to delineate core areas and corridors for carnivore conservation within human-modified landscapes.

Introduction

The massive rate of anthropogenic habitat alteration has made interactions across multiple landscape scales into a major topic in wildlife conservation. In fact, long term species population persistence in human-modified landscapes largely relates to theoretical concepts such as metapopulation dynamics or source-sink dynamics (e.g. Pulliam, 1988; Dunning *et al.*, 1992; Hastings & Harrison, 1994). Moreover, recent research shows that organisms within fragmented landscapes may be affected by landscape structure in a scale-dependent way; *i.e.* the same species may have different relationships, operating at different levels, within the same habitat type

---

* Corresponding author.

Mustelids in a modern world
Management and conservation aspects of small carnivore: human interactions
edited by Huw I. Griffiths, pp. 201–215
© 2000 Backhuys Publishers, Leiden, The Netherlands

(e.g. Wiens *et al.*, 1987). The effects of coarse-scale fragmentation can easily be seen only through "habitat specialist" species with extensive area requirements. The identification of these so-called "umbrella species" may thus be crucial for effective conservation planning (Noss & Cooperrider, 1994; Noss *et al.*, 1996).

Mustelid carnivores are known to be specialists from the point of view of habitat selection or feeding habits. According to Erlinge (1986) "most of the medium- and large-sized mustelids are habitat-specific, and the various species are adapted to different habitats: polecats to grasslands, sable and martens to woodlands, minks to marshes and semi-aquatic habitats, and the otter to aquatic habitats". Moreover, "the smaller-sized species (weasel, stoat) show a clear tendency towards food specialization". In human-dominated environments, the shift from small-scale, heterogeneous landscapes to large-scale, homogeneous ones, is detrimental to such species, pushing them towards lower population densities through many instances of local sub-population extinction. To identify the environmental correlates of such density changes, we organised a carnivore survey in an extensively human-modified landscape: north-western Lombardy.

General features

Lombardy in one of the most populated regions of Europe, with an overall average of 373 inhabitants/km^2, and peaking at more than 1,800 inhabitants/km^2 for the entirety of the Province of Milano (Milan). On the other hand, northern Lombardy lies in the central section of the southern Alps, and has a wide range of natural and semi-natural habitats, from the farmlands of the Po Valley to alpine tundra, through broad-leaved and coniferous woods. From the lowland to 1,000 m asl the potential vegetation is represented by heliophilous ("sun-loving") broad-leaved woodland, and between 1,000-2,200 m asl by skiophilous ("shade-loving") broad-leaved and coniferous woodlands. Above 2,200 m are subalpine shrubland and grassland, and alpine tundra.

We selected the north-western part of Lombardy as being an ideal study area with a clear-cut habitat gradient. This area (*c.* 4,000 km^2) ranges between 100-2,600 m asl, from the densely populated, agricultural and industrial Po Valley (immediately north of Milano), to the woodlands of the central Alps.

Of a total of 11 European mustelid species, Italy is host to seven, of which three are considered to be of conservation concern within Italy's national legislation. In northern Italy the otter almost became extinct during the 1970s (Spagnesi & Cagnolaro, 1981), the polecat is showing a general decline (AA.VV., 1992) and the pine marten is confined to a very limited range (Toschi, 1960). The carnivore fauna of the area also includes badger, stone marten, weasel, stoat and one canid, the red fox (Piozzi, 1993).

Our survey was conducted in 1997 by censusing one kilometre line transects performed within one km^2 grid squares as determined by a random sampling design within all the squares reported on regional thematic maps (scale = 1: 50,000). Transect surveys were performed by looking for any carnivore track or sign, and particularly scats. Similar techniques previously have been used for several groups of mammals, for example ungulates (Gaillard *et al.*, 1993), squirrels (Purroy & Rey,

1974) and other rodents (Guédon & Pascal, 1992), and canids (Andelt & Andelt, 1984; Cavallini, 1994). Each transect was divided into five tracts, each 200 m long. 375 squares were censused in total.

Identification of mustelid species

Some of the carnivore species' signs in the area are very easy to identify. Badger latrines and droppings are unmistakable, and their setts are easily checked for possible occupation by red fox (Kruuk, 1989). Badger tracks also are easily identified due to their clearly defined "hand-like" pawprint pattern (Bang & Dahlstrom, 1974). Red fox also are recognisable on the basis of their typically canid-type tracks and scats, although care is needed to exclude the more rounded tracks of small domestic dogs (Bang & Dahlstrom, 1974).

The field signs of the other mustelids require a more detailed analysis. The size of droppings is usually sufficient to allow discrimination between medium-sized and small-sized mustelid species. Amongst medium-sized species, the tracks of stone marten may differ from those of pine marten, despite their similar overall shape. Stone marten tracks are usually very well defined, whilst those of pine marten are less clear due to the presence of hairs under the paw (Bang & Dahlstrom, 1974). For the exact identification of these species, scat content analysis often is needed. Mustelids usually perform self-grooming, so that some body hairs may become ingested. By collecting scats and soaking them for two weeks in an ethanol bath, it is possible to separate hairs from other organic remains, prior to choosing isolated long hairs from the particular carnivore involved (Twigg, 1975). Hairs can be examined by mounting them on microscope slides as described by Teerink (1991). Here the hair is placed on an object glass so that its profile stands out as clearly as possible. Next, without the use of any mounting medium, a cover slip with a small drop of glue in each corner, is placed over the hair. Hair preparations were viewed under a Zeiss KF 10 x 3.2-40 stereomicroscope. Following Teerink (1991) we refer to the distal part of the hair as the shield, and to its proximal part as the shaft.

Stoat hairs differ from those of weasel by the medullar margins in the thickest part of the shield showing rather deep rather than shallow incisions (Teerink, 1991). In the stoat the medulla also has a more "dense" appearance (Keller, 1981); Teerink (1991) also mentions counting less than 40 or 45-50 bulges protruding into the cortex along *c.* 300 µm, respectively. The overhairs of the polecat are identified easily by the irregular medullary pigmentation along the shield where dark parts alternate with light (Teerink, 1991). The pine marten differs from the stone marten in the geometrical pattern of the medulla: the former has dark transverse medullar cells, often lying approximately perpendicular to the cortex of the central shield, whereas in the latter they have an oblique orientation (Keller, 1981; Teerink, 1991). Despite these differences, the discrimination of the two marten species from hair examination is often uncertain; as a result we have often classified them as "martens" within a single grouping. However, in the actual study area the pine marten (and the stoat) are known definitely to be absent from the lowlands below 1,000 m (Piozzi, 1993), so that the "martens" grouping may be regarded as being composed mainly of stone marten.

A multi-scaled approach

According to recent developments in landscape ecology, a multi-scaled approach is necessary to understand the responses of medium-sized carnivores to habitat changes, as mainly represented in human modified lands by forest fragmentation (e.g. Buskirk, 1992). As shown by Bissonette & Broekhuizen (1995) habitat fragmentation is one of the "most obvious characteristics that appear to influence marten numbers and distribution", but "it is not sufficient to take only a large-scale perspective"; thus a multi-scale approach is needed for the objective determination of habitat preferences. The necessity of having multiple-scale information on habitat requirements for conserving forest carnivores also has been stressed by Ruggiero *et al.* (1988). To fulfil this need, we took into account environmental data at three different levels (see Ruggiero *et al.*, 1988): (1) the habitat level (*i.e.* "site"), (2) the ecomosaic level (*i.e.* "plot"), and (3) the landscape level.

The local characteristics of each "site" are obviously important in determining whether they are selected positively or negatively (for or against) by each species. Habitat data were collected during field surveys. The characteristics of the "site" were assessed by recording the predominant habitat type (chosen from more than 100 habitat types) along each 200 m survey tract. Successive analyses were performed assembling all the recorded habitat types into eight different habitat categories: urban, rural, wetland, farmland, artificial woodlots, lowland woods, mountain woods and alpine habitats.

The different habitats found around the "site" contribute to the characterisation of the ecomosaic at the level of the plot. The carnivore assemblage present at each "site" is also dependent on the composition and distribution of the neighbouring habitats because of their potential value to the species (see Dunning *et al.*, 1992). Plots were selected from a one km^2 grid superimposed on regional thematic maps. Ecomosaic characteristics were identified by evaluating, within each plot, the percentage occurrence of the 55 different habitat variables listed in an established regional system of habitat classification, as reported on the maps and assembled into eight main categories: urban, farmland, woodland, uncultivated areas, wetland, barren land, glaciers, railways and arterial roads.

The influence of some habitat categories also is dependent on patch size and shape, as stated by metapopulation theory (e.g. Levins, 1970). At the landscape level, habitat fragmentation influences population size through habitat loss, thus decreasing the size of habitat patches and increasing their isolation (Wilcox & Murphy, 1985). As woodland rarefaction is one of the main conservation problems in the study area (Massa *et al.*, 1998), and also because of urban expansion, we focused our interest in landscape patterns on wooded and urban patches. We defined wooded cells as those containing at least 40% of any kind of woodland – this 40% threshold being derived from the empirical measures of Andrén (1994). Below this threshold the effects of habitat fragmentation may become apparent in both mammal and bird species. Moreover, we defined urban cells as those containing at least 20% urban habitat by assuming that this percentage occupation is enough to disturb landscape use by carnivores.

The utility of Geographic Information Systems (GIS) in the analysis of habitat suitability for wildlife species has been discussed by Donovan *et al.* (1987). By using a GIS (ArcView 3.0a), contiguous cells were gathered into woodland patches, identifying 87 wooded patches with an area equal to or larger than two km². Landscape effects were evaluated by considering the size, shape, and distance between those different patches. For each woodland patch we calculated its area, perimeter, minimum distance from the closest large wood, fractal dimension (a logarithmic relationship between patch perimeter and area) and degrees of interaction and isolation (see explanation below – these depend on size and distance from other wood patches in the study area) as follows:

Area $\qquad\qquad A = \Sigma\, a$

Where A is the total patch area and a is the area of a single wooded cell (*i.e.* one km²).

Perimeter $\qquad\qquad P = \Sigma\, s$

Where P is the patch perimeter and s is the length of each free side of a wooded cell (*i.e.* one km).

Fractal dimension $\qquad\qquad D = 2\ln(P/4) / \ln(A)$

Where D is the fractal dimension of a patch, A is the total patch area and P the total patch perimeter. The fractal dimension conveniently describes the irregular pattern of the patch shape. This estimation of the fractal dimension for continuous grouping of grid cells can be derived from Peitgen & Saupe's (1988) original equation.

Interaction $\qquad\qquad I = \Sigma\, (A/d^2)$

Where I is the degree of interaction of a given patch with all the neighbouring patches, A is the area of any neighbouring patch, and d is the distance between the edges of the given patch and any other patch (see Whitcomb *et al.*, 1981).

Isolation $\qquad\qquad r = 1/n \,\Sigma\, d$

Where r is an index of the isolation of a given patch, n is the number of neighbouring patches considered, d is the distance between the edges of the patch under consideration and any other patch (Forman & Godron, 1986).

Urban patches were taken into account by evaluating "site" occupancy according to their minimum distance from each of the surveyed squares. A total of 63 urban patches were identified.

Carnivore distributions

As a result of our field survey, we found carnivore tracks or signs in 305 transects (*i.e.* 903 tracts) out of a total of 375 transects (*i.e.* 1870 tracts). Five tracts were not searched due to the presence of landslides or over-dense vegetation. Species determinations were impossible in 22 cases. "Marten" observations in alpine areas were separated from those made on hills and in the lowlands and here are treated as pine marten.

Red fox appeared to be the most widespread species. The badger and martens were common (mainly because of the stone marten), weasel were moderately rare, but stoat and polecat were very rare (Table 1). Figure 1 shows the distribution of carnivores recorded within the study area in relation to woodland cover. This parameter is crucial in the distribution of the entire mustelid assemblage but, in contrast, red fox distribution also is widespread throughout the other habitats. The co-occurrence

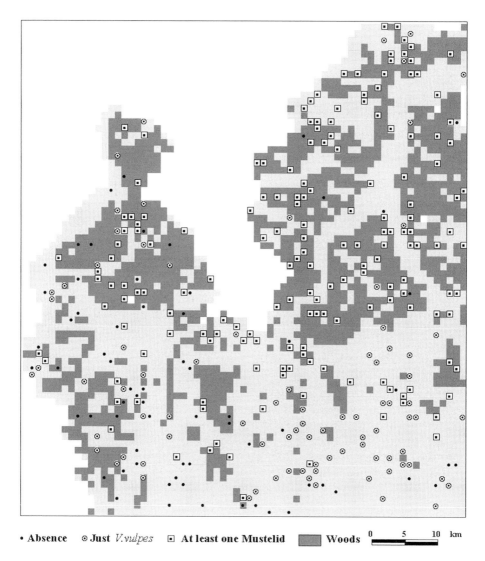

• **Absence**   ⊙ **Just** *V.vulpes*   ▣ **At least one Mustelid**   ▨ **Woods**   0   5   10   km

Fig. 1. Distribution of carnivore records in the study area according to the distribution of wooded cells (wood coverage >40%). The presence of at least one mustelid species is highlighted.

of the different species was evaluated by Complete Linkage Cluster Analysis (Gauch, 1982) (Fig. 2). In Cluster Analysis stoat segregate together with the alpine observations of marten. These are linked to particular, uncommon plot characteristics which are restricted to the northern part of our study area; notably stoat showed a significant correlation with the percentage of rocky habitat (r = 0.35, p << 0.01), whilst observations of marten correlated with the percentage of coniferous woods

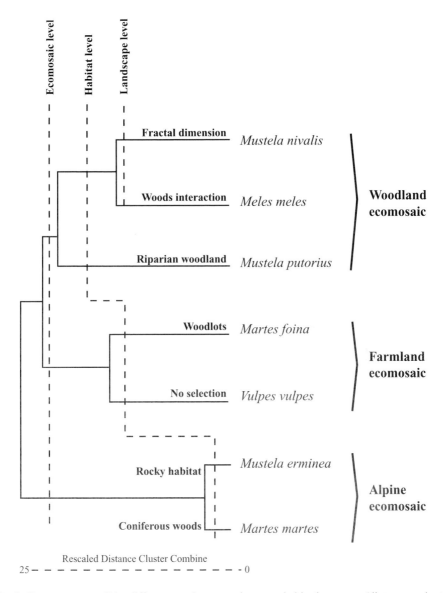

Fig. 2. Co-occurrence of the different carnivore species recorded in the survey (distance evaluated by Spearman's Rank Correlation, clustering by Complete Linkage (Gauch, 1982). See text for details.

(r = 0.20, p <<0.01). Both rocky habitats and coniferous woods are typical components of the alpine ecomosaic (Fig. 3). Looking at "site" characteristics, stoat was
also found in mountain shrubland with green alder, *Alnus viridis*, and dwarf mountain pine, *Pinus mugo*, and in alpine pasture. Signs of pine marten were found in the
same habitats, as well as in woods dominated by spruce, *Picea abies*, and birch,
Betula spp., or occasionally in mixed broad-leaved woods.

Martes martes

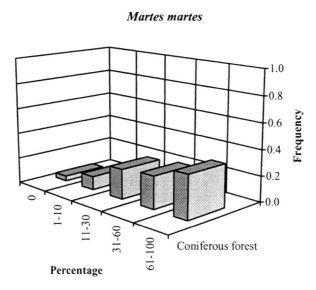

Mustela erminea

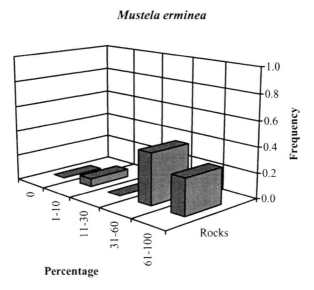

Fig. 3. Relationship between records of "martens" or stoat and alpine habitats at the ecomosaic
level.

Table 1. Numbers of occupied line transects and frequencies of carnivore species recorded during this survey.

Species	Line transects	Frequency
Red fox, *Vulpes vulpes*	272	72.5 %
Lowland martens, *Martes foina*	109	29.0 %
Badger, *Meles meles*	106	28.3 %
Weasel, *Mustela nivalis*	58	15.5 %
Alpine martens, *Martes martes, M. foina*	20	5.3 %
Stoat, *Mustela erminea*	6	1.6 %
European polecat, *Mustela putorius*	3	0.8 %

Stone marten and red fox share a separate pattern of ecomosaic occupation, with a general tolerance to high percentages of farmland and urbanisation (unless the degree of urbanisation is very high) (Fig. 4). On the other hand, within the same farmland dominated landscape, these two species show a quite different habitat ("site") selection: the highest recorded frequency of red fox is related to farmland habitat, while the highest recorded frequency of stone marten is linked to tree cover in both artificial and semi-natural woodlots (Fig. 5).

The three remaining species' distributions are related to woodland ecomosaics. Amongst them, polecat was found (just three times) in wooded plots close to three different low-lying (*i.e.* <300 m) lakes (Lago di Como, Lago di Mezzola and Lago di Lugano). Badger and weasel were found in plots characterised by high coverages of coniferous or deciduous woodland (Fig. 4) and low degrees of urbanisation and cultivation. These two species occupy "sites" in several woodland types, from oak, *Quercus* spp., and sweet chestnut, *Castanea sativa*, woods in the lowland, to beech, *Fagus sylvatica*, and spruce woods in the mountains. On the other hand, weasel and badger show some very interesting differences at the level of landscape utilisation. For badger, highly significant correlation values were found with minimum distance and interaction, underlining the link between this species and continuous wooded habitats (Table 2). Woodlot area also showed a significant relationship with the frequency of occurrence of badger; a similar negative relationship between badger and habitat fragmentation already has been shown in the Netherlands by Knaapen *et al.* (1995). In the case of the weasel we found a highly significant relationship with area, perimeter and fractal dimension – a typical situation for an "edge" species that is related to "good" habitats. At the level of ecomosaic selection, red fox and stone marten did not show any significant relationship to these parameters.

Habitat selection

The main divisions in habitat selection seem to occur at the ecomosaic level. However, between pairs of "similar" species, additional differences mainly derive from "site" characteristics, whilst the effect of landscape is evident only for those species occupying woodland habitat types in the densely populated lowlands. In this sense, habitat fragmentation is affecting mustelid distributions, both for core habitat species (badger) and ecotonal species (weasel). Moreover, at the landscape level

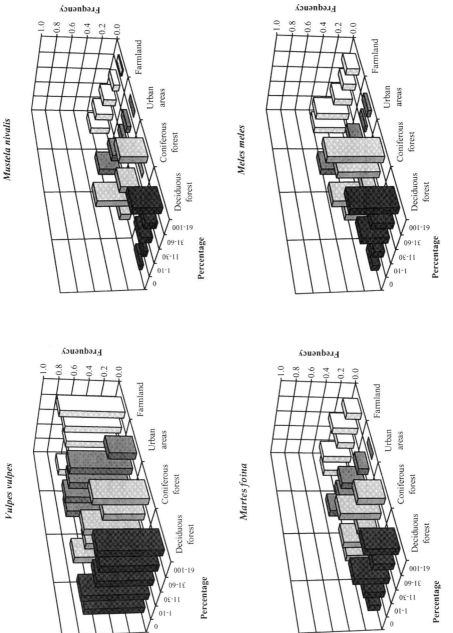

Fig. 4. Relationship between records of the four commonest species and the main four habitat categories at the ecomosaic level.

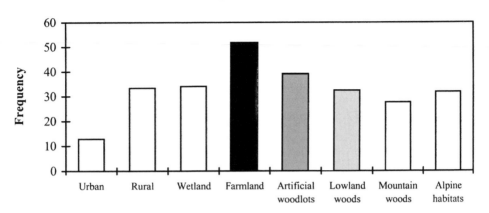

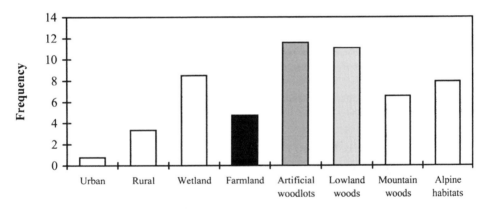

Fig. 5. Relationship between red fox or stone marten and the eight habitat categories at the level of "site".

Table 2. Relationship between records of the four commonest species and woodlot parameters (landscape level). Probabilities: * = P < 0.05, ** = P < 0.01

	V. vulpes	*M. foina*	*M. meles*	*M. nivalis*
Area	-0.117	0.132	0.383 *	0.601 **
Minimum distance	0.054	-0.269	-0.652 **	-0.419 *
Fractal dimension	-0.048	0.168	0.373 *	0.502 **
Interaction	-0.084	0.145	0.488 **	0.258
Isolation	0.069	-0.292	0.084	-0.180
Perimeter	-0.115	0.116	0.389 *	0.586 **

a common pattern for all carnivores (including the previous two species) was the negative relationship between frequency of occurrence and proximity to urban patches (*i.e.* unsuitable habitats and barriers to dispersal) as shown in Fig. 6.

To date much research on habitat connectivity has investigated the importance of linkages between patches of mature habitat, especially in anthropogenically fragmented forest. This approach was used in Downes *et al.*'s (1997) study of Australian mammals, and is very important in the Wildlands Project, which uses carnivore species' requirements for creating corridors among protected areas throughout North America (Noss, 1992, 1995). The fundamental importance of wildlife corridors for mammal dispersal has been stressed by several authors (e.g. Saunders & Hobbs, 1991; Noss & Coperrider, 1994; Tiebout & Anderson, 1997). Wildlife corridors that connect patches of remnant habitat can function as pathways for the movement and exchange of individuals amongst isolated remnant populations, thereby assisting in the maintenance of both populations and regional biodiversity (Harris, 1984; Simberloff, 1988). These corridors can be most effective when they are of sufficient size and habitat quality to support a resident population of the target species (Bennet, 1990; Downes *et al.*, 1997).

Even highly mobile organisms such as passerine birds suffer from the effects of habitat fragmentation. The decrease in forest coverage in the lowlands of northern Italy has caused significant density decreases and a number of local extinction of forest interior bird species, even when the overall amount of wood cover in the "plot" has remained the same (Massa *et al.*, 1998). In such situations, the pattern of

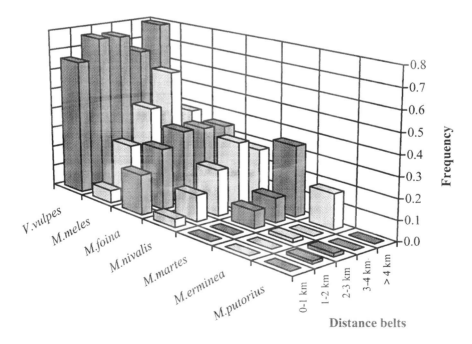

Fig. 6. Relationship between the occurrence of carnivore species and the minimum distance from urban patches (landscape level).

habitat use that we describe in the present paper may help in identifying "umbrella species" for the development of a landscape strategy directed at animal community conservation. From this point of view the best example of a "focal species" amongst the Lombardy carnivores seems to be the badger. This is due to the high positive correlation of badger presence with woodlot size and continuity (as measured by the parameters interaction and minimum distance).

By looking at the badger's distribution (Fig. 7) it becomes apparent how well this species fits with "core" woodland distribution. Amongst the other mustelid species weasel behaves as an edge species, polecat presently is too rare, stone marten is too

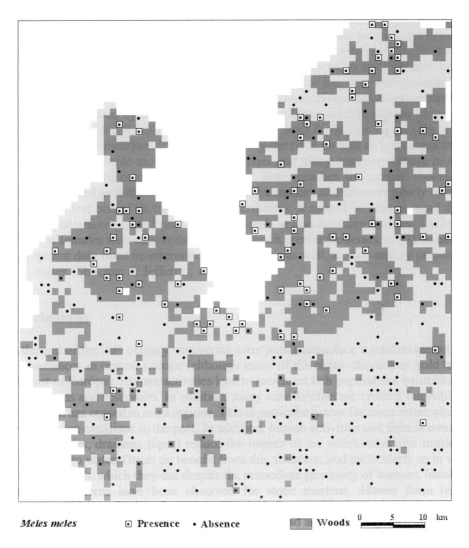

Meles meles   ▣ **Presence**   • **Absence**   ▨▨ **Woods** 0   5   10 km

Fig. 7. Distribution of badger records, according to the distribution of wooded cells (wood coverage >40%).

tolerant of human land-use, and pine marten and stoat select for different geographic areas in the alpine part of the region. In a situation such as this, the badger can be identified as an "umbrella" species in the sense of Lambeck (1997), *i.e.* as a species whose requirements encapsulate the needs of other species. The badger here appears as a forest interior species, so that planning core areas and corridors for its conservation may positively affect the conservation of the entire guild of forest mammals and birds.

A strategy for improving conservation planning should be based on the biological function desired of the landscape (Buchanan *et al.*, 1998). In our case, if the challenge of conserving the vertebrates of the interior forest has to be met, landscape connectivity has to be increased. In a similar case in the Netherlands, Knaapen *et al.* (1995) suggest a forecasting scenario that uses just the requirements of badger for planning landscape connectivity improvements. Here the main goal should be the conservation and restoration of potential habitats, together with restoration or development of dispersal corridors (woodlots, hedgerows) and the construction of tunnels or "ecoducts" to allow roads to be crossed. The gathering of spatial and habitat data into landscape scenarios and management plans will be of the greatest importance in the coming decades if European biodiversity is to be conserved.

References

AA.VV. (1992). *Relazione sullo stato dell'ambiente.* Roma; Istituto Poligrafico e Zecca dello Stato.

Andelt, W.F. & Andelt, S.H. (1984). Diet bias in deposition-rate surveys of coyote density. *Wildlife Society Bulletin*, **12**: 74-77.

Andrén, H. (1994). Effects of habitat fragmentation on birds and mammals in landscape with different proportion of suitable habitat: a review. *Oikos*, **71**: 355-366.

Bang, P. & Dahlstrom, P. (1974). *Animal tracks and signs.* Glasgow; Collins.

Bennett, A.F. (1990). *Habitat corridors: their role in wildlife management and conservation.* Melbourne; Arthur Rylah Institute for Environmental Research.

Bissonette, J.A. & Broekhuizen, S. (1995). *Martes* populations as indicators of habitat spatial patterns: the need for a multiscale approach. In W.Z. Lidicker Jnr. (ed.), *Landscape approaches in mammalian ecology and conservation*: 95-121. Minneapolis; University of Minnesota Press.

Buchanan, J.B., Fredrickson, R.J. & Seaman, D.E. (1998). Mitigation of habitat "take" and the Core Area Concept. *Conservation Biology*, **12**: 238-240.

Buskirk, S.W. (1992). Conserving circumboreal forests for martens and fishers. *Conservation Biology*, **6**: 318-320.

Cavallini, P. (1994). Faeces count as an index of fox abundance. *Acta Theriologica*, **39**: 417-424.

Donovan, M.L., Rabe, D.L. & Olson, C.E., Jnr. (1987). Use of Geographic Information Systems to develop habitat suitability models. *Wildlife Society Bulletin*, **15**: 574-579.

Downes, S.J., Handaside, K.A. & Elgar, M.A. (1997). The use of corridors by mammals in fragmented Australian eucalypt forests. *Conservation Biology*, **11**: 718-726.

Dunning, J.B., Danielson, B.J. & Pulliam, H.R. (1992). Ecological processes that affect populations in complex landscapes. *Oikos*, **65**: 169-175.

Erlinge, S. (1986). Specialists and generalists among the mustelids. *Lutra*, **29**: 5-11.

Forman, R.T.T. & Godron, M. (Eds.) (1986). *Landscape ecology.* New York; John Wiley.

Gaillard, J., Boutin, J. & Van Laere, G. (1993). Dénombrer les populations de chevreuils per l'utilisation du line transect. Etude de feasibilité. *Revue d'Ecologie*, **48**: 73-85.

Gauch, H.G. (1982). *Multivariate analysis in community ecology.* Cambridge; Cambridge University Press.

Guédon, G. & Pascal, M. (1992). Elément de validation d'une méthode d'échantilonage linéaire standardisée adaptée au campagnol provençal (*Pitymys duodecimcostatus*, De Sélys-Longchamps, 1839). *Revue d'Ecologie, La Terre et la Vie*, **47**: 85-102.

Harris, L.D. (1994). *The fragmented forest*. Chicago; University of Chicago Press.
Hastings, A. & Harrison, S. (1994). Metapopulation dynamics and genetics. *Annual Review of Ecology and Systematics*, **25**: 167-188.
Keller, A. (1981). Détèrmination des mammifères de la Suisse par leur pelage. V. Carnivora, Artiodactyla. *Revue Suisse de Zoologie*, **88**: 463-73.
Knaapen, J.P., van Engen, H.C., van Apeldoorn, R.C., Schippers, P. & Verboom, J. (1995). Badgers in the Netherlands: evaluation of scenarios with models. In: J.F.T. Schoute, P.A. Finke, F.R. Veeneklaas & H.P. Wolfert (eds.), *Scenario studies for the rural environment*: 549-554. Dordrecht; Kluwer Academic Publishers.
Kruuk, H. (1989). *The social badger: ecology and behaviour of a group-living carnivore (Meles meles)*. Oxford; Oxford University Press.
Lambeck, R.J. (1997). Focal species: a multi-species umbrella for nature conservation. *Conservation Biology*, **11**: 849-56.
Levins, R. (1970). Extinction. In: M. Gerstenhaber (ed.), *Some mathematical problems in biology (Lectures on Mathematics in Life Sciences 2)*: 77-107. Providence (Rhode Island); American Mathematical Society.
Massa, R., Bani, L., Bottoni, L. & Fornasari, L. (1998). An evaluation of lowland reserve effectiveness for forest bird conservation. *Biologia e Conservazione della Fauna*, **102**: (in press).
Noss, R.F. (1992). The Wildlands Project: land conservation strategy. *Wild Earth* (Special Issue): 10-25.
Noss, R.F. (1995). *Maintaining ecological integrity in representative reserve networks*. Toronto & Washington; World Wildlife Fund Canada/World Wildlife Fund US.
Noss, R.F. & Coperrider, A.Y. (1994). *Saving nature's legacy: protecting and restoring biodiversity*. Washington (DC); Island Press.
Noss, R.F., Quigley, H.B., Hornocker, M.G., Merrill, T. & Paquet, C. (1996). Conservation biology and carnivore conservation in the Rocky Mountains. *Conservation Biology*, **10**: 949-963.
Peitgen, H.O. & Saupe, D. (Eds.) (1988). *The science of fractal images*. Berlin; Springer-Verlag.
Piozzi, V. (1993). *Il "Progetto Atlante Mammiferi Lombardia": definizione metodologica ed applicazioni preliminari*. MSc thesis. Milano; Università degli Studi di Milano.
Pulliam, H.R. (1988). Sources, sinks, and population regulation. *American Naturalist*, **132**: 652-661.
Purroy, F.J. & Rey, J.M. (1974). Estudio ecologico y sistematico de la ardilla (*Sciurus vulgaris*) en Navarra: I) Distribucion. Densidad de poblaciones. Alimentacion. Actividad diaria y anual. *Boletin de la Estacion Central de Ecologia*, **3**: 71-82.
Ruggiero, L.F., Holthausen, R.S. & Marcot, B.G. (1988). Ecological dependency: the concept and its implications for research and management. *Transactions of the North American Wildlife and Natural Resources Conference*, **53**: 115-126.
Saunders, D.A. & Hobbs, R.J. (1991). *Nature conservation 2. The role of corridors*. Chipping Norton (New South Wales); Surrey Beatty & Sons.
Simberloff, D. (1988). The contribution of population and community biology to conservation science. *Annual Review of Ecology & Systematics*, **19**: 473-511.
Spagnesi, M. & Cagnolaro, L. (1981). Lontra. In: M. Pavan & M. Beretta Boera (eds.), *Distribuzione e biologia di 22 specie di mammiferi in Italia*: 95-101. Roma; Consiglio Nazionale delle Ricerche.
Teerink, B.J. (1991). *Hair of west European mammals*. Cambridge; Cambridge University Press.
Tiebout, H.M., III & Anderson, R.A. (1997). A comparison of corridors and intrinsic connectivity to promote dispersal in transient successional landscapes. *Conservation Biology*, **11**: 620-627.
Toschi, A. (1960). *Fauna d'Italia – Vol. VII – Mammalia (Lagomorpha – Rodentia – Carnivora – Ungulata – Cetacea)*. Bologna; Calderini.
Twigg, G.I. (1975). Finding mammals – their signs and remains. *Mammal Review*, **5**: 71-82.
Whitcomb, R.F., Lynch, J.F., Klimkiewicz, M.K., Robbins, C.S., Whitcomb, B.L. & Bystrak, D. (1981). Effects of forest fragmentation on avifauna of the eastern deciduous forest. In: R.L. Burgess & D.M. Sharpe (eds.), *Forest island dynamics in man-dominated landscapes*: 125-206. New York; Springer-Verlag.
Wilcox, B.A. & Murphy, D.D. (1985). Conservation strategy: the effects of fragmentation on extinction. *American Naturalist*, **125**: 879-887.
Wiens, J.A., Rotenberry, J.T. & Van Horne, B. (1987). Habitat occupancy patterns of North American shrubsteppe birds: the effect of spatial scale. *Oikos*, **48**: 132-147.

CHAPTER 14

Monitoring the very rare: pine marten populations in England and Wales

John E. Messenger & Johnny D.S. Birks

Abstract

The pine marten, *Martes martes*, is one of Britain's rarest carnivores. Exterminated from much of the island in the 19th century, it has been believed only to have survived through much of the 20th century as a relict population in Scotland. Over recent years, however, a continuous series of reports of martens by naturalists, foresters etc., has led to the suggestion that the pine marten also lives on in very small numbers in remote parts of northern England and Wales. Although their presence remains controversial, the probable existence of small, isolated, low-density populations is particularly significant given the present interest in restoring the marten to those areas from which it has been extirpated. The present study describes survey work being undertaken to investigate the presence and viability of marten populations in Britain outside of Scotland. We also highlight the difficulties associated with the quantifying the population distribution of very rare species, and present evidence for the continued presence of the pine marten outside Scotland.

Introduction

Following the Convention on Biological Diversity at the Earth Summit in Rio de Janeiro in 1992, attention has focused more closely on the need to monitor the status of scarce or vulnerable species. Associated with this is the thematic issue of biodiversity restoration, in which signatory states are required to attempt to recreate natural environments and biotic assemblages – restoring extirpated species where both necessary and practical.

The UK has recently proposed strategies for the long-term monitoring of its mammalian species (Macdonald *et al.*, 1999) and programmes for the reintroduction of several extirpated species are being evaluated at present (e.g. European beaver, *Castor fiber*; Macdonald *et al.*, 1995). Furthermore, there is growing public interest in the idea of biodiversity restoration, and in local-level species reintroductions in particular. This is because reintroduction programmes allow an unusual level of "grassroots" involvement by lay people, who feel that programmes such as these provide meaningful "hands-on" participation in the conservation experience (Griffiths *et al.*, 1996). Within this context, the collation of accurate data on species distributions and abundances is of paramount importance. There is a strong bioethical emphasis in the genetic aspects of population restoration (cf. the reintroduction of the red kite, *Milvus milvus*, to England; May *et al.*, 1993) and it is important that

Mustelids in a modern world
Management and conservation aspects of small carnivore: human interactions
edited by Huw I. Griffiths, pp. 217–230
© *2000 Backhuys Publishers, Leiden, The Netherlands*

introduced populations are genetically as close as possible to the original population. It is also crucial that reintroductions should not take place when relict (albeit small) populations persist still within the area in question (Griffiths *et al.*, 1996).

Within this context, carnivores present particular problems: carnivores are sometimes popular within the public's perception but also often are misidentified by them, whilst the species themselves usually live at relatively low population densities, are typically intelligent, alert and secretive, and have adaptively plastic behavioural and social patterns. For many mustelids, these aspects of the species' biology conspire to limit the range of workable monitoring approaches that are readily available. However, mustelids such as the pine marten, *Martes martes*, and the polecat, *Mustela putorius*, are amongst Britain's rarest species, with national population levels estimated at 3,650 (Harris *et al.*, 1995) and *c.* 38,000 (Birks & Kitchener, 1999) respectively. However, long-standing and effective monitoring programmes for mustelids (usually based on systematic searches for field signs) exist nationally only for otter, *Lutra lutra* (Strachan & Jefferies, 1996) and badger, *Meles meles* (Wilson *et al.*, 1997). Furthermore, as legal protection now prevents the killing of most British mustelids, indirect monitoring methods have tended to replace the more traditional approach based on game bag data (cf. Chanin & Jefferies, 1978). Despite this, gamekeepers' trapping records and hunters' bag data still are of value for assessing changes in some still-unprotected species, notably stoat, *Mustela erminea*, and weasel, *Mustela nivalis* (Tapper, 1992; McDonald & Murphy, this volume) and also in broad-scale, Europe-wide species monitoring (e.g. badger; Griffiths & Thomas, 1997).

The history of the pine marten in Britain is that it was well distributed throughout the mainland until about 1800, when declines and local extinctions are thought first to have occurred. These declines were probably due to direct persecution and habitat loss. The situation deteriorated during the 19th century when the effect of game keeping on the Victorian hunting estates began to cause serious declines in many of Britain's predatory birds and mammals. By the early part of the 20th century pine marten had become extinct throughout much of Britain, surviving only in the Scottish Highlands and a few of the less-populated areas of England and Wales (Langley & Yalden, 1977). Following the end of the First World War game keeping never returned to its pre-war levels, giving many of the by-now small populations of predators a chance to recover (Birks, 1993). The pine marten appears to be recovering well in Scotland (Balharry *et al.*, 1996) but this recovery is not evident in England and Wales, where small, possibly isolated, populations appear to survive (Velander, 1983; Strachan *et al.*, 1996). Some of these populations seem to be genuine relicts, but others may be the result of accidental or surreptitious reintroductions (Yalden, 1999). Exactly how rare the species is in England and Wales has been the subject of a lively debate, with current interest in promoting the recovery of British pine marten populations having fuelled a series of recent survey and monitoring efforts (e.g. Bright & Harris, 1994; McDonald *et al.*, 1994; Strachan *et al.*, 1996). These all have failed to generate consistent data on the presumably sparsely-distributed, low density marten populations outside the species' Scottish stronghold, leading to suggestions that either the monitoring methods used were unreliable (Messenger *et al.*, 1997) or that the species is completely or effectively extinct outside Scotland. Despite this, some confusion almost certainly has arisen because of the difficulties in developing and applying techniques appropriate to the location and monitoring of low-density marten populations. This uncertainty has led the Vincent Wildlife Trust (VWT) to examine a range of well-established and novel monitoring approaches to investigate the true status of the pine marten, particularly in Wales and northern England. We here review the techniques presently available for monitoring pine marten, and introduce some new approaches under trial by the VWT.

The problems of monitoring small, rare carnivores

"Searching for rare carnivores is expensive" (Zielinski & Kucera, 1995) and, in the context of monitoring, "expensive" means difficult. By simple virtue of their high trophic position carnivores tend to be relatively rare. In addition, they may have large home ranges, live in remote areas with difficult terrain, be active nocturnally and have a tendency to be elusive. Therefore, even in an ideal situation, carnivorous mammals are likely to pose significant problems to the field researcher.

1. Traditional methods

In North America small carnivores are of interest both for conservation *per se*, and also as harvestable furbearers. As a result, much of the ecological work on these species (and especially on *Martes* spp.) has been undertaken in the USA and Canada (see Proulx, this volume). Studies of martens, fisher, lynx and wolverine in western USA led Zielinski & Kucera (1995) to publish detailed accounts of three techniques which have been used successfully in detecting these species.

Photographic bait stations

This technique involves attracting the target species to a (usually meat-based) bait to feed, and to cause its own photograph to be taken simultaneously. A number of different systems have been developed to date. Infra-red, break-beam devices linked to dedicated, multi-shot, 35 mm camera systems such as the 'Trailmaster' (Goodson & Associates Inc., Lenexa, USA) are among the more sophisticated (there are also similar systems which use infra red or movement sensors). However, 'home-made' single shot systems, based on relatively inexpensive 'Instamatic'-type cameras, triggered mechanically by a fishing line tied to a piece of bait, have also been used successfully. Zielinski & Kucera (1995) recommend using a 4 mile^2 (2 miles x 2 miles) study unit for such surveys, suggesting the use of at least two of the multi-shot systems per study unit, or at least six single shot photo units.

The disadvantages of these systems include the high cost of equipment (one 'Trailmaster' system costs *c.* US$500) and comparatively high running costs (film, film processing and camera batteries). Furthermore, theft and/or vandalism may be a potential problem in some areas.

Track plates

This refers to a group of techniques whereby animal footprints are recorded when animals visit bait stations. Zielinski & Kucera (1995) describe two main systems, both employing aluminium plates which have been 'smoked' with an acetylene flame. The equipment is arranged so that an animal has to pass over the soot-covered plate in order to reach the bait. The simplest version of this is a large, uncovered plate with the bait placed in the centre; footprints are left by the animals which come to investigate. A second system employs a wooden 'tunnel' into which a smaller plate is set and which gives a degree of weather proofing. After crossing the soot-covered plate, animals pass onto tacky paper ('Con-Tact') which removes the soot particles from their feet, and leaves a clear print which easily can be removed and examined in the laboratory. Whichever type of device is used, it is recommended that they are placed at a density of six/4 mile^2 study area.

The VWT has also used a similar technique to study stoats and weasels. Our system uses a tunnel and a two-component dye system (King & Edgar, 1977). The tunnel contains a shallow tray in its centre into which is placed a cloth pad soaked with a ferric nitrate-based 'ink'. Either side of this are placed papers treated with tannic acid. Animals passing through the tunnel, pick up the 'ink' on their paws and this is deposited on the paper, leaving a permanent blue-black paw print.

Snow tracking

This technique is commonly used in boreal North America, Fennoscandia and Siberia. It involves either simply searching for tracks, or looking at tracks found around bait stations; however, considerable skill and experience are required in making confident species identifications (see Sidorovich, 1999). When simple track searching is employed, all roads and trails within the 4 mile^2 study unit should be searched. If examining tracks at bait stations, at least two per 4 mile^2 study unit should be employed. For many workers, including those in England and Wales, this technique is rarely of value because of a lack of snow cover in most winters.

These three techniques have been used successfully in grid-square based surveys in the western USA, where martens are described as having densities as low as one individual/2.5 km^2 (Zielinski & Kucera, 1995). However, whilst densities such as this may be considered low in North America, martens may be more abundant in western USA than the UK where, even in their Scottish stronghold, marten home ranges as large as 34 km^2 have been recorded (Balharry, 1993). The success of the first two of the above techniques is largely dependent on a fairly high rate of contact between the target species and the detection equipment. Skill in the placing of the equipment is clearly important, but in areas in which martens are very scarce and/or their movements are poorly understood, an unrealistically high density of detection stations may be needed in order to make any contacts at all. The high costs of hardware and limitations on surveyor man-hours may, therefore, contra-indicate the use of these techniques, at least in the initial stages of a survey.

2. Other methods used by the VWT

The VWT also has experimented with several other detection methods.

Live trapping

The VWT has undertaken a limited amount of live trapping work in Northumberland, northern England (near the Scottish border) and rather more in Wales. So far we have worked for over 800 trap nights (1 trap night = one trap placed for one night) in South Wales and over 1,200 trap nights in North Wales. The traps employed were 'Tomahawk' raccoon traps (Tomahawk Live Trap Co., Tomahawk, USA) and 'Fenn' feral cat/rabbit traps (A. Fenn & Co., Redditch, UK) usually set either on a grid or along a transect, with trapping largely being confined to the period from autumn to spring. The traps were set in areas of native broad-leaved woodland and coniferous plantations. The bait used was usually chicken, although eggs and fruit were also tried. After over 2,000 trap nights no pine martens have, as yet, been caught, although many non-target species have been captured (mainly polecats and feral domestic cats, *Felis catus*). Live trapping is very labour intensive and also inappropriate in areas where contact rates are likely to be low.

Photographic trail monitoring

The VWT has been using four 'Trailmaster' 1500 infra-red beam camera systems, mostly in conjunction with bait stations. However, recently we have been experi-menting with trail monitoring in an attempt to improve the chances of contact with martens with the limited amounts of detection equipment available to us. For exam-ple, currently we are investigating the use of pedestrian river bridges by nocturnal mammals. Where a river is deep and/or fast, such bridges may be important cross-ing points for wide-ranging species such as the pine marten.

Fur collecting baiting stations

Samples of hair from unknown species can be identified by microscopic examina-tion of casts of the hair in a suitable medium such a gelatine (Teerink, 1991). Furthermore, hair can be subjected to DNA analysis, especially if a follicle is still attached. The VWT has developed a technique for collecting hair samples from pine marten as they visit specially-designed baiting stations. The bait station takes the form of a wooden tunnel constructed from four 18" (500 mm) long pieces of 6" x 1" (150 mm x 25 mm) treated soft wood (see Fig. 1). This produces a tunnel of internal dimensions of 4" (100 mm) x 6" (150 mm) (width x height). One end of the tunnel is blocked with a piece of 1" (25 mm) galvanised weld-mesh (Sentinel Ltd., UK). Across the other end, half way up the opening, a galvanised metal spring (3" x 9/16" x 0.054 extension spring, zinc plated – Eliza Tinsley & Co. Ltd., Cradley Heath, UK) is attached horizontally so that its coils are just apart. One end of the spring is fixed using a small metal staple and the other end rests on the point of a L-shaped hook constructed from 3 mm brass rod. The hook is fitted through a small hole in the side of the tunnel body and held in place by bending the protruding end over (which allows for some rotational adjustment to its position). The hook and spring are set so that the spring is dislodged as an animal withdraws from the tunnel backwards after having entered to pick up bait at the far end. As the spring becomes detached at one end the coils snap shut, trapping a few guard hairs. Tests with captive pine martens showed that between 20-30 hairs were normally trapped and that this caused no obvious discomfort to the animal (some individuals raided four bait stations in quick succession). These bait stations have been field tested in Ireland and shown to work with wild pine martens. The use of a spring to collect fur has advantages over adhesives which, during trials, were found to either lose their "stickiness" quite quickly or become fouled with dust and other debris. A modification of this system, useful where disturbance from less agile species such as badgers is a problem, is to fix the bait stations away from the ground. In this case, the floor section of the tunnel can be 8" (200 mm) longer to form a platform at the entrance end.

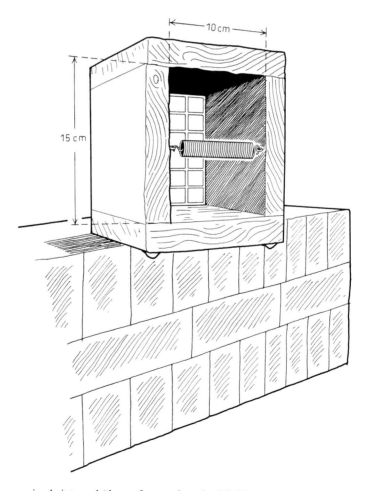

Fig. 1. Fur-snagging bait tunnel (drawn from a photo by J.E. Messenger).

One clear advantage of this system is that the bait stations are relatively cheap to build. As a result it may be possible to use them at a higher density than, for example, photographic systems. Even so, poor contact rates may still cause difficulties. During 1996, the VWT operated these devices for a total of 2,940 unit nights in an area from which reports of pine marten sightings are received regularly: Gwydyr Forest, north Wales. Interference from non-target species can be a problem, however, as these devices need to be reset after each event. During the trials in north Wales, we obtained samples of fur from polecat and badger, but none identified as being from pine marten.

All of the above techniques may be successful under the right circumstances but, with sparse and/or poorly understood populations, contact rates still may be unacceptably low. Even those systems with very low equipment maintenance costs (e.g. fur collecting bait stations) can be costly to run in the field if the study area is some distance away from the researcher. Another problem with low contact rates is the very real difficulty of maintaining the morale of the researcher! Many weeks of long hours in the field, inclement weather and long drives to the study site become very tedious when only negative observations are made.

Den location

In the Netherlands, workers have discovered that pine martens regularly den in old nest holes of the black woodpecker, *Dryocopus martius* (Kleef, 1997). Here it is possible to survey the forests during the winter and to identify and locate trees containing these holes. During the following summer the holes are revisited to look for signs of pine marten occupation – typically scats deposited from the hole. This is viewed as the most effective method of detecting and monitoring martens in the Netherlands (H. Wijsman, pers. comm.). Similar methods may have potential in the UK. Although black woodpeckers are absent as a breeding species in our study areas, this species may well colonise Britain in the near future (Gorman, 1998), thus providing martens with potential den sites and marten workers with the opportunity to fully exploit this detection/monitoring method.

Scat transects

Field work in Scotland for the VWT in the 1980s by Velander (1983) showed that, in some parts of the Scottish Highlands, pine martens were resident in areas of extensive conifer. Here their presence was very clearly displayed by characteristic scats deposited on vehicular tracks though forestry. It was assumed that the martens were using these convenient linear landscape features as territorial boundaries and were marking and counter marking with scats. The density of scats on some of these trackways can be high (e.g. 18 piles of scats in 300 m) and identifiable marten scats were found within 700 m of a transect in 94.1% of the sites surveyed (Velander, 1983). However, Velander notes that when transect walks were repeated at different times of the year, scat densities could be very different.

Using data obtained from field work in Wester Ross, Scotland (where pine marten are known to be well-established and breeding), Balharry *et al.* (1996) calculated that there was little chance of failing to find marten scats on a 2 km transect in a marten-occupied area ($P = 0.022\%$). Where a 4 km transect was walked, the data show that the probability of finding no scats fell to 0.0004%. As part of a recolonisation study, a survey protocol based on these findings was used to identify other areas in which pine martens were established and breeding. However, the authors appear to accept that the survey technique might not detect 'transient or dispersing marten'. Indeed, they suggest that the results of their survey may be explained because 'the methodology is not appropriate and scat density does not necessarily reflect an established population versus transient marten' (Balharry _et al._, 1996). Balharry (1993) also noted, during his research in Scotland, that "where martens are resident and have contiguous territories, scats are placed in prominent positions along forest tracks".

A thorough survey of pine marten in England and Wales was undertaken in 1987-88, again using scat transect work as the basis for field survey (Strachan _et al.,_ 1996). The survey was confined to areas in which reports of recent pine marten sightings concentrated. About six, two km-long transects were selected in each ten km map grid square within the target areas. Despite these efforts to maximise success, only 8.7% of transects were found to be marten positive during the initial survey. Of these, 41.5% were positive on the basis of a single marten scat being found and 73% of the positives contained no more than two scats. Field signs occurring at such a low densities carry the real risk of 'false negatives' being recorded.

It is clear from work in Scotland, England and Wales that scat transect-based surveys may be appropriate for detecting the presence of martens, but only in certain situations. This may, therefore, explain why the results of scat transect surveys in England and Wales have been disappointing. Indeed, there are a number of factors which might work against reliance upon this approach at low population densities:

1. A break-down in scat marking: at low population densities and/or where marten territories are not contiguous, territorial behaviour such as scat marking may cease. This has been reported in the case of Eurasian otter, in which spraint marking activity ceases when the population of a river catchment falls below a certain level (Strachan _et al._, 1990).
2. Identification difficulties: marten scats display a high degree of morphological variation, so shape and size alone are not adequate to confirm the species of origin (Strachan _et al._, 1996). However, pine marten scats, when very fresh, have a characteristically sweet odour which, combined with form, can be used to confirm species identity. Unfortunately, this odour is relatively short-lived, especially in wet and very dry weather. As a result, the majority of possible marten scats found in a survey may have to be rejected because of being insufficiently fresh. In situations where relatively few scats are found then the chance of finding fresh ones is likely to be low. Outside Scotland, where population densities are probably unusually low, scat encounter rates will be correspondingly lower, as will be the chance of finding fresh specimens.
3. Loss of scats: work is currently in progress in Wales (A. Braithewaite, pers. comm.) using scats from a captive marten to examine whether counter marking by wild martens can be stimulated. A high proportion of scats placed in the field was found to vanish within a few days. Further work showed that slugs (Mollusca) were often responsible, and could completely consume a marten scat

within 48 hours. On another occasion a fox was observed scraping out a freshly set out marten scat. In areas where scat densities are low, such effects are clearly significant.

4. Plantation bias: the scat transect technique was designed for use in habitats containing a reasonable density of tracks. In Britain, this means that such surveys are effectively restricted to areas of commercial, coniferous forestry. Although British pine martens certainly do use such habitat, its importance relative to other habitat types has never been established. It is not inconceivable that commercial forestry represents a less favoured habitat for martens.

5. The Dutch experience: attempts to monitor small populations of pine martens in the Netherlands have deployed a number of different techniques, including scat-searches (Canters & Wijsman, 1997). The scat transect technique was found to be wholly unreliable for determining the presence of viable breeding populations that had been identified by other methods (H. Wijsman, pers. comm.). A VWT visit to pine marten sites in the Netherlands in 1998, in the company of Werkgroep Boommarter Nederland, confirmed that scats are rarely found on tracks and rides through the forests occupied by the species in the core of its range. This suggests that patterns of scat-deposition behaviour may vary within the species' European range. Moreover, it raises serious doubts about any assumptions based upon the rigid application of the scat survey technique.

A new approach: the VWT sightings scheme

The VWT became interested in further work on pine marten in England and Wales at the end of 1994, following the production of a report by the Countryside Council for Wales: this was based on a brief survey of pine marten in Wales using scat transect surveys (McDonald *et al.*, 1994) and concluded that martens were effectively extinct in Wales. A further report based on a similar brief survey in Northumberland painted an equally gloomy picture in England (Bright & Harris, 1994). Suspecting that methodological failures may have played a major part in this conclusion, the VWT set out (in 1995) to review current knowledge of the species in England and Wales and to investigate marten survey methods. During the early stages of our review we became aware of reports of marten sightings which were being collected and collated by local naturalists in some areas (e.g. Brown, 1989; Morgan, 1993).

Inspired by the efforts of these naturalists, the VWT launched a widespread appeal for information on pine marten in England and Wales. Leaflets and posters appealing for information on sightings (including bilingual versions in Wales) were circulated to many countryside organisations. Wales was targeted first (in 1995) and the campaign was extended fully into northern England in late 1996. Our appeal for information is still being publicised widely through the local and national media. However, after a slow start, reports of martens have begun to come in. This is an ongoing exercise of unprecedented scale in Britain, and the publicity efforts will continue for the foreseeable future.

Persons reporting a marten are subjected to a standardised interview designed to gather all relevant information and avoiding "leading" questions such as "Did it have a creamy-white bib?". At the end of the interview a confidence score (on a scale 1-10) is assigned to each report on the bases of the quality of information given and the experience of the observer. We are careful to collect and record all reports which are offered to us as being possibly of pine marten, even if subsequently it is proven that the animal involved was not one (e.g. in the case of misidentified road kills) – these records are assigned a confidence score of zero.

Under this scheme a high scoring record is one which is given a confidence score of six or more. To date we have 97 high-scoring records of marten sightings from Wales during the 1990s, and 128 from England (see Fig. 2). For the same period, we

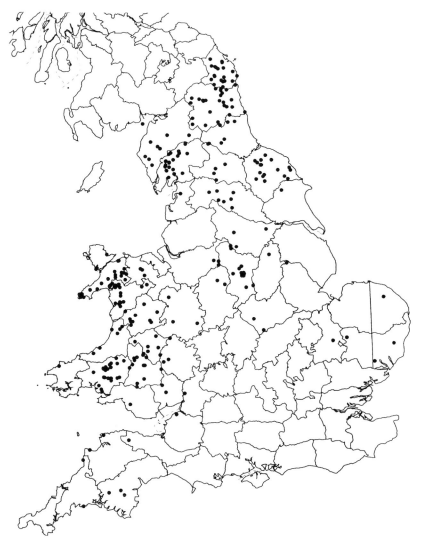

Fig. 2. Distribution of marten sightings in England and Wales (1990 onwards) with a confidence score of six or more.

have nine high-scoring road casualty records from Wales and four from England. Road casualties disappear quickly if not collected immediately, and only one, an animal run over near Chorley (Lancashire) in 1994, has been preserved (Birks *et al.*, 1997). A further three corpses and the skull of a trapped animal (Jefferies & Critchley, 1994) have been recovered from northern England since 1990 (pine marten are sometimes trapped inadvertently by gamekeepers during predator control). However, since the species is now fully protected in British law, trap captures are rarely reported. Although live sightings form by far the largest proportion of our records, other types of record are also collected (see Fig. 3).

We have attempted to assign those reporting recent, high-quality sightings to broad categories – a high proportion are from naturalists, countryside professionals (e.g. rangers, foresters) or scientists (see Fig. 4). This bias probably results from a bias in the distribution of publicity material towards county wildlife trusts, environmental groups and other countryside-related bodies. A few observers (less than 7%) have submitted reports of more than one sighting.

Whilst it is possible that some high-scoring records are, despite careful evaluation, cases of mistaken identity, it is inconceivable that all, or even most of them, are inaccurate. Equally, it is possible that some low-scoring (five or less) records are perfectly sound. A preliminary analysis of our marten records suggests a distribution which cannot be explained by observer bias or the misidentification of other species (see Fig. 2). The distribution of publicity material was carefully recorded and extended well away from the areas from which most reports were obtained. Most records come from within or close to the main marten population areas identified by Strachan in the late 1980s (Strachan *et al.*, 1996) and so confirm continuous marten presence since 1990.

Conclusions

Carnivores present a considerable array of problems to the monitoring ecologist. Where these populations are sparse, even by carnivore standards, the difficulties are greatly increased. When static field equipment is used, poor rates of contact may prevent enough, or even any, data being collected. Searches for field signs may also fail and, in Britain, much emphasis has been placed on surveys based on scat searches. But there are many reasons why such approaches may fail, including the changes in territorial marking behaviour which might occur at low population levels (e.g. Strachan *et al.*, 1990).

At a time when biodiversity has come to the fore in conservation planning, the importance of small, relict populations and their potentially unique genetic identity should not be underestimated. The use of inappropriate survey techniques can result in surveys producing negative findings, simply as a result of methodological failure. If this occurs, these important, relict populations may be ignored or, even worse, subjected to wholly inappropriate conservation management.

Attempting to monitor sparse pine marten populations using casual sightings is not, strictly speaking, possible as there can be no proper control on survey effort. Nevertheless, with care it is possible to use such data to good effect. The sightings approach may have shortcomings but, in these situations, it may be the only viable option. To date we have strong circumstantial evidence for the continuing existence of pine marten populations in some of the most remote areas of Britain. This needs to be taken into account, particularly in the light of an increasing dynamic towards the introduction of species to areas from which they are believed to be absent. Clearly this is a genuine problem, particularly if the "absence" of the species has been established by using potentially inappropriate methods. Here, as in many other aspects of conservation biology, the operation of the "precautionary principle" should be seen as paramount.

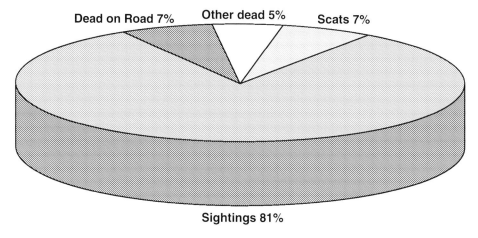

Fig. 3. The nature of pine marten reports received since 1990 (n = 405; all records, any confidence score).

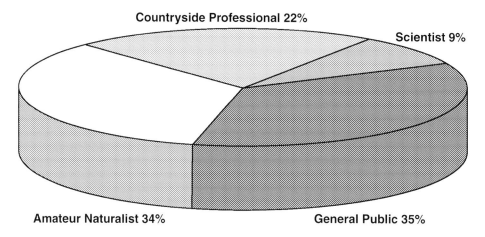

Fig. 4. Broad categories of reporters of reliable sightings of live martens in England and Wales in the 1990s (n = 241; only reports for which a category could be assigned are included).

Acknowledgements

Our thanks go to Tony Braithewaite, Alan Enock and Roy Bowen of Forest Enterprise, and to Chris Hall and Sue Wells for their help with trapping and other field work. Finally, we are indebted to all those who have taken the trouble to supply us with the details of their sightings of pine martens.

References

Balharry, D (1993). *Factors affecting the distribution and population density of pine martens* (*Martes martes L.*) *in Scotland.* PhD thesis. Aberdeen; University of Aberdeen.

Balharry, E.A., McGowan, G.M., Kruuk, H. & Halliwell, E. (1996). *Distribution of pine martens in Scotland as determined by field survey and questionnaire* (*SNH Survey and Monitoring Report No. 48*). Edinburgh; Scottish Natural Heritage.

Birks, J.D.S. (1993). The return of the polecat. *British Wildlife*, **5**: 16-25.

Birks, J.D.S. & Kitchener, A.C. (Eds.) (1999). *The distribution and status of the polecat Mustela putorius in Britain in the 1990s.* London; The Vincent Wildlife Trust.

Birks, J.D.S., Messenger, J.E. & Davison, A. (1997). A 1994 pine marten *Martes martes* (L.) record for Lancashire, including a preliminary genetic analysis. *The Naturalist*, **122**: 13-18

Bright, P.W. & Harris, S. (1994). *Reintroduction of the pine marten: feasibility study* (*Unpublished English Nature Contract Report, F72-11-10*). Bristol; University of Bristol.

Brown, D. (1989). *Bele'r Coed-Arolwg 1987, Y Canlyniadau.* Bangor; Cyngor Gwarchod Natur (in Welsh).

Canters, K.J. & Wijsman, H.J.W. (1997). *Wat Doen we met de boommarter.* Utrecht; Werkgroep Boommarter Nederland (in Dutch).

Chanin, P.R.F. & Jefferies, D.J. (1978). The decline of the otter *Lutra lutra* L. in Britain: an analysis of hunting records and discussion of causes. *Biological Journal of the Linnean Society*, **10**: 305-328.

Gorman, G. (1998). The spread of the black woodpecker in Europe – will it reach Britain next? *Birding World*, **11** (10): 390-395.

Griffiths, H.I. & Thomas, D.H. (1997). *The conservation and status of the European badger* (*Meles meles*) (*Nature & Environment No. 90*). Strasbourg; Council of Europe.

Griffiths, H.I., Davison, A. & Birks, J.D.S. (1996). Species reintroductions. *Conservation Biology*, **10**: 923.

Harris, S., Morris, P., Wray, S. & Yalden, D.W. (1995). *A review of British mammals: population estimates and conservation status of British mammals other than cetaceans.* Peterborough; Joint Nature Conservation Committee.

Jefferies, D.J. & Critchley, C.H. (1994). A new pine marten *Martes martes* (L.) record for the North Yorkshire Moors: skull dimensions and confirmation of species. *The Naturalist*, **119**: 145-150.

King, C.M. & Edgar, R.L. (1977). Techniques for trapping and tracking stoats *Mustela erminea*; a review, and a new system. *New Zealand Journal of Zoology*, **4**: 193-212.

Kleef, H.L. (1997). Boommarterinventarisatie in Nederland: aanpak en resultaten, toegespitst op Noord-Nederland. In: K.J. Canters & H.J.W. Wijsman (eds.), *Wat doen we met de boommarter*: 11-22. Utrecht; Werkgroep Boommarter Nederland (in Dutch).

Langley, P.J.W. & Yalden, D.W. (1977). The decline of the rarer carnivores in Great Britain during the nineteenth century. *Mammal Review*, **7**: 95-116.

Macdonald, D.W., Tattersall, F.H., Brown, E.D. & Balharry, D. (1995). Reintroducing the European beaver to Britain: nostalgic meddling or restoring biodiversity? *Mammal Review*, **25**: 161-200.

Macdonald, D.W., Mace, G. & Rushton, S. (1999). *Proposals for the future monitoring of British mammals.* Bristol; Department of the Environment, Transport & the Regions.

May, C.A., Wetton, J.H., Davis, P.E., Brookfield, J.F.Y & Parkin, D.T. (1993). Single-locus profiling reveals loss of variation in inbred populations of the red kite (*Milvus milvus*). *Proceedings of the Royal Society of London (Series B)*, **251**: 165-170.

McDonald, R., Bright, P.W. & Harris, S. (1994). *Baseline survey of pine martens in Wales* (*Unpublished English Nature Contract Report, FC 73-01-91*). Bristol; University of Bristol.

Messenger, J.E., Birks, J.D.S. & Jefferies, D.J. (1997). What is the status of the pine marten in England and Wales? *British Wildlife*, **8**: 273-279.

Morgan, I.K. (1993). Interim notes on the status of the pine marten in South and Mid Wales *Newsletter of the Llanelli Naturalists*, **1992-93** (Winter): 11-22.

Shaw, G. & Livingstone, J. (1992). The pine marten: its reintroduction and subsequent history in the Galloway Forest Park. *Transactions of the Dumfries and Galloway Natural History and Antiquarian Society (3rd Series)*, **67**: 1-7.

Sidorovich, V.E. (1999). How to identify mustelid tracks. *Small Carnivore Conservation*, **20**: 22-27.

Strachan, R., Jefferies, D.J. & Chanin, P.R.F. (1996). *Pine marten survey of England and Wales 1987–1988*. Peterborough; Joint Nature Conservation Committee.

Strachan, R. & Jefferies, D.J. (1996). *Otter survey of England 1991-1994*. London; The Vincent Wildlife Trust.

Strachan, R., Birks J.D.S., Chanin, P.R.F & Jefferies, D.J. (1990). *Otter survey of England 1984-86*. Peterborough; Nature Conservancy Council.

Tapper, S. (1992). *Game heritage*. Fordingbridge; The Game Conservancy Ltd.

Teerink, B.J. (1991). *Hair of West European mammals: atlas and identification key*. Cambridge; Cambridge University Press.

Velander, K.A. (1983). *Pine marten survey of Scotland, England and Wales 1980-1982*. London; The Vincent Wildlife Trust.

Wilson, G., Harris, S. & McLaren, G. (1997). *Changes in the British badger population, 1988-1997*. London; People's Trust for Endangered Species.

Yalden, D.W. (1999). *The history of British mammals*. London; T & AD Poyser.

Zielinski, W.J. & Kucera, T.E. (Eds.) (1995). *American marten, fisher, lynx, and wolverine: survey methods for their detection* (*US Department of Agriculture Forest Service (Pacific Southwest Research Station) General Technical Report PSW-GTR-157*).

CHAPTER 15

Factors influencing otter, *Lutra lutra*, numbers and distribution on part of the Blackwater catchment (Ireland)

Paola Ottino* & Paul Giller

Abstract

At present there is little information on the impact of landuse (and especially forestry) on Eurasian river otter populations, and little is known of otter habitat use in relation to different landscape types. This paper provides detailed information derived from a complete survey of a single large catchment featuring a variety of landuse types.

In the Blackwater catchment of southern Ireland otter signs were recorded by walking along both banks of watercourses, and environmental conditions (average river depth and width, vegetation cover, etc.) were recorded, as were signs of the presence of American mink. Correlations between the occurrence of otter spraints and other otter signs, between the percentage of otter signs and habitat parameters, and between otter signs and landuse were evaluated and multiple linear regression used to identify the measured variables that most influenced sprainting activity. During the study four active holts were found and three delineated home ranges were recorded, these being occupied by six or seven otters, including a family group.

A significant relationship was found between the number of spraints and other otter signs, and this can be used to validate otter presence, and to evaluate relationships with environmental variables. Significant correlations were found between signs of otter presence and river depth, river width and the availability of lying-up areas. No trends were recorded in bank type, vegetation cover or water flow velocity.

The relationship between the frequency of otter signs and percentage vegetation cover showed positive correlations in the agricultural areas and moorlands, but a negative correlation in forest plantation habitats. This particular trend may relate to the fact that relatively few large (3+) fish (their main prey item) have been recorded in streams in the forested areas of the catchment.

Introduction

The thirteen species of otter (Wozencraft, 1989) are distributed all over the World except for Australia. *Lutra* is the most widespread and best represented genus both in the Old and New World, and the species *Lutra lutra*, the Eurasian otter, is widespread in Europe, North Africa and much of Asia. However, in many parts of central Europe the otter population has declined over the last forty years, so that it is now rare or absent from many countries (Foster-Turley *et al.*, 1990). *Lutra lutra* is

---

* Corresponding author.

Mustelids in a modern world
Management and conservation aspects of small carnivore: human interactions
edited by Huw I. Griffiths, pp. 231–246
© 2000 Backhuys Publishers, Leiden, The Netherlands

classified as a vulnerable (V) species by the IUCN (1990). The most stable or thriving populations are located in the eastern and western parts of Europe, while in the rest of Europe the distribution of the otter is fragmented (Macdonald & Mason, 1992). Isolated populations exist in some countries of western Europe such as UK, Ireland, France, Germany, Belgium, Austria and Italy, but in other countries the otter has completely disappeared as, for example, in the Netherlands, Liechtenstein and Switzerland. Little information is available with regard to the states of the former USSR and the countries of eastern Europe, although quite large populations of otters have been found (e.g. Barus & Zejda, 1981).

Major contributing factors to the otter's decline include pollution, habitat destruction, sport hunting and accidental mortality (Chanin & Jefferies, 1978; Chanin, 1985; Macdonald & Mason, 1990). These factors, either singularly or collectively, may be responsible for this rapid decline, but there is open dispute between authors.

On examining British hunting records between 1907 and 1971, Chanin & Jefferies (1978) noted that the decline of otter had accelerated over the late 1950s and this coincided with the introduction of pesticides. The most important contaminant was dieldrin, used in agriculture. Probably poly-chlorinated biphenyls (PCBs) also may have been responsible for the otter's decline, but these authors did not examine these contaminants. In Sweden, Sandegren *et al.* (1980) studied 53 otters which had been found dead. They found high concentrations of PCBs in otter tissues and concluded that these pesticides were the most important cause of the otter's decline in Sweden.

PCBs are known to have marked effects on the reproduction, immune system and endocrine system of mammals (Mason, 1995). Mason (1995) maintains that in Britain otter distribution is negatively correlated with the mean concentration of PCBs in spraints, considered as an indicator of levels in body tissues, and reported standards for PCBs to protect otter populations (see Table 1). These standards can also be considered valid as organochlorine pesticide quality standards (Mason, 1995).

Studies carried out in the former Yugoslavia in 1986 (Taylor *et al.*, 1988) have shown that in the Drina catchment, with low industrial and agricultural output, the occurrence of otters was common (97.6%) compared to areas where industrialisation was high.

The importance of the otter as an environmental indicator and the reason for its decline lie in the fact that it is a "key species" in wetland habitats. Here, as it is at the top of the food chain, its population size and reproductive output are naturally relatively low. This means that the otter's capacity to recolonise is comparatively slow and also that it is particularly sensitive to changes in environmental conditions. It is necessary, on the basis of these aspects, to protect the habitats where the otter

Table 1. PCB quality standards for protecting otter populations: (A) safe, (B) requiring action (from Mason, 1995).

PCBs		
Tissue contents	**A**	**B**
In fish (fresh wt.): whole body mince or flesh	<0.026 mg.kg^{-1}	>0.05 mg.kg^{-1}
In otter (lipid wt.) (liver or muscle)	<10 mg.kg^{-1}	>30 mg.kg^{-1}
In otter spraints (lipid wt.)	<4 mg.kg^{-1}	>9 mg.kg^{-1}

still remains, and to restore areas where this species now is extinct. For this reason, a habitat network program is in progress in Germany to protect and restore habitats which can function as a network to connect thriving otter populations with isolated ones (Reuther, 1995).

In Ireland, little was known about the status of the otter prior to the first National Otter Survey (Chapman & Chapman, 1982). Stephens (1957) has stated that otters had decreased drastically in the country as they were hunted and trapped because their pelts were a sought-after commodity. However, otters were still relatively common (Fairley, 1972) and, in 1976, the species was protected by the Republic of Ireland's Wildlife Act.

The National Otter Survey was undertaken between January 1980 and February 1981, with alternate 50 km^2 of the National Grid of Ireland being surveyed. Sites were spatially distributed at 5-8 km intervals along rivers, canals, lakes and the coast. At each site a maximum of 600 m of bank was searched for otter signs and the search terminated when sign was found. A 600 m stretch was considered negative for otter presence when no signs were located. Of the 2,373 sites surveyed, 2,177 (91.7%) were found to be positive for the presence of otter. It was revealed that the otter was more numerous on the west coast than on the east coast and that the Burren (Co. Clare), the Dublin area (Co. Dublin), the River Barrow (Co. Carlow) and the lower Blackwater River system (southern Ireland) were relatively poor areas in comparison with the rest of Ireland. However, in general, the Irish populations of otters were considered to be internationally important.

On the basis of a later survey by Lunnon & Reynolds (1991) in some of the sites originally surveyed by Chapman & Chapman, no significant change in the otter population was apparent over the intervening years.

Further analyses were carried out by various authors on a more local scale. Kyne *et al.* (1990) surveyed otters in parts of the Connemara Bogland and, although otter signs were generally widespread, they found no evidence of otters on many stretches during an exceptionally dry summer, and the average number of positive sites was very low. On the other hand, in the Munster catchment of the Blackwater River, O'Sullivan (1991) described a very good otter population with no evidence of decline since the original survey. The results presented by Smiddy (1993) from the east Cork and west Waterford area of the catchment agree with that view, so the distribution of the species throughout the Blackwater catchment is considered to be relatively stable.

Several studies also have investigated the otter's diet in Ireland and recently, other studies have been focused on levels of organochlorine pesticides, PCBs and heavy metals in otters. In southern Ireland the concentration of PCBs tended to increase from west to east, with the highest levels of contaminants being found in Cork City (mean concentration of p,p-DDE = 0.84 mg/kg, Dieldrin = 0.21 mg/kg, PCB = 2.71 mg/kg) and in adjacent regions, and in Bantry Bay (mean concentration of PCB = 2.38 mg/kg) (O'Sullivan *et al.*, 1993). In general the mean levels of heavy metals found in otter livers were considered to be relatively low (mercury = 2.50 mg/kg, cadmium = 0.17 mg/kg, lead = 0.18 mg/kg) although zinc concentrations were higher at 41.30 mg/kg (Mason & O'Sullivan, 1993).

An interesting study was carried out by Lynch & O'Sullivan (1993) on the cranial morphology of Irish otters. Some authors classify the Irish otter as a separate subspecies, *Lutra lutra roensis* Ogilby, 1834 (see Hinton, 1920; Dadd, 1970) on the basis of a darker pelt and smaller white throat patches than seen in the nominate form (*Lutra lutra lutra* from Sweden), although there is little information about this in the literature (e.g. Miller, 1912; Fairley, 1972). An island phenomenon, such as competitive release, may have influenced the interspecific differences and evidence of sexual dimorphism (in both skull shape and size) found by Lynch & O'Sullivan (1993).

Despite this, more fundamental research is required to determine the precise ecological and habitat requirements of the otter. At present, the minimum amount of cover and food to support a population is unknown. Also there is no information on the impact of forestry and other landuse types on the otter, and very little is known of their habitat use in relation to different landscape types (woodland, moorland, farm land, etc.).

At present, we can only guess at the total size of the otter population in Ireland, even though we know that here the otter is widespread and common (O'Sullivan,1991). Thus attempts at estimating population densities at a local scale would contribute towards the construction of a better estimate of the national population. In the Araglin Valley, southern Ireland, the first analysis of otter distributions was carried out by Chapman & Chapman (1982) during the National Otter Survey. Of the 2,373 sites surveyed nationwide, only two sites were along the Araglin River: one at the confluence between the River Blackwater and the River Araglin (a positive record), and the other on the upper R. Araglin (a negative record). Further analyses were carried out in the Blackwater catchment by O'Sullivan (1991), who found new otter-positive sites in the Araglin Valley, but also recorded the two previously-examined sites as otter negative.

In this study the distribution, density and habitat use of otters in the Araglin Valley was examined and the factors affecting its distribution determined.

Study area

The study was carried out in the Araglin Valley, a designed Natural Heritage Area situated in the counties of Cork, Tipperary and Waterford. Detailed research was conducted on the R. Araglin and its tributaries, the River Douglas (including various streams in the area of Kilworth) and River Glenfinish (Fig. 1). The R. Araglin catchment and the R. Douglas are areas where intense studies have been undertaken on the relationship between forms of landuse, forestry practices and stream ecology. The present study forms part of this overall research programme.

The study area lies within a range of altitudes from 30 m to 500 m asl, and dominant vegetation types range from open moorland and rough pasture/improved grassland to coniferous or mixed coniferous and deciduous afforestation. With regard to fish populations in the study area, some studies of otter diet have been carried out (Ottino & Giller, in press). In the R. Araglin fish populations are composed of brown trout, *Salmo trutta*, Atlantic salmon, *Salmo salar*, common eel, *Anguilla anguilla*, three-spined stickleback, *Gasterosteus aculeatus*, stone loach, *Noemacheilus barbatulus*, and brook lamprey, *Lampetra planeri*. The R. Douglas, however, is essentially a trout stream and, in the R. Glenfinish brown trout and eel dominate, whilst Atlantic salmon are less common and only a few stone loach are present.

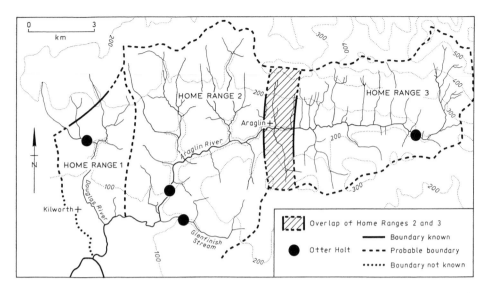

Fig. 1. Map of the study area showing home ranges of otters: (1 & 3) = home ranges of two sub-adult otters, (2) = home range of adult male including a family group.

Materials and methods

From October 1995 to June 1996 all watercourses in the study area were surveyed and each river was divided into 500 m-long stretches running from headwater to mouth. Both banks of the rivers were surveyed. Data were collected by walking along both banks of all watercourses and then were transposed onto a map of the area.

Otter signs, including the occurrence of spraints, anal secretions and tracks were recorded. The presence of holts, food remains and scrapes were accepted as being proof of otter presence only when supported by the co-occurrence of spraints and/or footprints in the near vicinity.

Otter tracks were measured and ascribed to size classes based on a scheme modified from those of Jenkins (1980) and O'Sullivan (1992) (see Table 2). Track size median values (*i.e.* width and length) were calculated and the raw results examined with the Kruskall-Wallis (KW) Test for significant differences among different track size classes (indicating animals of different sizes). The significance of the differences between pairs of size classes was analysed by Mann-Whitney Tests.

Mounds of scraped sand, mud or grass, often with spraints on top, and intensively marked areas or aggregations of spraints, sometimes separated by large stretches of river lacking spraints, were identified as home range boundaries. Range boundaries were drawn onto maps using the above data and the study area topography.

Average environmental variables were evaluated and scaled as shown in Table 3. The nature of the bank-side vegetation was evaluated in terms of percentage cover classes. The presence (1) or absence (0) of mink and otter holts were also recorded. As several environmental factors, e.g. heavy rain, may influence the reliability of otter survey results, all rivers were surveyed twice during each month of the study programme.

Table 2. Criteria used for distinguishing otter size classes from otter track sizes (see Jenkins, 1980; O'Sullivan, 1992). C = cub, Y = young otter, WGY = well-grown young otter, J = juvenile, SA = subadult, A = adult, SAM = subadult male, AF = adult female, AM = adult male.

Jenkins (1980)		O'Sullivan (1992)		Present study	
Track length (cms)	**Otter size class**	**Track width (cms)**	**Otter size Class**	**Track size (cms)**	**Otter size class**
<4.0	C	4.0	C	-	-
		-	>4.0 – 5.3	C/Y	- -
<5.0	Y	-	-	<5.0	C/J
>6.0	WGY/A	5.5 – 6.5	SAM/AF	>5.0 – 6.0	SA
6.0	AF	-	-	>6.0 – 7.0	AF
7.0	AM	>6.5	AM	>7.0	AM

Table 3. Scalable environmental parameters recorded during the survey. V = vegetation, which was scaled on a measure of percentage cover in the progression 1%, 2%, 3%, 5%, 7%, 10%, 15%, 20% 25%, 30%, 40%, 50%, 65%, 80%, 90%.

Parameters	Scale
Bank type	0 = grass/vegetation
	1 = silt
	2 = earth
	3 = sand
	4 = gravel
	5 = stone
River depth	1 = <0.3 m
	2 = 1.0 – 0.5 m
	3 = 0.5 – 0.7 m
	4 = 0.7 – 1.0 m
River width	1 = <1.0 m
	2 = 1.0 – 2.0 m
	3 = 2.0 – 3.0 m
	4 = 3.0 – 4.0 m
	5 = 4.0 – 5.0 m
	6 = >5.0 m
Flow regime	1 = slow
	2 = fast
Lying-up places	1 = none
	2 = low
	3 = medium
	4 = high

The relationships between spraints and other signs were examined using Spearman's Rank Correlation. This was also used to evaluate the correlation between the percentage of otter signs and the above mentioned habitat parameters. Correlations were also evaluated between otter signs and landuse type (moorland, forest and agriculture), and the proportion of otter spraints recorded in each month was calculated. In addition, multiple linear regressions were used to identify the measured variables that most appeared to influence sprainting activity.

Results

Of the 112 river survey stretches, otter spraints were found at 56 (50%). Otter signs were absent from river headwaters which had low water flow velocities (c. 0.052 m/sec) or which dried up temporarily in summer, or which were <0.3 m deep.

Figs. 2 & 3 show the percentage of signs/500-m length of river. The highest number of signs occurred around the holts: stretches 15 and 46 on the R. Araglin, stretch 1K1 in the Kilworth catchment area of the R. Douglas (Fig. 2) and stretch 3G of the R. Glenfinish (Fig. 3). The other peaks coincided with particular zones such as the boundaries of home ranges, bases of bridges, large boulders, or the points of confluence between two rivers. On the other hand, the lowest numbers of signs were found in the area of the village of Kilworth (Fig. 2) and on the headwater reaches of each river, where the rivers were shallow (Figs. 2, 3). Over the whole study period, the signs most commonly found were spraints, followed by tracks, lying-up areas and scrapes (Table 4).

The highest numbers of otter signs recorded were in spring and early summer, and the minimum was found in March – probably due to the heavy rain that occurred then (Fig. 4). This trend was mostly found in Home Range 2 (see below), while in Home Range 1 the lowest number of otter signs was recorded in winter, but increased in spring and early summer (Fig. 5).

Four holts were recorded in whole study area: two on the R. Araglin, one on the R. Glenfinish and one on the R. Douglas (Fig. 1). Three of these were located in tree root systems (sycamore, ash and oak) and one in a steep-sided earthen bank in an area with dense vegetation cover and low disturbance. Three home ranges can be delineated within the study area, but their exact extent up the various tributary streams is unknown (Fig. 1). Home range boundaries were located on the R. Araglin and on the catchment of R. Douglas near Kilworth. In these areas high levels of sprainting and scraping were recorded. The number of signs tended to decrease away from the home range boundaries and to increase near the holts.

There were strongly significant differences among the sizes of tracks (width: $KW = 24.06$, $P = 2.42 \times 10^{-5}$; length: $KW = 24.59$, $P = 1.87 \times 10^{-5}$), consequently there were significant differences amongst the four otter track size classes identified. In addition, the Mann-Whitney Test (Table 5) revealed significant differences between the pairs of otter size classes (median values of the track sizes are shown in Table 6). To judge from track sizes, cub/juvenile otters were recorded five times in December, three times in February and twice in May. The presence of one family group (indicated by cub/juvenile tracks found in association with the larger tracks of an adult female) occurred three times near the holt on the R. Araglin in Home Range 2 (Fig. 1) and twice near home range boundaries. An adult male utilised the central home range (Home Range 2; Fig. 1) which included that of the family group. Tracks of intermediate size were found at two home range boundaries and around the two holts in Home Range 1 and Home Range 3. These suggest the presence of solitary animals, presumed to be sub-adult males.

A combination of the total number of holts identified, the track sizes measured, home ranges identified and otter sightings, was used to estimate the number of otters in the study area. Track sizes suggested a minimum of two cubs, so it was possible to estimate that a minimum of six otters inhabited the Araglin Valley.

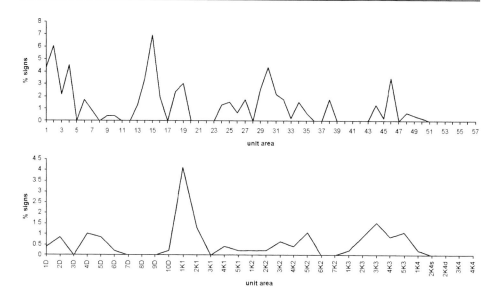

Fig. 2. Frequency of otter signs (both banks) per 500 m long length along the R. Araglin (above), and the R. Douglas (D) and its tributaries K1–K4 (below).

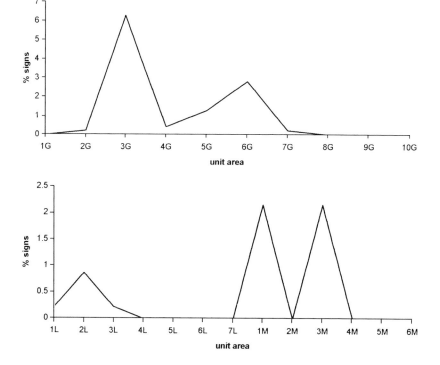

Fig. 3. Frequency of otter signs (both banks) per 500 m of the Glenfinish stream (G) (above), and a Muchnagh stream (M), and a tributary of the R. Araglin (L) (below).

Table 4. Statistical data on sprainting activity and other otter signs in the study area (SD = Standard Deviation, N = number of each sign).

	N	Mean	SD	Range (Min – Max)
Signs	462	4.12	6.58	0 – 32
Spraints	287	2.55	4.55	0 – 27
Tracks	125	1.12	3.04	0 – 15
Scrapes	24	0.20	0.91	0 – 7
Lying-up places	22	0.19	0.57	0 – 4

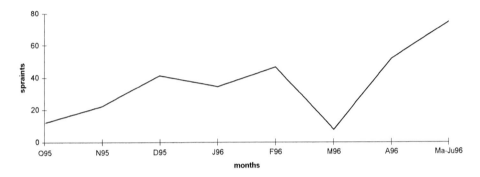

Fig. 4. The numbers of otter spraints recorded each month in the study area. O95 = October 1995, N95 = November 1995, D95 = December 1995, J96 = January 1996, F96 = February 1996, M96 = March 1996, A96 = April 1996, Ma-Ju96 = May-June 1996.

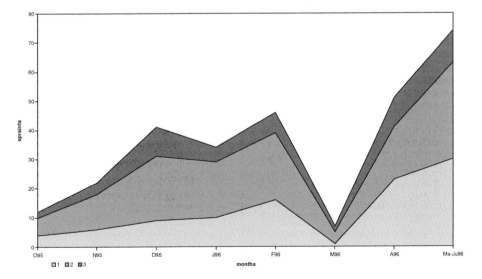

Fig. 5. Monthly changes in the numbers of otter spraints in the three home ranges recorded in the study area. O95 = October 1995, N95 = November 1995, D95 = December 1995, J96 = January 1996, F96 = February 1996, M96 = March 1996, A96 = April 1996, Ma-Ju96 = May-June 1996.

Table 5. Comparison of track sizes (U = Mann–Whitney Test, P = level of significance, N = number of tracks).

(a) track width				(b) track length			
Size classes	U	P	N	Size classes	U	P	N
AF – AM	2.35	0.0018	12	AF – AM	2.27	0.02	12
AF – C/J	3.44	5.74×10^{-4}	17	AF – C/J	3.39	6.89×10^{-4}	17
AF – SAM	3.18	1.45×10^{-3}	13	AF – SAM	2.90	3.68×10^{-3}	13
AM – C/J	3.06	2.14×10^{-3}	15	AM – C/J	3.05	2.31×10^{-3}	15
AM – SAM	2.97	2.99×10^{-3}	11	AM – SAM	2.84	4.40×10^{-3}	11
C/J – SAM	2.75	5.86×10^{-3}	16	C/J – SAM	3.26	1.09×10^{-3}	16

Table 6. Median values of track sizes (cms) measured in the study area (N = number of tracks in each size class).

Size classes	N	Median	Range (Min – Max)
Width AF	7	6	6 – 6.5
Length AF	7	6.5	6 – 7
Width AM	5	6.5	6.5 – 7
Length AM	5	7	7 – 8
Width C/J	10	3.75	3 – 5
Length C/J	10	4.25	3 – 5
Width SAM	6	5	5 – 5
Length SAM	6	5.5	5.5 – 6

Figures 6 & 7 show the percentage vegetation cover/500 m stretch of river. The highest values occurred in the R. Douglas catchment around Kilworth, in the middle areas of R. Araglin (Fig. 6) and in R. Glenfinish (Fig. 7). On the headwater reaches of the R. Araglin, moorland was predominant and the percentage cover was very low in comparison to the other stretches of the river (Fig. 6).

By using all the data from the entire study area and period, a significant correlation was found between the number of spraints and the presence of other otter signs (Table 7). Any of these signs can be used as confirmation of otter presence, and therefore used to evaluate the relationship between otters and environmental variables. Significant relationships were found between the number of otter signs and river depth (P <0.0001), river width (P <0.001), the availability of lying-up areas (P = 0.044) and otter holt presence (P <0.001). No significant trends were recorded for bank type (P = 0.996), vegetation cover (P = 0.817) or water flow velocity (P = 0.786) (see Table 8). The results of multiple linear regression analysis (Table 9) confirmed that the presence of holts is the most important parameter associated with otter presence, followed by river depth. None of the other parameters could explain a significant amount of the variation seen in otter signs. Mink presence seemed to have no affect on the Araglin otters (Table 9), in contrast to the results from other studies (Mason & Macdonald, 1983, 1986; Melquist & Hornocker, 1983; Wise *et al.*, 1981).

Using Spearman's Rank Correlation, the relationship between otter spraints and percentage of vegetation cover in the three different habitats was examined. A negative correlation was found with the forest habitat (rs = -0.216, P <0.005), while positive correlations were recorded in the agricultural area and the moorlands (rs = 0.144, P <0.005 and rs = 0.100, P <0.005, respectively).

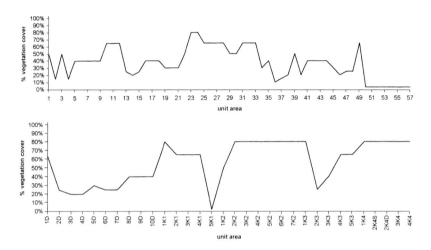

Fig. 6. Frequency of percentage cover of vegetation on the bank side (both banks) per 500 m length along R. Araglin (above) and R. Douglas (D) and its tributaries (K1–K4) (below).

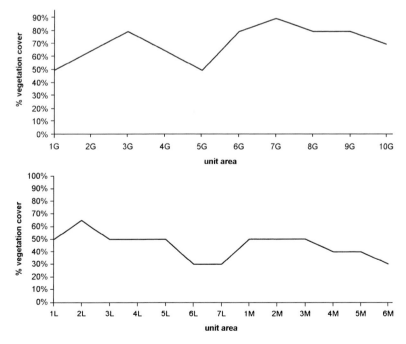

Fig. 7. Frequency of percentage vegetation cover on the bank side (both banks) per 500 m length along Glenfinish stream (G) (above), and Muchnagh stream (M) and a tributary of the R. Araglin (L) (below).

Table 7. Correlation between spraints and other signs of otter presence (values = Spearman's Rank Correlation Coefficient, P = probability, N = 12).

SIGNS	Spraints 0.88 P<0.001	Tracks 0.56 P>0.001	Scrapes 0.35 P<0.001	Lying-up places 0.37 P<0.001
SPRAINTS	-	Tracks 0.21 P = 0.002	Scrapes 0.17 P = 0.054	Lying-up places 0.21 P = 0.026
TRACKS	-	-	Scrapes 0.48 P<0.001	Lying-up places 0.05 P = 0.516
SCRAPES	-	-	-	Lying-up places 0.19 P = 0.037

Table 8. Correlation between signs and environmental parameters (values shown are Spearman's Rank Correlation Coefficient and levels of probability).

Environmental parameter	Sign	P
Bank type	- 0.046	0.996
% vegetation cover	0.022	0.817
River depth	0.461	<0.001
River width	0.326	<0.001
Speed of water	- 0.026	0.786
Lying-up places	0.190	0.044
Mink	0.184	0.052
Holt	0.322	<0.001

Table 9. Multiple linear regression analysis for identifying variables that influence sprainting activity (N = 112).

Environmental parameter	Sign	t	P
Bank type	- 0.046	0.996	0.255
% vegetation cover	0.022	0.817	0.955
River depth	0.461	<0.001	<0.001
River width	0.326	<0.001	0.213
Speed of water	- 0.026	0.786	0.161
Lying-up places	0.190	0.044	0.966
Mink	0.184	0.052	0.381
Holt	0.322	<0.001	<0.001

R = 0.762   **R^2** = 0.581   **Adjusted R^2** = 0.548   **S.E.** = 4.419

Discussion

Data on the estimated number of otter presences suggest that otters are widespread within the study area. Previously studied sites (Chapman & Chapman, 1982; O'Sullivan, 1991) considered as being otter negative were identified as being otter positive in the present study, with signs of otter being found at a number of new sites. Otter presence was also recorded in the headwater reaches and a holt was found in this zone of R. Araglin. The fact that the presence of otters was found at sites recorded as negative in the previous surveys suggests either an increase in the otter population of the Araglin Valley, or expansion of the area utilised by already existing otters.

Previous surveys of otter presence have usually been based on sites chosen at random and/or on the basis of access to the river; in the present study the field survey was carried out along entire watercourses. This method is more suited to the obtaining of more detailed information on otter presence in a relatively small area than is the traditional site-based survey method (see Ottino, 1995).

Spraints were the commonest otter signs found, but with a major decrease in abundance being noted in March – presumably in connection with meteorological conditions (heavy rain followed by flooding). The highest numbers of spraints were found in winter and spring. This trend was most clearly seen in the central home range (Home Range 2), and could be due to the emergence of cubs, or to the reinforcement of dominance relationships within the otter population when young animals become independent and establish their own home ranges (Chanin, 1985). Cub tracks were found in December near a holt in Home Range 2, with the larger tracks of an adult female. On their study rivers in Wales, Mason & Macdonald (1987), found that most births occurred between early winter and spring. Similarly, in a study carried out in central Scotland, Green *et al.* (1984) found most evidence for the presence of young cubs in winter and spring. On the basis of the very small size of tracks found near the holt, and because cubs leave the den about 70 days after birth, it is possible to suggest that a minimum of two cubs were born in early winter in the central home range. Other larger cub tracks recorded in the following months and near to the home range boundaries (sometimes associated with very small spraints) suggest that these cubs had grown up and had started to patrol the territory with their mother. Therefore, the increase in marking in winter and spring indicates the emergence of cubs during winter and their first territorial patrols in spring.

In Home Range 1, the monthly number of spraints showed a small peak in February, followed by a larger peak in spring. The low number of spraints in the autumn and winter months was probably due to different strategies for hunting salmonid fishes during the year, and accords with variations in water flow and temperature. Deep waters are favoured by salmonids in the autumn/winter seasons, when food consumption and energy expenditure are at a minimum, and also they provide good cover in the colder months (Bridcut, 1992). The R. Douglas' catchment around Kilworth has faster flowing waters and a lower number of pool habitats than R. Araglin. The first increase in the number of spraints was probably related to increased prey availability due to the occurrence of breeding season of frogs, *Rana temporaria*. The second increase in spraint numbers presumably reflects greater salmonid availability.

Comparisons of Figs. 2 & 3 and Figs. 6 & 7 show that the frequency of otter signs and the percentage vegetation cover in the Kilworth catchment area have opposite trends. However, in R. Glenfinish these two trends show a similar pattern. This is probably due to the different types of vegetation occurring in the two areas: widespread conifers in the Kilworth Forest and a prevalence of deciduous species around R. Glenfinish.

The lowest numbers of otter signs and spraints were recorded in the Kilworth catchment area where watercourses flow through conifer plantations. Other studies of interactions between forestry and freshwater ecosystems (Mason & Macdonald, 1987; Wallace, 1995) have identified changes in water chemistry, turbidity, flow regime and temperature that arise from forestry practices, and which may affect riverine flora and fauna (Mason & Macdonald, 1987; O'Halloran & Giller, 1993). In particular, the acidification of streams in conifer afforested catchments can affect fish densities negatively and consequently otter populations too. Despite this, in the Kilworth area fish populations are relatively high (Clenaghan, 1996). Giller *et al.* (1993) found that salmonid densities in the south of Ireland were lowest in moorland catchments and highest in agricultural ones, and also tended to decrease with increasing catchment afforestation. However, the fish present in the forest habitats were in as good condition as those in the two other habitats. This particular trend could be due to a negative physical habitat effect (Giller *et al.*, 1993). The low number of otter signs and spraints may relate to the relatively small size of the streams in the Kilworth area, to relatively low salmonid densities, or to the fact that relatively few large (3+) fish have been recorded in much of the catchment (Clenaghan, 1996). On the other hand, in the R. Glenfinish, the dominant tree species included ash, *Fraxinus excelsior*, willow, *Salix* spp., sycamore, *Acer pseudoplatanus* and *Rubus* spp., and there was a positive correlation between otter signs and percentage vegetation cover. Similar conclusions have been reached in other studies (Macdonald & Mason, 1983, 1985; Green *et al.*, 1984) where the marking activities of otters were mostly associated with mature ash and sycamore.

Another factor that has a limiting effect upon otters in the study area is river depth. At the headwater stretches, where the level of water was very low (and there where few fish), no signs of otter were found. Furthermore, freshwater pools were positively associated with otter signs, which agrees with the results of Macdonald & Mason (1982), Kruuk *et al.* (1986) and Kemenes & Demeter (1995). Water flow velocity also was negatively correlated with otter presence. Where the water flow velocity is low, the river tends to provide good fishing pools for otters.

All of these results suggest that in Ireland a suitable habitat for the otter must include (apart from low pollution levels, limited disturbance and good food availability) dense bank side cover (principally composed of deciduous species such as ash and sycamore), and good pools with relatively low water flow velocities, as is the case elsewhere in Europe (e.g. Macdonald *et al.*, 1978; Jenkins & Burrows, 1980; Macdonald & Mason, 1983; Adrian *et al.*, 1985). The Araglin Valley can be considered as being "good otter habitat", as particularly are the R. Glenfinish and the middle course of the R. Araglin. Other areas of the valley may only offer secondary habitats although they are utilised to some degree.

References

Adrian, M.I., Wilden, W. & Delibes, M. (1985). Otter distribution and agriculture in south-western Spain. In: *Proceedings of the XXVII Congress of the International Union of Game Biologists, Brussels, 1985*: 17-21.

Barus, V. & Zejda, J. (1981). The European otter (*Lutra lutra*) in the Czech Socialist Republic. *Acta Scientiarum Naturalium Academiae Scientiarum Bohemicae Brno*, **15** (12): 1-41.

Bridcut, E. (1992). *Diet, distribution and growth of natural field populations of brown trout* (*Salmo trutta L.*). PhD thesis. Cork; National University of Ireland.

Chanin, P.R.F. & Jefferies, D.J. (1978). The decline of the otter *Lutra lutra* in Britain: an analysis of hunting records and discussion of causes. *Biological Journal of the Linnean Society*, **10**: 305-328.

Chanin, P.R.F. (1985). *The natural history of otters*. London; Christopher Helm.

Chapman, P.J & Chapman, L.L. (1982). *Otter survey of Ireland, 1980-81*. London; The Vincent Wildlife Trust.

Clenaghan, C. (1996). *The spatial and temporal variation in the freshwater ecology and hydro-chemistry of an Irish conifer afforested catchment*. PhD thesis. Cork; National University of Ireland.

Dadd, M.N. (1970). Overlap of variation in British and European mammal populations. *Symposia of the Zoological Society of London*, **26**: 117-125.

Fairley, J.S. (1972). Food of otters (*Lutra lutra*) from Co. Galway, Ireland and notes on other aspects of their biology. *Journal of Zoology*, **166**: 469-474.

Foster-Turley, P., Macdonald, S.M. & Mason, C.F. (Eds.) (1990). *Otters: an action plan for their conservation*. Gland; International Union for the Conservation of Nature & Natural Resources.

Giller, P.S., O'Halloran, J., Hernan, R., Roche, N., Clenaghan, C., Evans, J., Kiely, G.K., Morris, P., Allot, N., Brennan, M., Reynolds, J., Cooke, D., Kelly-Quinn, M., Bracken, J., Coyle, S. & Farrel, E.P. (1993). An integrated study of forested catchments in Ireland. *Journal of the Society of Irish Foresters*, **50**: 70-88.

Green, J., Green, R. & Jefferies, D.J. (1984). A radio-tracking survey of otter *Lutra lutra* on a Perthshire river system. *Lutra*, **27**: 85-145.

Hinton, M.A.C. (1920). The Irish otter. *Annals and Magazine of Natural History*, **13**: 388-394.

Jenkins, D. (1980). Ecology of otters in northern Scotland. I. Otter (*Lutra lutra*) breeding and dispersion in mid-Deeside, Aberdeenshire, in 1974-79. *Journal of Animal Ecology*, **49**: 713-735.

Jenkins, D. & Burrows, G.O. (1980). Ecology of otters in northern Scotland. III. The use of faeces as indicators of otter (*Lutra lutra*) density and distribution. *Journal of Animal Ecology*, **49**: 755-774.

Kemenes, I. & Demeter, A. (1995). A predictive model of the effect of environmental factors on the occurrence of otters (*Lutra lutra* L.) in Hungary. *Hystrix (n.s.)*, **7**: 209-218.

Kruuk, H., Conroy, J.W.H., Glimmerveen, U. & Ouwerkerk, E.J. (1986). The use of spraints to survey populations of otters (*Lutra lutra*). *Biological Conservation*, **35**: 187-194.

Kyne, M.J., Kyne, M.J. & Fairley, J.S. (1990). A summer survey of otter sign on Roundstone Bog, South Connemara. *Irish Naturalists' Journal*, **23**: 273-276.

Lunnon, R.M. & Reynolds, J.D. (1991). Distribution of the otter (*Lutra lutra*) in Ireland, and its value as a indicator of habitat quality. In: D.W. Jeffrey & B. Madden (eds.), *Bioindicators and environmental management*: 435-443. London; Academic Press.

Lynch, M.J. & O'Sullivan, W.M. (1993). Cranial form and sexual dimorphism in the Irish otter *Lutra lutra* L. *Biology and Environment, Proceedings of the Royal Irish Academy (Series B)*, **93**: 97-105.

Macdonald, S.M. & Mason, C.F. (1982). The otter in central Portugal. *Biological Conservation*, **22**: 207-215.

Macdonald, S.M. & Mason, C.F. (1983). Some factors influencing the distribution of otters (*Lutra lutra*). *Mammal Review*, **13**: 1-10.

Macdonald, S.M. & Mason, C.F. (1985). Otters, their habitat and conservation in north-east Greece. *Biological Conservation*, **31**: 191-210.

Macdonald, S.M. & Mason, C.F. (1990). Action plan for European otter. In: P. Foster-Turley, S. Macdonald & C. Mason (eds.), *Otters: an action plan for their conservation*: 29-40. Gland; International Union for the Conservation of Nature & Natural Resources.

Macdonald, S.M. & Mason, C.F. (1992). *Status and conservation needs of the otter (Lutra lutra) in the Western Palearctic (Report for the Standing Committee of the Convention on the Conservation of European Wildlife and Natural Habitats)*. Strasbourg; Council of Europe Press.

Macdonald, S.M., Mason, C.F. & Coghill, I.S. (1978). The otter and its conservation in the River Teme catchment. *Journal of Applied Ecology*, **15**: 373 384.

Mason, C.F. & Macdonald, S.M. (1983). Some factors influencing the distribution of mink (*Mustela vison*). *Journal of Zoology*, **200**: 281-283.

Mason, C.F. & Macdonald, S.M. (1986). *Otters. Ecology and conservation*. Cambridge; Cambridge University Press.

Mason, C.F. & Macdonald, S.M. (1987). The use of spraints for surveying otter *Lutra lutra* populations: an evaluation. *Biological Conservation*, **41**: 167-177.

Mason, C.F. & O'Sullivan, W.M. (1993). Heavy metals in the livers of otters, *Lutra lutra* from Ireland. *Journal of Zoology*, **231**: 675-678.

Mason, C.F. (1995). Habitat quality, water quality and otter distribution. *Hystrix (n.s.)*, **7**: 195-207.

Melquist, W.E. & Hornocker, M.G. (1983). Resource partitioning and coexistence of sympatric mink and river otter populations. In: J.A. Chapman & D. Pursley (eds.), *Proceedings of the World Furbearer Conference, Frostburg, Maryland, USA*: 187-200.

Miller, G.S. (1912). *Catalogue of the mammals of western Europe exclusive of Russia in the collection of the British Museum*. London; British Museum (Natural History).

O'Halloran, J. & Giller, P.S. (1993). Forestry and the ecology of streams and rivers: lessons from abroad. *Irish Forestry*, **50**: 35-52.

O'Sullivan, W.M. (1991). The distribution of otters *Lutra lutra* within a major Irish river system, the Munster Blackwater catchment, 1988-90. *Irish Naturalists' Journal*, **23**: 442-446.

O'Sullivan, W.M. (1992). *An estimate of otter density on part of the Blackwater catchment in summer*. PhD thesis. Cork; National University of Ireland.

O'Sullivan, W.M., Macdonald, S.M. & Mason, C.F. (1993). Organochlorine pesticide residues and PCBs in otter spraints from southern Ireland. *Biology and Environment, Proceedings of the Royal Irish Academy (Series B)*, **93**: 55-57.

Ottino, P. (1995). *La lontra. Ricerche in Abruzzo. Andromeda Editrice*, **30**: 1-80.

Ottino, P & Giller, P.S. (in press). Food habits of the otter in the Araglin Valley, Southern Ireland. *Biology and Environment, Proceedings of the Royal Irish Academy (Series B)*.

Reuther, C. (1995). Habitat networking: a new change for the otters in Europe? *Hystrix (n.s.)*, **7**: 229-238.

Sandegren, F., Olsson, M. & Reuthergardh, L. (1980). Der ruckgang der Fischotterpopulation in Schweden. In: C. Reuther & A Festetics (eds.), *Der Fischotter in Europa - Verbreitung, Bedrohung, Erhaltung*: 107-113. Oderhaus u. Göttingen; privately published.

Smiddy, P. (1993). The status of the otter in East Cork and West Waterford. *Irish Naturalists' Journal*, **25**: 236-240.

Stephens, M. (1957). *The otter report*. London; Universities' Federation for Animal Welfare.

Taylor, I.R., Jefferies, M.J., Abbot, S.G., Hulbert, I.A.R. & Virdee S.R.K. (1988). Distribution, habitat and diet of the otter *Lutra lutra* in the Drina catchment, Yugoslavia. *Biological Conservation*, **45**: 109-119.

Wallace, J.L. (1995). *The interaction between forestry and freshwater ecosystems in South West Ireland*. MSc thesis. Cork; National University of Ireland.

Wise, M.H., Linn, I.J. & Kennedy, C.R. (1981). A comparison of the feeding biology of mink (*Mustela vison*) and otter (*Lutra lutra*). *Journal of Zoology*, **195**: 181-213.

Wozencraft, W.C. (1989). Classification of the recent Carnivora. In: J.L. Gittleman (ed.), *Carnivore biology, ecology and evolution*: 569-593. London; Chapman & Hall.

CHAPTER 16

Wildlife management and scientific research: a retrospective evaluation of two badger removal operations for the control of bovine tuberculosis

Frank A.M. Tuyttens*, Lucy Barron, Lucy M. Rogers, Peter J. Mallinson & David W. Macdonald

Abstract

Problems caused by wildlife rarely allow sufficient time for rigorous scientific research to be conducted so that the effectiveness of various management strategies can be tested and compared before application in the field. An appropriate example is that of the Eurasian badger, *Meles meles*, in SW England. Badgers have been subjected to various government-organised culling strategies between 1975 and 1997 because of their (presumed) role in the transmission to cattle of the bacterium *Mycobacterium bovis*, the causative agent of bovine tuberculosis (TB). However, after 22 years of badger culling little can be concluded about the effectiveness of the different disease control strategies because of the lack of a scientific control experiment. Data show, however, that the two most recent strategies, the Interim Strategy and the Live Test Strategy, did not halt the rising incidence of TB infection in cattle. Our study of a badger population that was subjected to both strategies allowed us to highlight, quantify and compare the practical difficulties of applying these strategies in the field. Although these operations failed to prevent further infections in cattle in the study area, they drastically reduced TB prevalence in the badger population. However, decisions about which badgers to kill often seemed illogical and inconsistent because it was not known where the boundaries between social groups lay. The small proportion of badgers subjected to a low-sensitivity diagnostic test, occupiers refusing access to their land, and imperfect badger sett surveys, were likely to exacerbate this problem in the Live Test Strategy. The Interim Strategy was much less expensive and time-consuming, but the small area of badger removal combined with poor trapping success may have resulted in an operation that was irrelevant epidemiologically. We use this case study to illustrate how detailed research, conducted in parallel with wildlife management strategies, can be useful in elucidating why some strategies appear more effective than others. Therefore, such case studies can also be a useful addition to, but not a replacement for, a proper scientific experiment where one or more strategies are tested against a no-treatment control.

Introduction

Wildlife managers are often faced with problems caused by wildlife which call for immediate action. Unfortunately, the efficacies of different management options have rarely been investigated fully by scientific research before they are applied in the field. The urgency and scale of the problems caused by wildlife often leave lit-

---

* Corresponding author.

Mustelids in a modern world
Management and conservation aspects of small carnivore: human interactions
edited by Huw I. Griffiths, pp. 247–265
© *2000 Backhuys Publishers, Leiden, The Netherlands*

tle opportunity for conducting rigorous, expensive, and time-consuming scientific experiments.

In Britain, the Ministry of Agriculture, Fisheries and Food (MAFF) has responsibility for dealing with one wildlife problem which illustrates these points exceedingly well. The Eurasian badger, *Meles meles*, is highly protected in this country and has even become a symbol of wildlife conservation. However, as much as this animal is loved by conservationists and many others, it is believed to cause serious problems to farmers. There is strong, albeit circumstantial, evidence that the badger is a wildlife reservoir of bovine tuberculosis (TB), caused by the bacterium *Mycobacterium bovis* (Muirhead *et al.*, 1974; Hayden, 1993; Nolan & Wilesmith, 1994). The failure to eradicate this disease has been linked to cross-species infection from badgers to cattle, particularly in SW England where badger densities are highest (Krebs *et al.*, 1997).

Between 1975 and 1997, MAFF implemented a series of reactive strategies to kill badgers that were suspected of having spread TB to cattle - the so-called Badger Removal Operations or BROs (Zuckerman, 1980; Dunnet *et al.*, 1986; Krebs *et al.*, 1997). As the same strategy was used throughout Britain, it was impossible to compare the efficacy of different strategies with one another, or with doing nothing. At the end of 1994, however, an experiment was put into operation to compare the effectiveness of two disease control strategies. Following a confirmed herd breakdown (*i.e.* the detection of a cow reacting to skin tests for TB) of presumed badger origin, the extant "Interim BRO" or the new "Live Test BRO" were randomly allocated. Under the Interim BRO Strategy badgers were trapped and shot on that part of the farm (called the "reactor land") where disease transmission between badgers and cattle was believed to have taken place. Under Live Test BROs badgers were trapped not only on the breakdown farm, but also in surrounding areas in which other cattle herds could have been at risk from the same badgers. During the first four days (the "Live Test Week") live-trapped badgers were blood tested for *M. bovis* with an indirect ELISA test using a 25 kDa antigen (Goodger *et al.,* 1994). Badgers with a positive ELISA test, and badgers trapped at a sett where another badger had been found to be ELISA-positive, were killed. All other badgers were released. The trapping and shooting of badgers from TB-positive setts identified during the Live Test Week was continued afterwards until no more badgers were caught for a fortnight. The Live Test BRO Strategy had raised high hopes as a new policy to deal with the TB problem in SW England that specifically targeted those live-trapped badgers that were found to have a positive reaction to the ELISA test. Unfortunately, the sensitivity of the ELISA test on an individual basis was found to be below expectation so that badger setts (rather than individual badgers) were taken as the unit of badger removal.

In September 1999, however, the experiment was abandoned because of poor statistical power and the lack of a non-interference 'control' (virtually no farmers refused MAFF permission to carry out a BRO) made data from this comparative trial difficult to interpret (Krebs *et al.*, 1997). The resource-intensive nature of the Live Test trial had also created a considerable backlog of BROs that were still to be carried out. Furthermore, a steady rise since 1986 in the prevalence of *M. bovis* in badgers and in the number of badger-related herd breakdowns in SW England aroused much concern about the effectiveness of both Interim and Live Test strategies (Krebs *et al.*, 1997; Tuyttens & Macdonald, 1998).

In brief, despite 22 years of government-organised badger culling, very little could be concluded regarding the effect of different types of BROs on the incidence of TB in cattle. One could only speculate about the likely reasons why neither the Interim Strategy nor the Live Test Strategy had resulted in the hoped-for decline of the TB problem in Britain. Following the recommendations of a scientific review group (Krebs *et al.*, 1997) MAFF has recently decided to adopt a more rigorous scientific approach to evaluate the relative effectiveness and costs of proactive and reactive badger culling strategies, as compared to no culling (MAFF, 1997).

We have studied a badger population in an area in SW England with a long history of repeated herd breakdowns. Since the start of our study in 1995, this population has been subjected to MAFF's two most recent reactive culling strategies (a Live Test and an Interim BRO). The general aim of this study was to investigate the consequences of such culling operations on the behaviour and population dynamics of badgers, with respect to the control of TB in particular. In addition, the study has provided a unique opportunity to conduct a detailed evaluation of the practicalities and effectiveness of these operations in the field. The specific objective of this paper is to illustrate how practical difficulties encountered in field implementation of these control strategies may have contributed to their apparent failure to control TB in England. Such information is likely to be useful for the design of a more successful TB-control strategy in the future. The more general objective is to illustrate how, even in situations where strategies for dealing with wildlife problems are being applied in the field without leaving room for a no-treatment control, research conducted in parallel with wildlife management can help to highlight the strengths and weaknesses of one, or various, control strategies.

Methods

In March 1995 we established a 16-17 km² study area around North Nibley (Gloucestershire, UK) where there has been a long history of repeated TB infections in cattle (see Tuyttens, 1999). Since the start of our study there have been two BROs in our study area. The first one was a Live Test Strategy BRO and was conducted in late summer 1995. The second BRO took place almost a year later and was of the Interim Strategy type. Thus we were able to compare the practicalities associated with these two types of badger control and to investigate their success at eradicating TB in the local badger population.

As shown in Table 1, the behaviour and ecology of this badger population was studied using a variety of established field techniques such as annual bait-marking in spring (Kruuk, 1978; Delahay *et al.*, in press), live-trapping in late spring, summer and autumn (Cheeseman & Harris, 1982), radio-tracking in June-August, September and October (Cheeseman & Mallinson, 1980; Tuyttens, 1999), and automatic night video-surveillance for at least a month during July-August (Stewart *et al.*, 1997a,b). We also conducted badger sett surveys in March 1995 (recording all active main, subsidiary and annexe setts but not outliers; for a description of these different types of setts, see Wilson *et al.*, 1997) and in the winter of 1997-1998 (recording all types of setts). All badgers that we live-trapped were anaesthetised, identity-tattooed (on initial capture) and had various biological parameters measured.

Table 1. Fieldwork schedule in North Nibley from the beginning of the study in March 1995 until the end of 1997. The shaded areas indicate the middle of the BROs.

Month	Technique	1995	1996	1997
J				
F				
M	Establish study area (incl. active sett survey)	✓	–	–
A	Bait-marking	✓	✓	✓
J	'Spring' trap-up	✓	✓	✓
J	Radio-tracking (period A) and	✓	✓	✓
A	night video-surveillance	✓	✓	–
S	'Summer' trap-up	–	✓	✓
	Radio-tracking (period B)	✓	✓	✓
O	Radio-tracking (period C)	✓	✓	✓
N	'Autumn' trap-up	✓	✓	✓
D	Sett survey	–	–	✓

Their TB-status was diagnosed by ELISA (Goodger *et al.*, 1994) and by isolation of the bacterium from faeces, urine, tracheal aspirate and pus from wounds (Pritchard *et al.*, 1986). Badgers killed during road-traffic accidents in North Nibley or during MAFF's BROs also were examined for the presence of *M. bovis* by biological and cultural tests as described by Little *et al.* (1982).

We describe the different stages of each BRO and the scale of the two operations in terms of area of removal, time and labour. We also critically evaluate which badgers were and were not trapped/killed during the removal operations. From bait-marking, trapping, and radio-tracking results it could be determined which setts belonged to the same social groups and which of these groups had used latrines on the reactor land (*i.e.* fields grazed by infected cattle). RANGES V (ITE, Wareham, Dorset, UK) was used to derive group and individual home ranges using the 95% minimum convex polygon method (see Tuyttens, 1999). The percentage of reactor land included in the range of each social group and radio-tracked individual then was calculated using a Geographic Information System (MapInfo). The setts found during the surveys conducted by MAFF prior to BROs were compared with our sett surveys in March 1995 and winter 1997-1998. However, as these surveys were not conducted at the same time, differences may not always reflect survey inadequacies. The probability that badgers, which in theory should have been targeted according to the prescribed BRO procedures, were actually trapped (and/or killed) in practice was also estimated.

Results

Live Test BRO

In January 1995 two cows from a farm in the centre of our study area had a positive reaction during routine testing for TB using the intradermal skin test. By method of elimination, badgers had been identified as the likely source of the infection, so a BRO was approved in March 1995. The treatment allocated by MAFF was a Live Test Strategy. Table 2 shows the time and man-days required for the different procedures of this BRO.

Table 2. Time-scale and labour associated with the different stages of the Live Test BRO *vs.* the Interim BRO that took place in North Nibley.

	Live Test	**Interim**
1. Badger activity survey:	10.06 – 04.07.95	03.06.96
- duration (days):	25	0.5
- area (in km^2):	17.5	<0.25
- man days:	33	1.5
2. Occupier visits:	12.07 – 03.08.95	03.06.96
- duration (days):	23	0.5
- number of occupiers:	34	1
- man days:	8	0.5
3. Siting traps:	14.08 – 18.08.95	04.06.96
- duration (days):	5	1
- number of traps:	65	6
- man days:	8.5	2
4. Pre-baiting traps:	21.08 – 01.09.95	04.06 – 10.06.96
- duration (days):	11	7
- man days:	40	5
5. Live Test Week:	04.09 – 08.09.95	N/A
- duration (days):	5	
- mandays:	30.5	
6. Trap-out:	11.09 – 16.10.95	11.06 – 09.07.96
- duration (days):	36	29
- number of traps (initially):	14	6
- man days:	?	19.5
7. Clear-up:	04.10 – 16.10.95	09.07.96
- man days:	7	0.5
SUMMARY:		
- total duration (days):	129	37
- total man days (excl. Trap-out)	127	9.5
- area trapped/removed (km^2):	6.5	0.2
- number of badgers killed:	27	2
(of which culture positive)	(10)	(1)

Determining where to site traps

One of the first steps of a Live Test BRO was the determination of the area around the breakdown farm in which badgers ought to be trapped and tested for TB with the Live Test. This required a Zone of Influence to be drawn around the breakdown farm (Fig. 1). In theory, the boundaries of this zone should delineate how far badgers using the reactor land travelled. MAFF personnel established a 4.1 km^2 Zone of Influence on the basis of a survey for badger field signs (setts, latrines and runs) covering a large area around the breakdown farm. This zone was only a very rough representation of the actual area travelled by badgers using the reactor land as suggested by bait-marking (Fig. 1a) and radio-tracking (Fig. 1b). This first stage of the Live Test BRO also was hampered because four of the 34 landowners refused MAFF access to their land. Although none of that land directly bordered onto the reactor land, these refusals could have had considerable practical importance as they prevented MAFF from siting traps in the vicinity of at least four main badger setts.

N

↑

1km

——— range of non-removed social groups

━━━ range of removed social groups

▓▓▓ reactor land

- - - zone of influence

⊔⊔⊔⊔ trial area (herds at risk)

● position of main sett

Fig. 1. Map of the North Nibley study area with (A) the social group ranges (estimated as the 95% minimum convex polygons drawn around the outermost latrines used by each group as revealed by bait-marking in the spring of 1995), and (B) the individual home ranges of radio-tracked badgers (estimated as the 95% minimum convex polygons drawn around the outermost fixes collected in June-August 1995), plotted on top of the reactor land, Zone of Influence and Trial Area of the Live Test BRO. The numbers indicate the position of the 'main' sett of the corresponding social group given in Table 3. Note that the range of one of the removed groups (3, New Sett) was not known in 1995 because it was not included in the bait-marking trial that year.

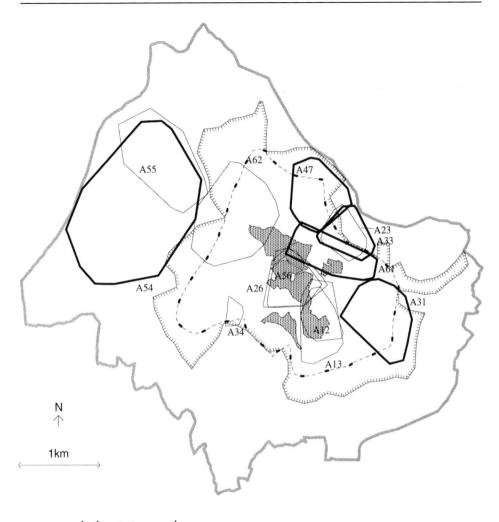

A62   badger tattoo number

⎯⎯   home range of adult female

▬▬   home range of adult male

▦   reactor land

•---   zone of influence

⊥⊥⊥⊥   trial area (herds at risk)

Fig. 2. Active setts found in the North Nibley study area during our survey in March 1995 (non-outlier setts only) (small symbols), during MAFF's survey in June-July 1995 as part of the Live Test operation (medium-sized symbols), and during our survey in the winter of 1997-1998 (large symbols). Setts identified as infected during the Live Test Week are shaded.

As the Zone of Influence cut through farms, a Trial Area was drawn up, the boundaries of which were usually the outer boundaries of cattle-owning farms containing land in the Zone of Influence (Fig. 1). Cattle herds within the Trial Area were termed 'herds at risk'. In this case ten herds at risk had been identified. During their survey for badger activity MAFF had found 49 setts (of which 20 were inactive) in the 6.5 km^2 Trial Area (Fig. 2). Forty-three traps were positioned in the vicinity of active setts and pre-baited daily for two weeks. Another 22 traps were sited near the inactive setts and baited only once (unless the sett became active).

MAFF staff found 93% (13/14) of the active non-outlier setts that we had found in the Trial Area in March of the same year. The main sett of the Brackenbury social group was not found during MAFF's survey and the main sett of the Villa social group was wrongly classified as inactive (Table 3). MAFF found 66% (23/35) of the active setts that were found during our survey in January 1998. Most setts that had not been found were small outlier setts. Although the possibility cannot be ruled out that some of these setts had become active after MAFF's survey, it is likely that a small proportion of badgers in the Trial Area evaded capture because the setts they were using at that time had not been found.

Live Test Week

During Live Test week, 36 badgers were trapped from 19 setts. The number of badgers trapped/sett ranged from one (10 setts) to four (three setts). The TB status of 31 badgers was tested with the ELISA test. Nine (29%) badgers from eight different setts had a positive ELISA test and were killed. In total 18 badgers were killed during the Live Test Week as eight more badgers trapped at these ELISA-positive setts were shot instantly at the trap site and one badger from an ELISA-negative sett was killed erroneously.

From our bait-marking studies five months earlier in the year, it was deduced that the 49 setts from which MAFF attempted to trap badgers during the Live Test Week belonged to 14 social groups, and that the eight infected setts that MAFF had identified fell within the ranges of six social groups (Table 3, Fig. 1a). Only five out of these 14 groups (with some or all setts trapped during the Live Test Week), and only two of these six groups from which infected setts had been identified, actually used the reactor land in March 1995. The range of one of the removed groups (Steep Bank) did not even include part of the Zone of Influence (Fig. 1a). On the other hand, eight groups in our study area were not trapped during the Live Test Week, although our bait-marking indicated that in spring half of these groups had used latrines in the Trial Area (Table 3). On the basis of the bait-marking results it appeared, therefore, that MAFF tested and removed badgers from too large an area if the objective was to target badgers that only had access to the reactor land. On the other hand, MAFF seemed to have operated in too small an area if the objective was to target badgers that had access to the Trial Area. We do not believe that this conclusion is invalidated by seasonal differences in space use, because it is backed up by the results of radio-tracking in June-August 1995, *i.e.* just before the BRO took place (Fig. 1b, Table 3). All home ranges of the badgers radio-tracked in June-August 1995 that included reactor land or Trial Area belonged to social groups whose March 1995 bait-marking ranges also included reactor land or Trial Area, respectively (Table 3).

Table 3. Indications from our pre-BRO bait-marking and radio-tracking studies about which social groups were using the reactor land of, and the Trial Area around, the first breakdown farm in our study. The number of total latrines (L) of each group on the reactor land and Trial Area, as well as the percentages of the estimated ranges (%) of social groups and of individual radio-tracked badgers that included reactor land and Trial Area are given.

	REACTOR LAND			TRIAL AREA		
	Bait-marking	Radio-telemetry		Bait-marking		Radio-telemetry
	L	%	%	L	%	%
Removed groups:						
1. Maitlands	0/26	0	N/A	25/26	97.8	N/A
2. Millend	2/10	37.8	19 (A61)	10/10	100	100 (A61)
3. New Sett*	N/A	N/A	0 (A34)	N/A	N/A	96 (A34)
4. Park Bank	0/24	0	0 (A47)	24/24	100	88.6 (A47)
5. Steep Bank	0/14	0	N/A	9/14	82.7	N/A
6. Westridge	3/17	19.3	37.5 (A12)	17/17	100	100 (A12)
			25.5 (A13)			100 (A13)
Non-removed groups with main setts trapped during the Live Test Week:						
7. Monument	1/21	14.6	N/A	16/21	64.1	N/A
8. Quarry	3/9	42	59.3 (A56)	9/9	95.4	100 (A56)
			59.9 (A26)			100 (A26)
9. Sharncliffe	0/33	0	N/A	20/33	82.4	N/A
10. Villa	0/12	0.7	4.1 (A62)	12/12	94.5	91.5 (A62)
11. Waterley	0/39	0	0 (A31)	36/39	96.6	96.6 (A31)
Non-removed groups with some setts (exc. its main sett) trapped during the Live Test Week:						
12. Footpath	0/7	0	N/A	4/7	86.8	N/A
13. Nuclear	0/11	0	0 (A23)	9/11	57.6	58.2 (A23)
			0 (A33)			48.2 (A33)
14. Ruby's	0/27	0	N/A	11/27	39.4	N/A
Groups with no setts trapped during the Live Test Week:						
15. Ammonite	0/28	0	0 (A54)	0/28	0	0 (A54)
			0 (A55)			0 (A55)
16. Boisley	0/7	0	N/A	3/7	38.4	N/A
17. Brackenbury	0/8	0	N/A	6/8	71	N/A
18. Helicopter	0/13	0	N/A	0/13	0	N/A
19. Lay-by	0/21	0	N/A	4/21	0.9	N/A
20. Maggs	0/6	0	N/A	0/6	0	N/A
21. Spuncombe	0/8	0	N/A	2/8	28.9	N/A
22. Yercombe	0/16	0	N/A	0/16	0	N/A

* New Sett was not bait-marked in the spring of 1995.

Furthermore, these percentages of the home ranges and corresponding group ranges that included reactor land or Trial Area were correlated significantly (reactor land: r_s = 0.979, n = 12, P <0.001; Trial Area: r_s = 0.643, n = 12, P <0.05).

It is also interesting to compare the ELISA results from the Live Test Week with those obtained for badgers that we had trapped a couple of months earlier during June 1995. During the latter, we captured 36 badgers from the same 14 social groups that had been targeted during the Live Test Week. Only seven of these 36 badgers were then found to be ELISA-positive. Within a period of only two to three months the prevalence of ELISA-positive badgers from these 14 groups thus appears to have increased from 19.4% to 29%, however, this difference is not statistically significant ($\chi^2 = 0.4$, d.f. $= 1$, P $= 0.527$). The decision of which setts to label as TB-infected and, hence, to remove, would have been very different if the BRO had been conducted a couple of months earlier. On the basis of the June trap-up, at least one ELISA-positive badger would have been found at six of the 14 social groups again, but only four of these social groups (Maitlands, New Sett, Steep Bank and Westridge) would have been the same as the ones identified by MAFF (Table 4). Two social groups would have been targeted on the basis of the first set of test results but not on the basis of the second, and *vice versa*.

The discrepancy in the identification of infected setts (or social groups) from the badgers sampled during these two trapping periods is due to the same badgers having a different reaction to the ELISA test at different times, and to different badgers being captured and ELISA-tested. Regarding the former, Table 4 shows that five badgers that were found to be ELISA-positive during the Live Test Week also had been TB tested in June but only two were found to be positive. This may reflect true sero-conversion. Alternatively, it may reflect the poor diagnostic power of the ELISA test (Clifton-Hadley *et al.*, 1995). Regarding differences in which individuals were tested, 39% (12/31) of the badgers ELISA tested during the Live Test Week had not been tested in June, and 44% of the 36 badgers tested in June were not ELISA tested during the Live Test Week. This could be due partly to badgers having died or dispersed during the time between these two trapping periods, and partly due to different animals evading capture at different times. Our conservative estimate is that only 50% of the cubs and 44% of the adults from the groups whose main setts were included in MAFF's trap rounds (see Table 3) were trapped during the Live-Test Week (see Tuyttens, 1999).

Trap-out of ELISA-positive setts

Following the Live Test Week, trapping at the ELISA-positive setts continued for four to six weeks (*i.e.* until no more badgers had been trapped for about a fortnight). Nine more badgers were trapped during this period. Post-mortem and bacteriological testing later revealed that of the 27 badgers killed during the entire BRO, ten were culture positive for *M. bovis* (Table 4).

The only known survivors from the six removed groups were a male cub and a radio-collared adult boar from the Park Bank group and a female cub from the Westridge group, despite records from trapping, video-surveillance (at Westridge only), radio-tracking and sett watching. Both badgers from Park Bank had been trapped at an ELISA-negative sett during the Live Test Week but released because MAFF did not know that this sett was linked to a TB-positive sett of the same social group.

There was one obvious example of a badger being killed because it had moved into the range of a TB-positive group during the BRO. A radio-collared adult boar (33A) from the ELISA-negative group Nuclear, was killed because it was captured after it had started to make excursions deep into the range of the neighbouring Millend group shortly after this group's TB-infected resident male (61A) had been killed during the Live Test Week. On post-mortem, badger 33A was found to be TB culture-positive as well.

Table 4. History of ELISA (e) and culture (c) test results for all badgers trapped by us in spring (Spr), summer (Sum) or autumn (Aut) or during MAFF's BROs that were found to be positive in at least one of the TB-tests between 1995 and 1997. Culture testing of badgers live-trapped by us consisted of the bacteriological examination of clinical samples of live-trapped badgers (faeces, urine, tracheal aspirate and bite wound swabs) for TB, while culture-testing of badgers killed by MAFF during BROs involved biological and bacteriological examination for TB post-mortem. '?' indicates that this animal was not tested. The ID numbers in bold indicate badgers killed during a BRO.

ID	Group	1995 Spr e	Spr c	BRO e	BRO c	Aut e	Aut c	1996 Spr e	Spr c	BRO e	BRO c	Sum e	Sum c	Aut e	Aut c	1997 Spr e	Spr c	Sum e	Sum c	Aut e	Aut c
4A	Spuncombe	+	-	?	?	?	?	-	-	?	?	-	-	-	-	-	-	?	?	?	?
7A	Sharncliffe	+	-	-	?	-	-	?	?	?	?	?	?	?	?	?	?	?	?	?	?
8A	Sharncliffe	+	-	-	?	-	-	+	-	?	?	?	?	?	?	-	-	-	-	?	?
13A	Westridge	+	-	?	+																
14A	Westridge	-	-	-	+																
16A	Steep Bank	-	-	+	+																
27A	Quarry	+	-	?	?	?	?	?	?	?	?	?	?	?	?	?	?	?	?	?	?
28A	Quarry	-	+	?	?	?	?	?	?	?	?	?	?	?	?	?	?	?	?	?	?
32A	Steep Bank	+	+	-	+																
33A	Nuc/Millend	-	-	?	+																
34A	New Sett	+	-	+	+																
39B	Sharncliffe	?	?	?	?	?	?	?	?	?	?	+	-	?	?	+	-	?	?	?	?
40A	Boisley	+	-	?	?	?	?	?	?	?	?	?	?	?	?	?	?	?	?	?	?
41A	Boisley	-	-	?	?	?	?	?	?	?	+										
43A	Maitlands	+	-	+	+																
47A	Park Bank	-	-	+	-																
61A	Millend	-	-	+	+																
72A	Piers court	?	?	?	?	+	-	?	?	?	?	?	?	?	?	?	?	?	?	?	?
134A	Maitlands	?	?	+	+																
139A	Westridge	?	?	+	-																
155A	Park Bank	?	?	+	+																
157A	New Sett	?	?	+	-																

Following the BRO the proportion of ELISA-positive badgers within the Trial Area had been reduced drastically, at least until the end of 1997 (Tuyttens, 1999). During our seven trapping periods after the Live Test BRO we have found only two ELISA-positive badgers (8A & 39B) in the Trial Area, and one (72A) outside the Trial Area (Table 4). Not a single culture positive badger was found, apart from 41A which was killed during the second BRO (see below).

Interim BRO

The second herd breakdown in our study area occurred on a farm which was within the Trial Area of the above Live Test BRO. In November 1995 and January 1996, three and two reactors to tuberculin-testing, respectively, were found and removed from the cattle herd. As the origin of infection was believed to be badgers, a BRO of the Interim Strategy type was conducted in early summer 1996. As under the Interim Strategy badger control was confined to the reactor land only, this was a much smaller operation than the Live Test BRO (Table 2).

(A)

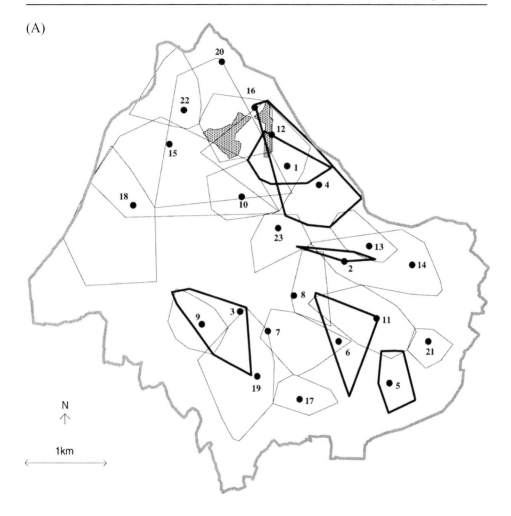

— range of non-removed social group

— range of removed social group

▓ reactor land

● position of main sett

Fig. 3. Map of the North Nibley study area with (A) the social group ranges (estimated as the 95% minimum convex polygons drawn around the outermost latrines used by each group as revealed by bait-marking in the spring of 1996), and (B) the individual home ranges of radio-tracked badgers (estimated as the 95% minimum convex polygons drawn around the outermost fixes collected in September 1996), plotted on top of the reactor land of the second breakdown farm. The numbers indicate the position of the 'main' sett of the corresponding social group given in Table 3.

(B)

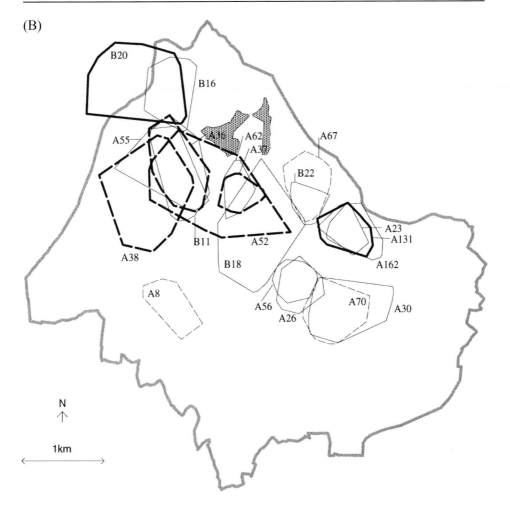

—— home range of adult female

—— home range of adult male

– – home range of yearling female

—— home range of yearling male

A62 badger tattoo number

▨ reactor land

Fig. 3. (Cont.)

In June 1996 MAFF personnel surveyed the 0.2 km² reactor land for badger activity. Three latrines, eight runs and two inactive setts were found. Six traps were put down and set to catch after a six day pre-baiting period. Three badgers were caught in total. A sow was found to be lactating and released; she was not trapped again. Two adult boars (41A from Boisley group and 58A from Footpath group) were killed. The BRO was closed in July 1996 due to lack of activity since the last badger was caught. One of the two boars (41A) was found to be positive for *M. bovis* in the post-mortem culture test.

During bait-marking in spring 1996 four active latrines were found on the reactor land. Three of these had been used by the Boisley social group, two by Footpath, one by Maitlands, and one by Park Bank. Figure 3a shows that on the basis of the bait-marking study it could be deduced that the spring ranges of two other groups (Ammonite and Maggs) included at least parts of the reactor land. Unlike the previous year, however, the determination of which groups of badgers used the reactor land on the basis of bait-marking results did not always agree with findings from the radio-tracking trial that took place in July-August. For example, none of the home ranges of the badgers from Ammonite and Park Bank that were radio-tracked immediately after the Interim BRO included reactor land (Fig. 3b).

Figure 2 shows that during our sett survey in 1995 we did not find any active non-outlier setts on the reactor land, but during our survey in January 1998 we found one subsidiary sett. Although the capture probability during this BRO could not be calculated, there is evidence that only a minority of the badgers from Boisley and Footpath - the two groups that most heavily used, and whose main setts were closest to, the reactor land - had been killed. Three badgers known to be alive evaded capture, and a fourth one was trapped but released because it was lactating. However, after this BRO we have not trapped any badger that had had a positive ELISA or culture test from these two groups. Hence our data suggest that the two BROs together have eradicated TB - at least in the short term - from all social groups within our study area, with the arguable exception of badger 39B from Sharncliffe that has had a positive ELISA-test but a negative culture-test twice (Table 4).

Discussion

The Live Test and Interim BROs investigated in this study have been very successful at reducing the prevalence of *M. bovis* amongst the badger population in our study area to very low levels for at least one to two years so far. Yet, our investigation of the practical difficulties encountered when implementing either control strategy in the field has exposed various stages during which infectious badgers could have escaped removal. That this appears not to have occurred in this particular case study may have involved a considerable amount of luck. Furthermore, the Live Test BRO did not prevent the breakdown of a 'herd at risk', and tuberculin-testing at the end of 1997 has just revealed that the index farm experienced another breakdown. This may suggest that badgers are not the only source of infection.

On a larger scale, neither strategy seemed able to halt the rising TB-incidence in cattle in SW England. This study has attempted, for the first time, to quantify and evaluate the practical difficulties encountered when conducting a Live Test or an

Interim Strategy in the field. It has also enabled us: (1) to compare the scale of these two reactive BROs in terms of area, time and labour (and hence approximate costs), (2) to investigate in considerable detail which badgers had been targeted, and (3) whether these targeted badgers had been removed effectively. Such information is likely to be useful for devising TB control strategies in the future.

Time and labour

There were striking differences in the time-scale, cost and labour associated with these two types of reactive BROs (Table 2). The Interim Strategy targeted only bad-gers using the reactor land (or the breakdown farm if this could not be identified), while Live Test operations aimed to remove badgers from contaminated setts from all land used by the badgers that could have caused the index breakdown. The lat-ter includes land extending out beyond this to the boundaries of all land with cattle herds considered to be at risk from these badgers. As a result, the mean area of removal was much larger for Live Test strategies (our study = 6.5 km², mean = c. 12 km²) than for Interim strategies (our study = 0.2 km², mean = c. 1 km²; Krebs *et al.*, 1997). The Interim BRO in our study area was completed in about five weeks while the Live Test BRO took three to four times as long. As Interim Strategies sim-ply required the non-selective removal of badgers (apart from lactating females) from the reactor land there was no need for a badger activity survey outside this area, or to visit neighbouring occupiers, or to test the TB status of live badgers. It was these three procedures that made Live Test BROs so much more costly and labour intensive. The long time-lag between the confirmation of TB in cattle and the actual BRO (>6 months in both our case studies) was a consequence of insufficient man power to cope with the work-load associated with Live Test operations. On the other hand, post-mortems revealed that ten times as many badgers with a positive culture test for TB had been killed during the Live Test BRO as compared to the Interim BRO. It could be argued that, ignoring labour and other expenses, the Live Test BRO in our study area was time better spent than the Interim Strategy: it removed 0.13 TB-positive badgers/day while the corresponding rate for the Interim Strategy was only 0.03 TB-positive badgers/day (Table 2).

Determining which badgers to target

As badgers live in social groups share a communal range and setts, the relevant epi-demiological unit for removal is the social group. However, under neither badger removal strategy were boundaries determined between social groups As a conse-quence, MAFF could not take account of the fact that as many as six social groups might have had access to part of the reactor land of the second breakdown farm (whilst only badgers from two social groups were removed). Neither could MAFF take account of the fact that during the Live Test Strategy the ranges of three groups that were not trapped overlapped the Trial Area, that badgers were killed that were unlikely to have foraged within the Zone of Influence, nor that several badgers trapped at uninfected setts were released while infected badgers had been found at other setts from the same social group. Although it is obvious that bait-marking and radio-tracking would have allowed MAFF to make more informed decisions about which badgers to target, both field techniques are too time consuming to be of practical value as part of a BRO.

Krebs *et al.* (1997) recognised this problem and recommended the use of the Dirichlet Tesellation Method (Doncaster & Woodroffe, 1993) as a low-cost alternative for identifying boundaries between social groups. This technique assumes that boundaries between neighbouring social groups are positioned halfway between their main setts. Although this method has been shown to be of some use at predicting the group ranges in undisturbed badger populations where the locations of the main setts were known already (Doncaster & Woodroffe, 1993; but see Delahay *et al.*, in press), our study indicates that the application of this method to other badger populations might be more problematic for two reasons. Firstly, the method crucially depends on identifying main setts correctly. Our sett survey has revealed that this is not straightforward in disturbed areas. Some groups appear to have more than one main sett, while some groups appear not to have any setts with the typical characteristics of a main sett. Secondly, in disturbed areas the social group ranges do not form a tight mosaic as in undisturbed areas, but instead ranges overlap considerably. Unoccupied patches also occur frequently (Figs. 1 & 3). Figure 4 illustrates that the boundaries between social groups predicted by the Dirichlet Tessellation Method agree poorly with the boundaries estimated from a bait-marking study.

In Live Test BROs the identification of TB-infected setts, or rather groups, has proven to be variable. Only 67% of the groups identified by MAFF as having at least one TB-infected sett also had been identified by us on the basis of the serological results from the badgers that we had trapped in the same area a couple of months earlier. The low trapping success during Live Test Week, coupled with the poor sensitivity of the Live Test (41%; Clifton-Hadley *et al.*, 1995) make it possible that many setts occupied by infected badgers were diagnosed incorrectly as being free from infection (Krebs *et al.*, 1997). In addition, a considerable number of active setts were not interfered with because they were on land to which MAFF was refused entry, or because they had not been found during the sett survey. The latter is unlikely to have been a problem in Interim Strategies as the area to be surveyed for badger activity belonged only to the owner of the breakdown farm and was typically much smaller.

Effectiveness of the removal of targeted badgers

Our study suggests that the majority of the badgers from the groups that used the reactor land had survived the Interim BRO. For the Live Test BRO on the other hand, there was evidence that only a small minority of badgers from infected setts identified during the Live Test week had survived. Some caution is required, however, because anecdotal observations revealed that most of these setts retained the appearance of active setts after the BRO, which could indicate that the survival of some trap-shy and sight-shy badgers might have gone unnoticed during our study. These results should not be generalised, however, because weather conditions and seasons when the BROs took place in our study area were generally favourable to high trapping probability (Tuyttens, 1999). We speculate tentatively that failure to site traps near setts might have been responsible in part for the apparently lower capture probability during the Interim Strategy as compared to the Live Test

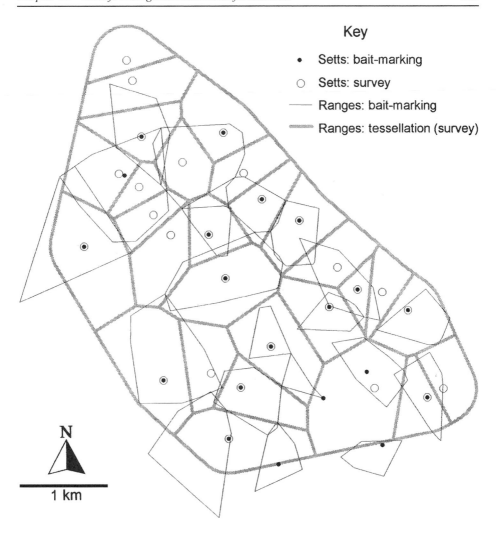

Fig. 4. Comparison of the social group boundaries predicted by the Dirichlet Tessellation Method and by the 95% minimum convex polygons drawn around the outermost latrines by each group as revealed by bait-marking in the spring of 1997. The active main setts identified during our sett survey of the winter of 1997-1998 were used for the former method.

Strategy. Another possible explanation is that low trapability during the Interim Strategy was a consequence of the removal operation that had taken place the previous year (Tuyttens, 1999). It also should be noted that policy regulations necessitated the release of one of the three badgers trapped during the Interim BRO because it was a lactating sow. No lactating sows were trapped during the Live Test BRO which took place a couple of months later in the year when cubs already had been weaned.

Conclusion

This is the first time that a Live Test BRO and an Interim BRO have been studied. Although they failed to prevent further herd breakdowns in the study area (but we do not know what would have happened without them), these two BROs appear to have been effective in the sense that they reduced TB prevalence in the badger population successfully. More detailed investigation revealed, however, that the apparent success of these two BROs in our study area was surprising, given the many difficulties encountered when applying these strategies in the field. Apart from the long delay between herd breakdown and the BRO, the lack of knowledge about social group boundaries was a major problem. As a consequence, decisions about which badgers to target/kill often seemed illogical and inconsistent under both strategies. In Live Test BROs this problem was exacerbated by the low sensitivity of the ELISA test, the low number of badgers Live Tested for TB per sett, the ability of landowners to refuse MAFF access to their land, and (probably) the inability to find all relevant badger setts if large areas were to be surveyed for badger activity. The Interim BRO was much less expensive and time consuming. However, the restriction of badger culling to the reactor land, combined with poor trapping success and the release of lactating females, may result in very small, ineffective and possibly epidemiologically irrelevant operations. All these practical difficulties may have contributed to the failure of both strategies to halt the rising incidence of TB infection in cattle in SW England. However, with only one study site we cannot generalise on how successful BROs have been in other areas.

A case study as described in this paper is, of course, no replacement for a proper scientific experiment, in which the effects of one or more wildlife management strategies are compared against a no-interference control in a sufficient number of replicate study areas. We cannot, therefore, deduce from our study how effective Live Test and Interim BROs have been as compared to doing nothing. It does illustrate, however, that scientific research conducted in parallel with wildlife management can help to highlight and quantify inefficiencies and problems associated with certain management procedures. It may give detailed insight about the reasons why one strategy works better than another one, or why a control strategy that should be effective in theory fails to work in practice. Hopefully, problems caused by wildlife can be solved more efficiently in the future on the basis of such knowledge.

Acknowledgements

We thank MAFF for funding and collaborating in this research programme. In particular we wish to thank the Gloucestershire Wildlife Unit, the Veterinary Laboratory Agencies, the Central Science Laboratory and the Chief's Scientists Group for their support and help throughout. We also thank the landowners in North Nibley for allowing us access to their land and the many volunteers, students and researchers at WildCRU and CSL who have carried out the fieldwork. We also thank Tim Robinson, Matt Waldram and Barney Long for helping with the preparation of some of the figures. This paper has been improved greatly by comments from Richard Clifton-Hadley, Richard Delahay, Chris Cheeseman, Steve Gillgan, Barney Long, Hans Kruuk and two anonymous referees.

References

Cheeseman, C.L. & Harris, S. (1982). Methods of marking badgers (*Meles meles*). *Journal of Zoology*, **197**: 289-292.

Cheeseman, C.L. & Mallinson, P.J. (1980). Radio tracking in the study of bovine tuberculosis in badgers. In: C.J. Amlaner & D.W. Macdonald (eds.), *A handbook of biotelemetry and radio tracking*: 649-656. Oxford; Pergamon Press

Clifton-Hadley, R.S., Sayers, A.R. & Stock, M.P. (1995). Evaluation of an ELISA for *Mycobacterium bovis* infection in badgers (*Meles meles*). *Veterinary Record*, **137**: 555-558.

Delahay, R.J., Brown, J., Mallinson, P.J., Spyvee, P.D., Handoll, D., Rogers, L.M. & Cheeseman, C.L. (in press). The use of marked bait in studies of the territorial organisation of the European badger (*Meles meles*). *Mammal Review*.

Doncaster, C.P. & Woodroffe, R. (1993). Den site can determine shape and size of badger territories: implications for group living. *Oikos*, **66**: 88-93.

Dunnet, G.M., Jones, D.M. & McInerney, J.P. (1986). *Badgers and bovine tuberculosis*. London; Her Majesty's Stationary Office.

Goodger, J., Nolan, A., Russell, W.P., Dalley, D.J., Thorns, C.J., Stuart, F.A., Croston, P. & Newell, D.G. (1994). Serodiagnosis of *Mycobacterium bovis* infection in badgers: development of an indirect ELISA using a 25 kDa antigen. *Veterinary Record*, **135**: 82-85.

Hayden, T.J. (1993). The badger: epidemiological darkness is plight enough. In: T.J. Hayden (ed.), *The Badger*: 196-211. Dublin; The Royal Irish Academy, Dublin.

Krebs, J., Anderson, R., Clutton-Brock, T., Morrison, I., Young, D., Donnelly, C., Frost, S. & Woodroffe, R. (1997). *Bovine Tuberculosis in cattle and badgers*. London; MAFF Publications.

Kruuk, H. (1978). Spatial organisation and territorial behaviour of the European badger (*Meles meles*). *Journal of Zoology*, **184**: 1-19.

Little, T.W.A., Swan, C., Thompson, H.V. & Wilesmith, J.W. (1982). Bovine tuberculosis in domestic and wild mammals in an area of Dorset. II. The badger, its ecology and tuberculosis status. *Journal of Hygiene*, **89**: 211-224.

MAFF (1997). *The Government's response to the Krebs Report on bovine tuberculosis in cattle and badgers*. London; MAFF Publications.

Pritchard, D.G., Stuart, F.A., Wilesmith, J.W., Cheeseman, C.L., Brewer, J.I., Bode, R. & Sayers, P.E. (1986). Tuberculosis in East Sussex. III Comparison of post-mortem and clinical methods for the diagnosis of tuberculosis in badgers. *Journal of Hygiene*, **97**: 27-36.

Stewart, P.D., Ellwood, S.A. & Macdonald, D.W. (1997a). Remote video-surveillance of wildlife - an introduction from experience with the European badger *Meles meles*. *Mammal Review*, **27**: 185-204.

Stewart, P.D. & Macdonald, D.W. (1997b). Age, sex, and condition as predictors of moult, and the efficacy of a novel fur-clip technique for individual marking of the European badger (*Meles meles*). *Journal of Zoology*, **241**: 543-550.

Tuyttens, F.A.M. (1999). *The consequences of perturbation caused by badger removal for the control of bovine tuberculosis in cattle: a study of behaviour, population dynamics and epidemiology*. DPhil thesis. Oxford; University of Oxford.

Tuyttens, F.A.M. & Macdonald, D.W. (1998). Sterilisation as an alternative strategy to control wildlife diseases: bovine tuberculosis in European badgers as a case study. *Biodiversity and Conservation*, **7**: 705-723.

Tuyttens, F.A.M., Macdonald, D.W., Swait, E. & Cheeseman, C.L. (in press). Estimating population size of Eurasian badgers (*Meles meles*) using mark-recapture and mark-resight data. *Journal of Mammalogy*.

Wilson, G., Harris, S. & Mclaren, G. (1997). *Changes in the British badger population 1988-1997*. London; The People's Trust for Endangered Species.

Zuckerman, L. (1980). *Badgers, cattle and tuberculosis*. London; Her Majesty's Stationary Office.

CHAPTER 17

Changes in badger, *Meles meles*, social organisation in response to increasing population density at Woodchester Park, south-west England

Lucy M. Rogers*, Richard J. Delahay, Tim D. Hounsome & Chris L. Cheeseman

Abstract

Changes in the social organisation of badgers, *Meles meles*, at Woodchester Park (UK) are described and related to a steady increase in population density. The data used in this analysis, from 1981 to date, show that as the density of badgers at Woodchester Park approached the carrying capacity of the population, badger spatial organisation apparently became more exclusively territorial. This was most explicitly seen in the decrease in the area of overlap between territories over time, but also in the increase in the number of social groups since 1990. In addition, the decrease in the percentage of badgers with bite wounds suggested that aggressive behaviour also changed. The most likely proximate explanation for the change in spatial organisation over time is that it has adjusted towards an optimum for exploitation of resources as the population density has increased to its carrying capacity. These findings have implications for attempts to manage bovine tuberculosis, *Mycobacterium bovis*, in the UK by reducing badger density, since years of higher population density at Woodchester Park were associated with a more stable social structure which may mitigate against disease transmission.

Introduction

Data from the longest running capture-mark-recapture study of Eurasian badgers, *Meles meles*, in an undisturbed wild population at Woodchester Park in Gloucestershire (UK) has provided a unique opportunity to describe the changes in social organisation which have accompanied a steady increase in population density. An understanding of the dynamics of badger populations is particularly important in the context of the management of bovine tuberculosis in badgers and cattle. Tuberculosis (TB) is endemic in British badgers and, since the early 1970s, the badger has been implicated as an important source of infection of the TB-causing organism, *Mycobacterium bovis*, to cattle (Muirhead *et al.*, 1974). Woodchester Park is located in an area associated with a high risk of TB for cattle, and represents the only source of data on the ecology and epidemiology of an important wildlife disease reservoir.

---

* Corresponding author.

Mustelids in a modern world
Management and conservation aspects of small carnivore: human interactions
edited by Huw I. Griffiths, pp. 267–279
© 2000 Backhuys Publishers, Leiden, The Netherlands

At Woodchester Park a badger density of 7.8 adults/km^2 was recorded in 1978 and 25.3 adults/km^2 in 1993 (Rogers *et al.*, 1997a). There is evidence that this increase in density has resulted in a reduction in badger body weight (Rogers *et al.* 1997b), suggesting that the population may be approaching its carrying capacity: that is the population size that the environment can just maintain (Begon *et al.*, 1986). The population at Woodchester Park was evidently well below carrying capacity at the beginning of the study in the 1970s, probably as a result of human persecution. Population recovery at Woodchester and elsewhere in Britain is likely to have been facilitated by the introduction of comprehensive protective legislation which ensures full protection for both badgers and their setts (Neal & Cheeseman, 1996). Indirect estimates of abundance suggest a 77% increase in badger numbers in Britain over the last ten years (Wilson *et al.*, 1997).

The social and spatial organisation of European badgers is flexible, which is unusual for carnivores (Gittleman, 1989). For example they can exist as large groups (up to 27; Rogers *et al.*, 1997a) in optimal habitats such as the pastoral farming regions of south-west England, but are solitary or live in pairs elsewhere (e.g. Kruuk & Parish, 1982). Social groups are of mixed age and sex, and are formed by the recruitment of juveniles on to the natal territory (Cheeseman *et al.*, 1988). Individuals forage alone but share in territorial defence and occupy a communal den. It is believed that variations in group size are regulated by the availability of food, whilst territory size is determined by the distribution of food patches and is independent of the number of badgers in the group (Kruuk & Parish, 1987).

The advantages of group living in badgers are still not fully understood (see review by Woodroffe & Macdonald, 1993) but may involve defence of food resources (Kruuk & Parish, 1982; Da Silva *et al.*, 1993), the economics of sharing sett sites (Roper, 1993) or the defence of mates (Roper *et al.*, 1986).

Changes in social organisation have been seen following changes in population structure or changes in food supply. Previous work has shown that if the population size is artificially reduced then social organisation may temporarily break down. For example, following the complete clearance of 11 social groups at Woodchester Park, social organisation in the recovering population was disrupted severely. Recolonising badgers occupied much larger, overlapping home ranges incorporating several main setts for the first few years, and travelled over greater distances than usual. Social groups were re-established before territorial boundaries. Eventually territories were re-established as the population density rose, with territorial boundaries being reconfigured almost exactly where they had been prior to the removal (Cheeseman *et al.*, 1993). This is also illustrated in a study by Roper & Lüps (1993) in which the simultaneous death of all the males in a social group severely disrupted social organisation, resulting in substantial overlap of territories. Changes in habitat, such as an increase or decrease in the food supply, might change the carrying capacity of the population and so also may cause a change in territoriality. For example Da Silva *et al.* (1993) observed that when the food supply was increased, existing territories split, and new setts were excavated. Conversely, Kruuk & Parish (1987) found that a decrease in the local biomass of earthworms, *Lumbricus terrestris* (the main item in the badger's diet in Britain) resulted in an increase in individual range sizes and a decrease in overlap in a population of badgers in Scotland.

In this paper we describe the changes observed in the spatial organisation of badgers at Woodchester Park over time and discuss possible causes, using indirect measures of social and spatial interactions such as the amount of territory overlap, bite wound frequency and the number and type of latrines used.

Methods

Study site

The core of the Woodchester Park study area covers approximately 7 km^2 on the Cotswold Sandstone Escarpment between 47 m and 210 m asl. The study area is optimal badger habitat, rich in earthworms and with a mild, wet climate. The landscape is hilly, dominated by permanent pasture (39%) and deciduous woodland (12%), with smaller areas of arable farmland, rotational grassland, scrub and coniferous and mixed woodland. Farming is mainly for beef and dairy cattle, with some sheep. Over the study period the proportions of the key feeding habitats, permanent pasture and deciduous woodland (Kruuk, 1978a), remained relatively constant in the study area. There are 25 contiguous badger social group territories in the core of the study area, with setts concentrated along an outcrop of Cotswold Sand in a band of woodland on the lower valley slopes (Cheeseman *et al.*, 1981).

Trapping

From 1981 to date, a continuous live-trapping and sampling regime of the resident badger population has provided ecological and epidemiological data in a long-term study of TB in badgers and cattle (see Delahay *et al.*, 1998). Each badger social group was trapped four times a year using cage traps positioned at the active setts. After a period of prebaiting with peanuts, traps were set for two nights. On initial capture trapped animals were anaesthetised by an intramuscular injection of ketamine hydrochloride (0.2 ml Vetalar/kg) and permanently marked with a tattoo in the inguinal region (Cheeseman & Harris, 1982). Data such as location, age (if year of birth was known), sex, breeding status, body weight and length, frequency of bite wounds and physical condition were recorded. Following a period of recuperation, captured badgers were released at the point of capture.

Population estimates

Known-age badgers were those classified at first capture as cubs or yearlings on the basis of their appearance. Age classes used in this analysis were cubs (<1 year) and adults (>1 years). Population size and density were estimated annually for the core social groups. Population size was estimated using the Minimum Number Alive (MNA) (Krebs, 1966; Rogers *et al.*, 1997a). Population density, expressed as the number of adult badgers/km^2, was calculated each year from the MNA estimate.

Bite wounds

Badgers may inflict bite wounds on each other during fights, either as a result of territorial disputes between intruder and resident males over access to females, or between female badgers from the same group over opportunities to rear cubs (Cresswell *et al.*, 1992; Kruuk, 1978b). Bite wounds were expressed as the percentage of badgers with any type of bite wound/annum.

Social organisation

The territorial boundaries of badger social groups are characterised by the presence of shared boundary latrines where members of adjacent groups deposit faeces and secretions from specialised subcaudal scent glands (Kruuk, 1978b). Each year the configuration of territorial boundaries at Woodchester Park was monitored using bait-marking during the peak of territorial activity in spring. At each active main sett, badgers were fed indigestible plastic pellets in a palatable bait of peanuts and syrup. A different coloured marker was used for each social group. During a subsequent survey all the latrines were searched for the coloured markers, and well-used badger paths, occurring between adjacent territories, were identified. Both boundary and hinterland latrines were recorded. Boundary latrines were those within 30 m of the social group boundary (as determined by bait marking), whereas hinterland latrines were further away. The results were plotted using a Geographical Information System (GIS) to show the position of the main setts, their territories and latrines. Territorial boundaries were then constructed by joining the outermost latrines for each social group according to the Minimum Convex Polygon method (Hayne, 1949; Mohr, 1947), unless a record for a boundary run existed, in which case the latter formed the territorial boundary (see Delahay *et al.*, 1999).

Results

Badger density

Population density has continued to increase since the most recently published figures (Rogers *et al.*, 1997a; Fig. 1). It is likely that the dip in numbers for 1995 and 1996 is an artefact of the MNA method and simply represents the proportion of the population that were still alive but had not been recaptured yet. Direct enumeration suggests more of a plateau in numbers caught. The population has increased through an average increase in group size (Rogers *et al.*, 1997a) but also in recent years through an increase in the number of social groups (Fig. 3).

Bite wounds

The percentage of badgers with bite wounds decreased over time from a peak of 0.25% in 1984 to 0.02% in the period 1993 to 1995 (Fig. 2). This decrease was significantly negatively correlated with the increase in adult badger density (Pearson's Correlation: $r = -0.695$, $n = 16$, $P < 0.001$).

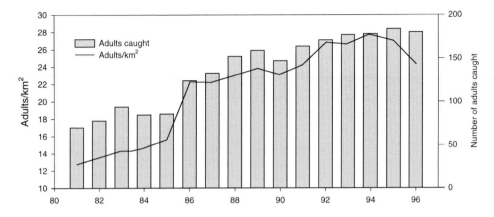

Fig. 1. Number of adult badgers caught and badger density (adults/km²) at Woodchester Park as calculated from MNA data (1981-1996).

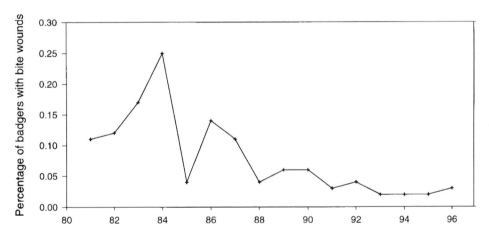

Fig. 2. The annual percentage of badgers with bite wounds at Woodchester Park (1981-1996).

Changes in social and spatial organisation

The number of social groups in the core study area increased over time from 21 up until 1989, to 22 in 1990, 23 in 1995, 24 in 1996 and 25 in 1997 (Fig. 3). The main setts of the four new groups were formed by a change in the status of setts within existing group territories, rather than by the excavation of new setts. Territory sizes did not expand, rather the two new territories occupied the same approximate area as the previous single territory. (The appearance of new territories was detected by annual bait marking.) Trapping data confirmed that the new territories appeared to have formed by fission of one group into two rather than by a coalescence of the members of several groups. The example in Fig. 4 shows the process of fission that led to the formation of the 'Wych Elm' group from the 'Kennel' group in 1992. In 1989 returns from bait marking indicated movement of badgers between the two

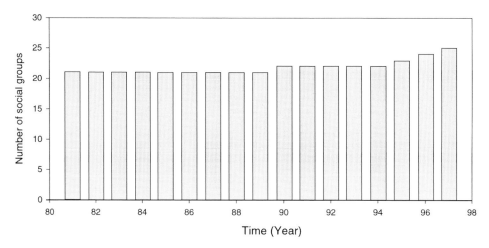

Fig. 3. The number of badger social groups in the core study area at Woodchester Park estimated from bait marking studies (1981-1997).

setts, with latrines being used by both setts throughout. Through 1990 and 1991 the degree of overlap was reduced, to the point where, in 1992, both social groups maintained exclusive territories with a clearly defined boundary between them.

The mean territory size (Fig. 5) and the number of groups overlapping (Fig. 6) neither increased nor decreased over time, although the mean area of overlap did decrease (Fig. 7). For example, the area of overlapping badger territories decreased from 22% of the total area of badger territories in 1982 to 0.45% in 1996. The area of overlap was significantly negatively correlated with adult density (Pearson's Correlation: $r = -0.486$, $n = 16$, $P < 0.05$).

Latrines

The total number of latrines in the study area increased over time. Hinterland latrines increased from a minimum of 73 in 1981 to a maximum of 228 in 1994. To control for changes in boundary length the number of boundary latrines was expressed per metre of boundary. This measure increased from its minimum of 0.007 in 1981 to its maximum of 0.0115 in 1994 (Fig. 8). Adult badger density and the total number of latrines were significantly positively correlated (Pearson's Correlation: $r = 0.682$, $n = 16$, $P < 0.05$). A Poisson regression model was fitted on the log scale to the number of latrines, including a term for the log group size. The increase in latrines was, however, not proportional to the increasing number of badgers since the slope of the regression line (0.54 ± 0.092 for log group size) was significantly less than unity ($t = 4.98$, $df = 307$, $P < 0.001$).

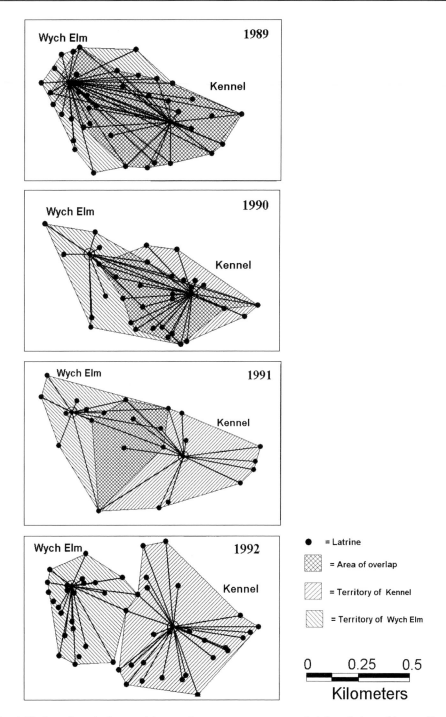

Fig. 4. Fission of one badger social group into two groups as recorded from bait marking studies.

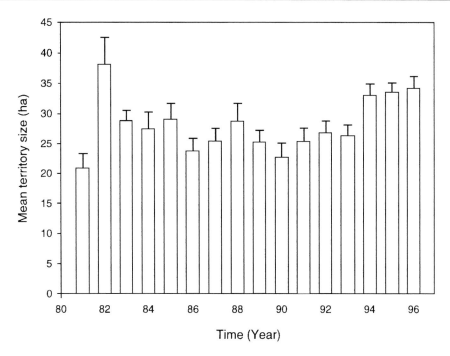

Fig. 5. Mean (plus 1 SE) social group territory sizes from annual bait marking studies (1981-1996).

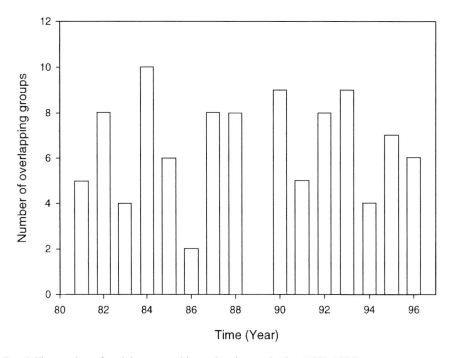

Fig. 6. The number of social groups with overlapping territories (1981-1996).

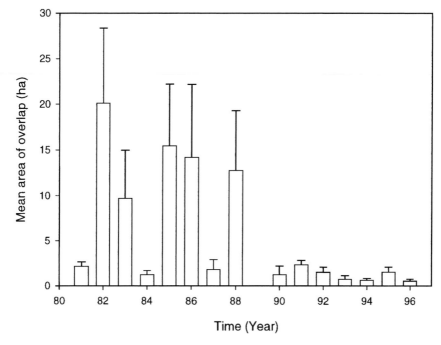

Fig. 7. The mean area (plus 1 SE) of territorial overlap per social group (1981-1996).

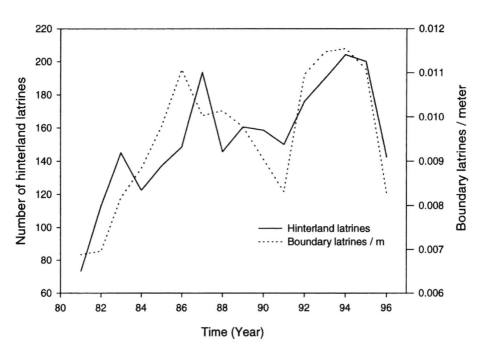

Fig. 8. The number of boundary and hinterland latrines in the core study area recorded during bait marking studies (1981-1996).

Discussion

As the density of badgers at Woodchester Park has increased to the carrying capacity of the population, badger social organisation has changed. The increase in density has been accommodated by an increase in social group size (Rogers *et al.*, 1997a) and more recently by the formation of new groups covering the same area but with a different pattern of space use. In addition there has been an increase in the exclusivity of space use, shown by a decrease in the area of overlap between territories over time. This has been accompanied by a reduction in the frequency of bite wounds suggesting that aggressive behaviour has also decreased. Together, these findings suggest that social organisation has adjusted towards an optimum, becoming more structured and more refined, as the population density has increased.

Territoriality has been defined in various ways, with the emphasis usually on the active defence of an area containing resources (such as food, setts or mates) by means of behaviour such as scent marking at the boundaries and aggression towards intruders (see Maher & Lott, 1995). However, the most fundamental feature of territoriality is that it involves a degree of exclusiveness. Territoriality is at one end of a continuum of spacing patterns with varying degrees of overlap between ranges (Maher & Lott, 1995). The flexibility observed in badger spatial organisation may reflect different points along this continuum.

Evidence for territorial behaviour in badgers is extensive (see Kruuk, 1978b; Kruuk, 1989; Neal & Cheeseman, 1996; Roper *et al.*, 1986). For example, badgers deposit secretions from specialised anal and caudal glands at shared latrines which are frequent on territorial boundaries. Boundary latrines are often visited by animals from more than one social group, and may be important for olfactory communication between groups. Radio-collared badgers have been recorded to patrol the boundaries of their territory regularly, visiting one latrine after another (see Brown, 1993). Kruuk (1978b) observed that badgers often appeared to avoid entering the neighbours' territory and witnessed several aggressive encounters between members of adjacent groups. The dominant individuals of a social group are mainly responsible for scent marking the territory and also each other, so that the group and its territory have the same odour (Gorman *et al.*, 1984; Kruuk *et al.*, 1984).

In the present study mean territory size remained broadly similar over time, which supports previous work suggesting that there is no relationship between group size and territory size (Kruuk & Parish, 1982). Indeed Kruuk & Macdonald (1985) described badgers as a 'contractionist' species living in social groups which occupy the smallest economically defensible territory, and increasing their group size within this area if resources allow.

It is difficult to assess the observed changes in territoriality at Woodchester Park in terms of the defence of the minimum area required for food resources (the 'contractionist' theory suggested by Kruuk & Macdonald, 1985). Under this hypothesis the fission of a social group into two would need to occur in response to a change in the dispersion of resources. In the present study we detected no gross changes in habitat coincident with changes in social organisation, although changes in the dispersion of an ephemeral and unpredictable resource such as earthworms might be difficult to detect from monitoring changes in habitat types alone. If patterns of resource dispersion have not changed at Woodchester Park then the fission of groups observed here is likely to represent some other, perhaps social, influence. However, it is not possible to determine whether the changes observed here are consistent with the 'contractionist' theory of badger social organisation without data describing food patch dispersion and richness at the appropriate scale.

At present we do not know the mechanism for group fission. It is thought that females make up a greater proportion of colonists of cleared areas than males (Cheeseman, unpubl.) which is consistent with the idea that opportunities for breeding might be important. Da Silva *et al.* (1993) discussed territory fission at Wytham Woods after an increase in food supply and suggested that, once carrying capacity was reached, competition within the group might favour division, which was facilitated by the excavation of new setts.

Changes in territoriality may function to maintain an optimum group size or structure, indeed territoriality seems only to occur in higher density populations (Cresswell *et al.*, 1992). Changes in territoriality could also provide enhanced opportunities for breeding sites for females. It may be that in high density populations some stability in social organisation and group structure is essential for successful breeding (Cresswell *et al.*, 1992). A further function of changes in territoriality could be for males to restrict access to oestrus females, although there is as yet no evidence to support this (Cresswell *et al.*, 1992).

Evidence from the present study is also consistent with a change in aggressive behaviour in the population over time. A reduction in the frequency of bite wounds as observed here would be expected if aggressive encounters between members of different social groups had diminished. However the extent to which bite wounds result from inter or intra-group aggression is not yet known.

Also in the present study the total number of latrines increased over time, but the increase was less than proportional to the rise in badger numbers, and so did not suggest an increase in territorial marking over time. However data were not available to test whether the intensity of latrine use had increased as badger territories became more exclusive.

The higher the density of badgers at Woodchester Park, the more stable the social organisation appears to be. This brings into question attempts to control the spread of bovine tuberculosis in high density badger populations by reducing badger density. It is known that the incidence of *M. bovis* in badgers at Woodchester Park was significantly related to the pattern of movement over time (Rogers *et al.*, 1998). In low density or perturbed populations where there is more movement (Cheeseman *et al.*, 1993) the risk of transmission of *M. bovis* between social groups may be even greater. Further, bite wounds are implicated as an important route for the transmission of infection between social groups (Wilkinson *et al.*, in press). If reductions in density (by culling, for example) were to reverse the observed trends of increasing social stability and decreasing bite wound frequency then disease transmission might become more likely.

Acknowledgements

We would like to thank the farmers, landowners and members of the public in the Woodchester Park study area who have given access to their property in order for the field work to be carried out. We also thank Tim Roper for comments on the script, Andy Mitchell for assistance with GIS and Steve Langton for statistical advice. We are indebted to Dave Handoll, John Howell, Peter Mallinson and Paul Spyvee at Woodchester Park for their expertise in the field and the staff in the Bacteriology Section of the Veterinary Laboratory Agencies for expert technical assistance. The project was funded by the UK Ministry of Agriculture, Fisheries and Food (MAFF).

References

Begon, M., Harper, J.L. & Townsend, C.R. (1986). *Ecology: individuals, populations and communities*. Oxford; Blackwell Scientific Publications.

Brown, J.A. (1993). *Transmission of bovine tuberculosis* (*Mycobacterium bovis*) *from badgers* (*Meles meles*) *to cattle*. PhD thesis. Bristol; University of Bristol.

Cheeseman, C.L., Cresswell, W.J., Harris, S. & Mallinson, P.J. (1988). Comparison of dispersal and other measurements in two badger (*Meles meles*) populations. *Mammal Review*, **18:** 51-59.

Cheeseman, C.L. & Harris, S. (1982). Methods of marking badgers (*Meles meles*). *Journal of Zoology*, **197:** 289-292.

Cheeseman, C.L. & Mallinson, P.J. (1981). Behaviour of badgers (*Meles meles*) infected with bovine TB. *Journal of Zoology*, **194:** 284-289.

Cheeseman, C.L., Mallinson P.J., Ryan, J. & Wilesmith, J.W. (1993). Recolonisation by badgers in Gloucestershire. In: T.J. Hayden (ed.), *The badger*: 78-93. Dublin; The Royal Irish Academy.

Cresswell, W.J., Harris, S., Cheeseman, C.L. & Mallinson, P.J. (1992). To breed or not to breed: an analysis of the social and density-dependent constraints on the fecundity of female badgers (*Meles meles*). *Philosophical Transactions of the Royal Society of London, Series B*, **338:** 393-407.

Da Silva, J., Woodroffe, R. & Macdonald, D.W. (1993). Habitat, food availability and group territory in the European badger, *Meles meles*. *Oecologia (Berlin)*, **95:** 558-564.

Delahay, R.J., Cheeseman, C.L., Mallinson, P.J., Rogers, L.M. & Smith, G.C. (1998). Badgers and bovine tuberculosis: a review of studies in the ecology of a wildlife disease reservoir. *Cattle Practice*, **6:** 83-87.

Delahay, R.J., Brown, J.A., Mallinson, P.J., Spyvee, P.D., Handoll, D., Rogers, L.M. & Cheeseman, C.L. (in press). The use of marked bait in studies of the territorial organisation of the European badger (*Meles meles*). *Mammal Review*.

Gittleman, J.L. (1989). Carnivore group living: comparative trends. In: J.L. Gittleman (ed.), *Carnivore behaviour, ecology and evolution*: 183-207. London; Chapman & Hall.

Gorman, M.L., Kruuk, H. & Leitch, A. (1984). Social functions of the sub-caudal scent gland secretion of the European badger (*Meles meles*, Carnivora, Mustelidae). *Journal of Zoology*, **204:** 549-559.

Hayne, D.W. (1949). Calculation of the size of home range. *Journal of Mammalogy*, **30:** 1-18.

Krebs, C.J. (1966). Demographic changes in fluctuating populations of *Microtus californicus*. *Ecological Monographs*, **36:** 239-273.

Kruuk, H. (1978a). Foraging and spatial organization of the European badger, *Meles meles*. *Behavioural Ecology and Sociobiology*, **4:** 75-89.

Kruuk, H. (1978b). Spatial organisation and territorial behaviour of the European badger *Meles meles*. *Journal of Zoology*, **184:** 1-19.

Kruuk, H. (1989). *The social badger: ecology and behaviour of a group-living carnivore* (*Meles meles*). Oxford; Oxford University Press.

Kruuk, H. & Macdonald, D.W. (1985). Group territories of carnivores: empires and enclaves. In: R.M. Sibley & R.H. Smith (eds.), *Behavioural ecology: ecological consequences of adaptive behaviour*: 521-536. Oxford; Blackwell Scientific Publications.

Kruuk, H. & Parish, T. (1982). Factors affecting population density, groups and territory size of the European badger, *Meles meles*. *Journal of Zoology*, **196:** 31-39.

Kruuk, H. & Parish, T. (1987). Changes in the size of groups and ranges of the European badger (*Meles meles*) in an area in Scotland. *Journal of Animal Ecology*, **56:** 351-364.

Kruuk, H., Gorman, M.L. & Leitch, A. (1984). Scent-marking with the subcaudal gland by the European badger (*Meles meles*). *Animal Behaviour*, **32:** 899-907.

Maher, C.R. & Lott, D.F. (1995). Definitions of territoriality used in the study of variation in vertebrate spacing systems. *Animal Behaviour*, **49:** 1581-1597.

Mohr, C.O. (1947). Table of equivalent populations of North American small mammals. *American Midland Naturalist*, **37:** 223-249.

Muirhead, R.H., Gallagher, J. & Bun, K.J. (1974). TB in wild badgers in Gloucestershire: epidemiology. *Veterinary Record*, **95:** 552-555.

Neal, E. & Cheeseman, C.L. (1996) *Badgers*. London; T. & A.D. Poyser.

Rogers, L.M., Cheeseman C.L., Mallinson, P.J. & Clifton-Hadley, R.S. (1997a). The demography of a high-density badger (*Meles meles*) population in the west of England. *Journal of Zoology*, **242:** 705-728.

Rogers, L.M., Cheeseman, C.L. & Langton, S. (1997b). Body weight as an indication of density dependent population regulation in badgers (*Meles meles*) at Woodchester Park, Gloucestershire. *Journal of Zoology*, **242:** 597-604

Rogers, L.M., Delahay, R.J., Cheeseman, C.L., Langton, S., Smith, G.C., & Clifton-Hadley, R.S. (1998). Movement of badgers (*Meles meles*) in a high density population: individual, population and disease effects. *Philosophical Transactions of the Royal Society of London, Series B*, **265:** 1269-1372.

Roper, T.J. (1993). Badger setts as a limiting resource. In: T.J. Hayden (ed.), *The badger*: 26-34. Dublin; The Royal Irish Academy.

Roper, T.J. & Lüps, P. (1993). Disruption of territorial behaviour in badgers *Meles meles*. *Zeitschrift für Säugetierkunde*, **58:** 252-255.

Roper, T.J., Shepherdson, D.J. & Davies, J.M. (1986). Scent marking with faeces and anal secretion in the European badger (*Meles meles*): seasonal and spatial characteristics of latrine use in relation to territoriality. *Behaviour*, **97:** 94-117.

Wilkinson, D., Smith, G.C., Delahay, R.J., Rogers, L.M., Cheeseman, C.L. & Clifton-Hadley, R.S. (in press). The effects of bovine tuberculosis (*Mycobacterium bovis*) on badger (*Meles meles*) mortality in a badger population in the west of England. *Journal of Zoology*.

Wilson, G., Harris, S. & McLaren, G. (1997). *Changes in the British badger population, 1988 to 1997*. London; People's Trust for Endangered Species.

Woodroffe, R. & Macdonald, D.W. (1993). Badger sociality - models of spatial grouping. *Symposia of the Zoological Society of London*, **65:** 145-169.

CHAPTER 18

Mustelids in the Balkans – small carnivores in the European biodiversity hot-spot

Boris Kryštufek

Abstract

Ten of the eleven mustelids occurring in Europe are native to the Balkan Peninsula. Species densities are highest in the north-east of the region and decline towards the west and south, and are particularly low on the islands (up to three species per island). Mustelid research has attracted less attention in the Balkans than most other mammalian groups. As a result, their distributional ranges are poorly understood which, surprisingly, is particularly true for the widespread and common species. In fact, much more information has been published on rare taxa, especially otter, steppe polecat and marbled polecat. In spite of these incomplete data sets, some extinction events and population trends can be deduced for the region, and the data available from official hunting statistics reveal considerable oscillations in mustelid game bags. The European mink, which was fairly widespread in the Carpathian Basin within historical times is now mainly extirpated from the region. Clearly evident in the last few decades are the decline of the European polecat and the increase of the stone marten. Pine marten show no sign of a decline in Slovenia where forestry practices are based on selective cutting, although the species is of conservation concern in other regions. Due to low market prices for mustelid skins, direct hunting pressure is not particularly crucial to the continued survival of the majority of Balkan mustelids – habitat destruction is more important. Widespread introduction of a market economy and the privatisation of previously public forests, following the collapse of communism a decade or so ago, may result in rapid degradation and destruction of forest habitats. This kind of threat is likely to pose a serious problem for native biota in the future.

Introduction

The Balkan Peninsula is an area that is full of controversies – even its boundaries are far from unequivocal. Although the River Danube and River Sava are usually considered to mark the northern limit of the region (*i.e.* the Balkan Peninsula *sensu stricto*), some authors consider the Carpathian Basin (the lowland basins of Pannonia and Dacia) to be a natural part of the peninsula (*i.e.* the Balkan Peninsula *sensu lato*). The region thus includes all the states of former Socialist Federal Republic of Yugoslavia (SFRY), *i.e.* Croatia, Slovenia, Macedonia, Bosnia-Herzegovina and the Federal Republic of Yugoslavia (FRY, *i.e.* Serbia and Montenegro), plus Albania, Greece, Bulgaria and European Turkey, but Hungary and Romania also can be added if the broader definition is accepted. Politically and ethnically the Balkan Peninsula is the most varied part of Europe, being a mosaic of at least ten different nations, and including groups as diverse as Slavs, Roma

Mustelids in a modern world
Management and conservation aspects of small carnivore: human interactions
edited by Huw I. Griffiths, pp. 281–294
© *2000 Backhuys Publishers, Leiden, The Netherlands*

("gypsies"), Albanians, Greeks, Magyars and Turks. The range of languages present makes even communication difficult and, until recently, this was strengthened by the political division of the region between the West and the East – divisions that remain pronounced because of disastrous economic conditions, military conflicts and political instability. On the other hand, this area is also the "hot spot" for European biodiversity (Gaston & David, 1994). Thus, although numerous field biologists have been attracted by the high biological diversity that occurs in the Balkans, very few of them have managed to overcome the numerous problems that arise from political, linguistic and ethnic barriers, and have managed to study the region as a whole. In addition, due to the complex history of the region, in some countries faunal studies have a tradition lasting less than a century. It is thus not surprising that, considered as a whole, the Balkan fauna is the least well-known in Europe, and some areas almost completely lack reliable data supported by voucher specimens – Albania is a typical example.

Because of their very different histories, the various Balkan nations have developed markedly different attitudes towards their environments and these are reflected in hunting practices and conservation attempts. Thus it seems nearly impossible to provide a balanced review of the mustelids of the entire peninsula, and my article certainly is biased towards the situation in Slovenia, of which I have most first-hand experience (cf. Kryštufek, 1991). However, although Slovenia is perhaps the least "typical" Balkan state, it does allow me to present data in the form of long-term statistics.

Status in the Balkans

Ten of the eleven mustelid species occurring in Europe are native to the Balkan Peninsula: weasel, *Mustela nivalis*, stoat, *Mustela erminea*, European polecat, *Mustela putorius*, steppe polecat, *Mustela eversmannii*, European mink, *Mustela lutreola*, marbled polecat, *Vormela peregusna*, pine marten, *Martes martes*, stone marten, *Martes foina*, badger, *Meles meles,* and otter *Lutra lutra* – only the wolverine, *Gulo gulo*, is absent. The European mink, which was fairly widespread along the main rivers of the Carpathian Basin within historical times (Youngman, 1982) is now extirpated throughout all of the states of the former SFRY (Kryštufek *et al.*, 1994) and Bulgaria (Spiridonov & Spassov, 1998); the only post-1970 records come from the Danube Delta (Mitchell-Jones *et al.*, 1999). The introduced American mink, *Mustela vison*, is known from a few scattered records in Hungary and the SFRY, mostly of fur-farm escapees (Kryštufek *et al.*, 1994), but its pressure on the native biota has been insignificant when compared with that reported in northern Europe.

Mustelids – information gaps

To talk about mustelids in the Balkans is to talk about a group of mammals that has been largely ignored except by hunters. For example, whilst surveying the mammal fauna of the Balkans, mainly during the first decades of the 20th century, mammalogists proposed numerous subspecific names for local forms. Although many of these names are not valid (even though their number certainly reflects genuine geographical variation) they do reflect the interest researchers invested in particular groups. If the number of subspecies/species is considered to be a reflection of scientific interest, then mustelids attracted less attention than any other group of terrestrial, non-flying mammals (Table 1). Among seven mustelid subspecies described from the Balkans, five are island forms and restricted to the Aegean islands of Crete and Rhodes. Of the remaining two subspecies one, the Bosnian stone marten, *Martes foina bosniaca*, was created on the basis of minor colour differences and almost certainly is invalid (Mirić, 1970), whilst the other, the Hungarian steppe polecat, *Mustela eversmannii hungarica*, originates from the Carpathian Basin, *i.e.* north of the Balkans *s.s.*

Furthermore, the distributional ranges of mustelids in the Balkans are poorly understood. Of the ten species occurring in the region, three have island populations: weasel, stone marten and badger, and all of these are generally distributed on the mainland. These island occurrences seem to be fairly well known, although discrepancies exist between species distribution maps in Niethammer & Krapp (1993a,b) and Mitchell-Jones *et al.* (1999). Six of the remaining mustelid species (*i.e.* all the others except the otter) have restricted ranges. Somewhat surprisingly, ranges are best documented (in the sense of the largest density of documented records/unit area) in the two "rarest" taxa: the steppe polecat and the marbled polecat. However, most of the records for the marbled polecat are old and need confirmation: of 31 localities known in the SFRY, eleven were published between 1929-1937 and have not been repeated since (Mirić *et al.* 1983). It is thus not surprising that, as recently as 1993, Spassov & Spiridonov (1993) interpret improbable and extra-limital records as being a possible indicator of a wider former distribution of the marbled polecat: in their opinion the species' probable original range extended to *c.* 400 km north-west of its actual distribution. On the basis of this dubious information, Spiridonov & Spassov (1998) then speculate on the possible extinction of the species in the Pannonian Plain during the last 200 years!

Furthermore, the lack of basic knowledge on morphological variation in the various Balkan polecat species has resulted in the geographical range of the steppe polecat being uncertain. For example, Milenković (1990) published an isolated

Table 1. The number of subspecies from different taxonomic groups of mammals described from the Balkan Peninsula *s.l.* Note that the ratio of the number of Balkan subspecies to Balkan species is lower in mustelids than in any other group.

Group	No. species	No. subspecies	Ratio (ssp / sp)
Insectivora	13	24	1.85
Rodentia	25	108	4.32
Artiodactyla	5	10	2.00
Carnivora	16	17	1.06
Canidae	3	5	1.67
Ursidae	1	1	1.00
Felidae	2	4	2.00
Mustelidae	10	7	0.70
Total	77	176	2.29

record of steppe polecat from Macedonia which suggested a southwards shift in the known range of the species by >200 km. However, this record might well result from misidentification because of increased local variability in an important species-diagnostic character (the interorbital constriction), as seen also in European polecats from European Turkey (Kurtonur *et al.*, 1994). In conclusion, uncertainties about the actual geographic ranges of some mustelid species are so marked that extralimital records, which may shift supposed distributional borders by several hundred kilometres, sometimes can seem plausible.

In the Balkans species distribution borders are poorly documented for both the stoat (Reichstein, 1993) and the European polecat (Wolsan, 1993). The situation with the pine marten is even worse, there being an almost complete lack of data from the southern part of its range (Stubbe, 1993a). In fact, the only recent species distribution surveys undertaken in the region have been river corridor-based surveys for otter (e.g. Liles & Jenkins, 1984; Taylor *et al.*, 1988; Paunović & Milenković, 1996; MacDonald & Mason, 1982; Gaethlich, 1988). A recent attempt by the European Mammal Society (*Societas Europaea Mammalogica*) to prepare dot maps for all European mammal species (Mitchell-Jones *et al.*, 1999) seems to suggest that mustelid distributions are not as neglected as the above suggests. This is because there is a high density of comparatively large map cells in which the presence of particular species is confirmed, and because the majority of records are "new" (*i.e.* originate after 1970). However, the quality of the primary data utilised cannot be deduced from the Atlas, and a comparison of the mustelid species maps with those for small mammal species (where records are usually based on the results of trapping surveys) strongly suggests that few of the mustelid records are supported by voucher specimens: many originate from questionnaires or other, similar sources, which are difficult to verify. Hunters, even professional ones, are not always reliable sources of such information, at least when morphologically similar congeneric species are involved. This is particularly true for both polecats and martens, as well as for weasel and stoat. For example, in European Turkey hunters frequently do not distinguish between European polecat and stone marten, and use the same name ("sansar") for both of them. I was interested in the reliability of official game statistics for pine and stone martens, which led me to ask Slovenian hunters to send the heads of martens with their identifications and other information (locality, date, sex, habitat, etc.). All 47 pine marten and 28 stone marten skulls received were identified properly (Kryštufek, 1984). However, the sample size was small, and the results probably were biased by only hunters with a keen interest in martens having been willing to respond to the survey. Elsewhere in Europe, hunters may often confuse the two species and, as a result, some national hunting statistics simply "lump" the two together (H. Griffiths, pers. comm.).

In conclusion, the distributions of mustelids in the Balkans are poorly documented, with the otter being the sole exception. Furthermore, in most cases the available data do not permit any firm conclusions to be reached on possible changes in distributions. In the case of the European mink it can be stated with certainty that its range shrank to such a degree in this part of Europe during the 20th century that the species became extinct in the major part of the region.

Population trends

Population trends can be followed only when population size has been estimated, either in absolute or in relative terms. To my knowledge, there are no reliable estimates of mustelid population sizes available for any of the Balkan states. Here animal numbers are usually derived from "direct counts" by hunters or forest guards which, at best, provide only a rough estimate of actual densities. Data from the official statistics of the Slovenian Hunters' Association suggest a suspiciously low level of interannual variation in the majority of species (Table 2). It is hard to believe that coefficients of variation (a measure of population oscillation that is independent of actual population size) are <6% in four mustelid species. For example, weasel populations (which can sustain harvests of *c.* 80%) are unlikely to be so stable over a four-year period as to vary between 3,520 (in 1990) and 4,309 (in 1988), with a coefficient of variation of only 5.18%. On the other hand, population density estimates (inds./100 km²) might be close to actual densities (e.g. 27.8 stone marten/100 km² in Slovenia may be reasonable; see Table 2) and estimates from different countries result in comparable numbers. Thus, the stone marten population was estimated at *c.* 35,000 in Bulgaria by Grigorev (1986) which gives an overall density of 35.6 inds./100 km² – a value very similar to that from Slovenia. However, different sources often report different estimates. Population estimates for badgers in Bulgaria range from 35,000 (Griffiths & Thomas, 1993) to 40-60,000 (Velichkov & Profirov, 1998), *i.e.* a difference of almost two-fold. It seems unlikely that the density of badgers in Bulgaria would be twice that of the stone marten. The Slovene Hunters' Association usually rejects the "direct count" method as a means of providing a sound basis for wildlife management, even for large ungulates (e.g. Simonič, 1976). Such approaches are considered to be subjective, and often are not based on a standardised methodology. Recently, in Slovenia the population status of mustelids has been estimated by graded scores which range from 1 (presence occasional, species rare) to 5 (species common). However, this has done little to improve overall accuracy, or to provide a better insight into species population dynamics.

Table 2. Average spring populations of mustelids in Slovenia for the four year period 1988-1991 (based on official statistics of the Slovenian Hunters' Association). Data are derived from "direct counts". The Coefficient of Variation is the Standard Deviation expressed as a percentage of the mean spring population. Density (inds./100 km²) is calculated for the entire territory of Slovenia (area 20,251 km²) although the actual area under hunting management is considerably smaller (*i.e.* 17,170 km²). Red fox, *Vulpes vulpes*, is given for comparative purposes.

Species	Mean	Coefficient of Variation	Density per 100 km²
Badger	4,518	5.01	22.3
European polecat	4,169	3.70	20.6
Pine marten	4,003	2.07	19.8
Stone marten	5,622	16.70	27.8
Stoat	3,253	9.89	16.1
Weasel	4,007	5.18	19.8
Otter	72	15.39	0.4
Fox	7,984	12.59	39.4

On the other hand, the Bulgarian authorities do consider direct counts to reflect actual animal densities, albeit with an error range of ±15% (Velichkov & Profirov, 1998).

Other sources of indirect population density estimates include indices such as the annual game bags, or the numbers of pelts on the market. This sort of information also contains a lot of "noise", particularly as harvesting is strongly influenced by variations in pelt price. Anecdotal evidence from 20th century Slovenia strongly supports this conclusion. For example, in the years before World War II, when stone marten pelts were expensive, the hunting pressure on the species was said to be so severe that it resulted in a considerable decline in marten numbers.

When compared with estimates from direct counts, Slovenian annual game bags show significantly higher coefficients of variation for all mustelid species except stone marten (Table 3). Furthermore, annual game bags (as a percentage of the estimated spring population) are surprisingly similar in four mustelids, ranging between *c.* 10-20% (Table 4). However, this value is more than five times higher in the red fox, *Vulpes vulpes*. It seems unlikely that the annual game bag removes <20% of the estimated spring population, particularly as the harvest starts in autumn when the young-of-the-year have been recruited into the adult population. The annual game bags most likely reflect either: (i) a lack of interest among hunters in the hunting of mustelids, or (ii) incomplete or inaccurate statistics, or (iii) some combination of the two. In any case official data on game bag statistics should be considered with extreme caution since they often include several sources of error (Myrberget, 1988).

In the last century there have been considerable oscillations in mustelid game bags in Slovenia (Fig. 1). The higher bag numbers in the post-World War II period presumably reflect real population increases – a consequence of changes in land use (Adamič, 1974). During this period, extensive areas of abandoned arable land

Table 3. Average annual Slovenian game bag for the four year period 1987-1990 (based on official statistics of the Slovenian Hunters' Association). Stoat, weasel and otter are protected all the year around; fox is given for comparison. (See Table 2 for further explanation.)

Species	Mean	Coefficient of Variation	Density per 100 km^2
Badger	669	19.89	3.3
European polecat	547	33.93	2.7
Pine marten	431	5.43	2.1
Stone marten	775	9.70	3.8
Fox	5.647	19.55	27.9

Table 4. Annual Slovenian game bag as a percentage of the estimated spring population over a three year period (based on the official statistics of the Slovenian Hunters' Association); fox is given for comparison (see Table 2 for further explanation.)

Species	1988	1989	1990
Badger	17.0	12.1	18.2
European polecat	11.4	19.0	8.7
Pine marten	11.0	10.3	11.3
Stone marten	10.7	14.0	17.3
Fox	68.5	59.1	65.2

underwent succession to form forests. Thus increases in mustelid numbers were due mainly to their colonisation of new areas of habitat. On the other hand, water pollution and habitat destruction resulted in a considerable decline in otter numbers throughout the region, although the process was not documented directly in any of the Balkan countries.

Over the last few decades clear trends can be seen in two species (Figs. 2 & 3). The first trend is the decline of the European polecat (Fig. 2) – this seems to be genuine and, as a similar decline has been reported from Bulgaria (Spiridonov & Spassov, 1997), the process is likely to be occurring on a broad geographic scale. Stone martens, on the other hand, are in expansion (Fig. 3) and this trend has been reported from the majority of European countries (Stubbe, 1993b), including Bulgaria (Velichkov & Profirov, 1998). This process also involves the invasion of urban environments (reported in Slovenia and Bulgaria) which is well known in central Europe (Stubbe, 1993b). Scattered anecdotal reports suggest that during the last few decades the polecat has been replaced by the stone marten in and around Slovenia's rural settlements.

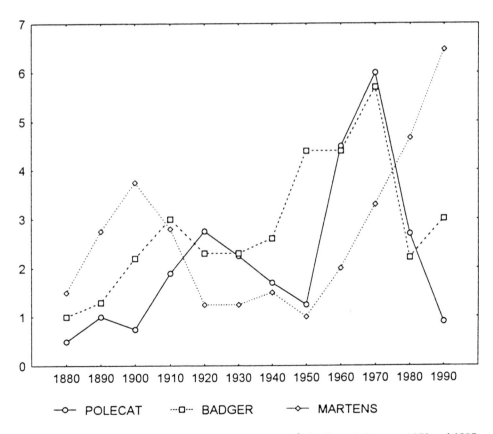

–⋄– POLECAT   ⋯□⋯ BADGER   –⋄– MARTENS

Fig. 1. Trends in annual mustelid game bags (kills/100 km²) in Slovenia between 1978 and 1997. Values given are average annual game bags per decade. Bags of pine marten and stone marten are pooled. Based on Adamič (1974) and the official statistics of the Slovenian Hunters' Association.

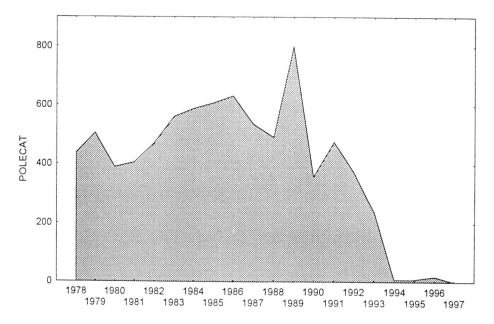

Fig. 2. Trends in the European polecat game-bag (kills/100 km²) in Slovenia between 1978 and 1997. The decline in the 1990s presumably reflects a genuine crash in polecat populations (based on the official statistics of the Slovenian Hunters' Association).

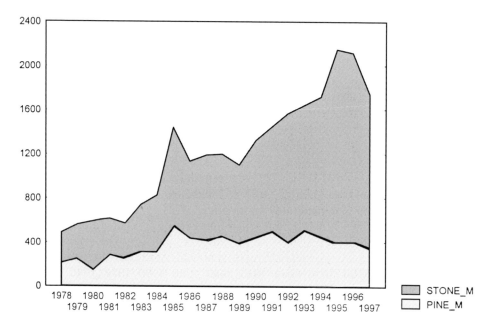

Fig. 3. Trends in the pine marten and stone marten game-bags (kills/100 km²) in Slovenia between 1978 and 1997. The increase in values for the stone marten is presumably real. Based on the official statistics of the Slovenian Hunters' Association.

Human impact

Human impacts on mustelids are twofold, acting through: (i) direct pressure by hunting, and (ii) habitat degradation and destruction. The effects of hunting pressure on badger populations were evaluated by Griffiths (1991), Griffiths & Kryštufek (1993) and Griffiths & Thomas (1993). Because of the differences between hunting practices in different countries, combined with an almost universal lack of reliable data, it hardly seems possible that the impact of hunting on badger populations can be estimated. Although the species has had complete legal protection in Greece since 1985, *c.* 1,500 badgers are said to be killed each year and even strychnine baits are used still on Crete (Griffiths & Thomas, 1993). Pressure on badgers increased drastically in Bulgaria in the 1980s and is also high (>10,000 badgers killed/year) in Yugoslavia (FRY), where the species' Red Data Book status is considered to be Lower Risk-conservation dependant (LR-cd) (Savić *et al.*, 1995). The number of badgers killed/hunter.year[-1] varies between 0.015 (FRY) and 0.180 (Romania). During the last thirty years hunting pressure on the badger in Slovenia has decreased steadily despite a considerable increase in the number of licensed hunters. This decrease can be seen both as fewer badgers killed/hunter.year[-1] (*c.* a five-fold decrease from 1960 to 1990) as well as in lower total annual game-bags (>900 badgers/year in the first half of 1960s *vs.* <800 badgers/year in the second half of 1980s; Kryštufek, 1993).

Little attention has been paid to the effect of direct pressure on other mustelid species, which is presumably an important threat to the survival of the majority, if not all, species. Velichkov & Profirov (1998) are of opinion that "There are no threatened predatory species ..." in Bulgaria. On the other hand, Spiridonov & Spassov (1998) consider overhunting to be the main reason for low numbers of both stone and pine marten in Bulgaria between the 1940s and 1960s, and regard it as being a real threat to the continued survival of the latter. At the present time mustelid pelt prices are low. For example, in 1994, near Demirköy in European Turkey, I purchased eight stone marten skins for only 600,000 Turkish lira (at that time *c.* 30 German marks). The pelt price in Bulgaria is 130 leva (*i.e.* $US 5.2) for martens and 23 leva ($US 0.9) for badger and polecat (the average monthly salary in Bulgaria is *c.* 1,200 leva, and the annual fee for membership of the hunters' organisation is 120 leva including taxes; Velichkov & Profirov, 1998). Carnivore pelts are also of little value in Slovenia, which mainly reflects the influences of the animal welfare lobby. Fox pelts are sold at 3,000 Slovenian tolars (*c.* 30 German marks), but martens command still lower prices. This is in strong contrast with prices in the pre-World War II period, when four marten skins could be exchanged for a cow, and three marten skins were equivalent to the pay from several months logging during the winter period. Badger fur is now of little or no commercial value, but in the same period Crete annually exported >3,000 badger pelts to Germany alone (Zimmermann, 1949).

Habitat degradation is frequently considered to be a basic threat to some rare or endangered mustelids. Putting aside the otter, which was badly affected by freshwater pollution, and the little-known European mink (which possibly was extirpated by the same problem), this is true for marbled polecat, steppe polecat and pine marten. All these species have restricted distributions in the Balkans. In Bulgaria, besides over-hunting, the pine marten suffered marked habitat loss due to deforestation and increased competition with the stone marten, which is competitively superior in early successional stages and in secondary forest (Spiridonov & Spassov, 1998). It is interesting to compare this with Slovenia, where logging is based on the cutting of single trees or small tree groups. In contrast to the clear-cutting system this type of management results in mixed-aged woodland. Since selective cutting most closely mimics the natural disturbances in temperate forest regions, it results in managed forests which are more like natural ones (Peterken, 1996). In fact, the pine marten population seems to have been stable for the last few decades (Fig. 3). However, even though stone marten numbers increased significantly during the same period, there is no evidence of increased competition between the two species.

The steppe polecat is presumed to depend strongly upon populations of their main prey item, the European souslik, *Spermophilus citellus* (Mirić, 1976). From the late 1940s until the middle 1970s, souslik populations decreased to between a twentieth and an eightieth of previous levels in Vojvodina (in the northern lowlands of FRY); in many places this ground squirrel has completely disappeared (Ružić, 1979). It is generally agreed that the souslik's decline has followed human-mediated habitat transformation. Surprisingly, Savić *et al.* (1996) do not consider the steppe polecat to be of any great conservation concern in FRY. On the other hand, Spiridonov & Spassov (1998) assume that the mass poisoning of rodents in the late 1980s "proved fatal for the steppe polecat". In the Red Data Book of the former Czechoslovakia, the European souslik is listed as endangered (E) and the steppe polecat as intermediate (I) (Baruš *et al.*, 1989). Similarly, the Austrian Red Data Book lists both the European souslik and the steppe polecat in the same category: rare (R) (Bauer, 1989). The above suggests that steppe polecat may be far less dependent on this particular diurnal and colonial rodent than has been generally believed. However, this link may reflect the well-known and widely-publicised dependence of the black footed ferret, *Mustela nigripes*, on prairie dogs, *Cynomys* spp., rather than any real ecological relationship.

The eventual impact of habitat degradation on the marbled polecat is enigmatic (see Milenković *et al.*, this volume). Spiridonov & Spassov (1998) report habitat loss due to the transformation of Bulgarian steppe habitats into arable land. They also consider "large colonies of rodents (hamsters, dormice *sic!*)" to be essential for the species' survival. Furthermore, they believe in the occurrence of "strongly competitive" interactions between marbled and steppe polecats, although the ranges of the two barely overlap in Bulgaria. Summarising all these contradictions, one only may conclude that the lack of data (as explicitly emphasised by Spiridonov & Spassov for both species) prevents any firm conclusions from being reached.

Throughout eastern Europe major changes have resulted through the demise of socialism: one of the most notable being the reprivatisation of state assets. Included amongst these are the former state forests, many of which now have passed into private hands. The effects of this on the Balkan fauna are completely unknown. However, there are concerns that the development of high-intensity, industrialised, free-market economy driven forestry may adversely affect a range of wildlife species.

Table 5 gives a summary of the threatened mustelids in five of the nine countries from the Balkan Peninsula *s.s.* Six mustelid species are considered to be of conservation concern, one of them (the European mink) being already extinct (Ex).

The otter is listed as being either endangered (E) or vulnerable (V) in all these countries. The marbled polecat is of special concern wherever it occurs, and the pine marten is under threat along the southern margin of its distributional area (Bulgaria). The badger seems to be safe on the mainland, but the two island subspecies (the Cretan badger, *Meles meles arcalus* and the Rhodian badger, *Meles meles rhodius*) are vulnerable due to direct human impacts. The number of threatened mustelids is highest in Bulgaria (five species) and lowest in Slovenia and Croatia (a single species). This might result partly from the higher number of mustelid species actually occurring in Bulgaria (all ten Balkan species) whereas Slovenia and Croatia host only seven species each. However, the FRY has the same number of species as in Bulgaria (ten), and here four species are considered to be threatened; besides, the degree of overlap between the threatened species of the two countries is the lowest possible. It seems likely, therefore, that the different countries have not applied the IUCN's conservation listing criteria in exactly the same manner.

Is there anything special about the Balkan mustelids?

The species density of mustelids in the Balkans is highest in the north-east of the region, with up to ten species occurring in individual 100 x 100 km grid squares (Fig. 4). Species-richness declines towards the west and south, and is particularly low on the islands. This type of pattern seems to be common among "continental" species, which avoid Mediterranean shrubland habitats (Kryštufek & Griffiths, 1999). Thus, areas with high mustelid species-richness are outside the Balkan Peninsula *s.s.* The western part of the Balkans is regarded as a "hot spot" for European biological diversity (Gaston & David, 1994) and demonstrates a higher degree of rodent endemism than any other part of the continent (Kryštufek, unpubl). Mustelids evidently contradict these trends.

First of all, the majority of mustelid species are widely distributed. Three species (from the ten living in the Balkans) are restricted to the Western Palaearctic

Table 5. Threatened mustelids in the countries of the Balkan Peninsula *s.s.* IUCN categories: Ex = extinct, E = endangered, V = vulnerable, R = rare, LR-cd = lower risk, conservation dependent, K = insufficiently known.

	Slovenia[1]	Croatia[2]	FRY[3]	Bulgaria[4]	Greece[5]
Otter	E	E	V	V	V
pine marten				V	
Marbled polecat			V	V	K
Steppe polecat				R	
European mink			Ex	Ex	
Badger			LR-cd		V[6]

[1] Kryštufek (1996), [2] Draganović (1994), [3] Savić *et al.* (1995), [4] Botev & Peschev (1985), Spiridonov & Spassov (1998), [5] Karandinos (1992), [6] refers only to the subspecies *M. m. arcalus* (Crete) and *M. m. rhodius* (Rhodes).

(European polecat, European mink and pine marten), five have wider palaearctic distributions, and two more (stoat and weasel) have holarctic ranges. The often-quoted Pleistocene refugium on the Balkan Peninsula seems not to have been sufficiently long-lasting to enable speciation amongst top predator species, which live at low densities (in contrast with small primary consumers such as rodents, which include many Balkan endemics). It seems highly unlikely that even recognisable geographic races (*i.e.* subspecies) have originated on the Balkan mainland. The only undisputed subspecies are restricted to Aegean islands, where it is presumed that their populations were "marooned" following Pleistocene sea level changes. Furthermore, one of these islands (Crete) is well known for its richness in endemic animal species and subspecies (Legakis & Kypriotakis, 1994).

Due to their broad habitat tolerances, the majority of mustelid species presumably did not find the boreal habitats north of the Alpine glaciers hostile. It seems likely that the Balkan refugium led to little genetic isolation in mustelid species, even during the peaks of Pleistocene glaciation. In an evolutionary sense, the Balkans contain little mustelid diversity which cannot be found in the rest of the continent. Despite this, the species-richness of mustelids in the Balkans is high, and there are genuine conservation concerns for some of the species living there.

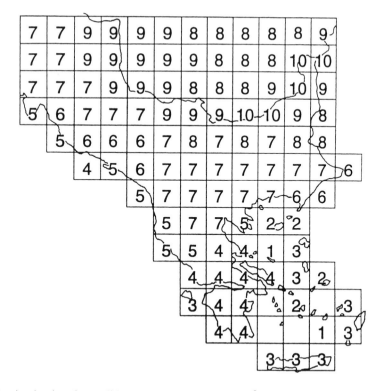

Fig. 4. Species density of mustelids (number of species/100 km²) in the Balkan Peninsula and adjacent regions. Based on distribution maps in Niethammer & Krapp (1993a, b). European mink was considered within its presumed historical borders, although now it is almost completely extirpated from the Balkans.

Acknowledgements

I would like to thank the Slovenian Hunters' Association (Lovska zveza Slovenije) for access to their files, and the referees for their comments on this paper.

References

Adamič, M. (1974). [Zahlenschwankung der Populationen wichtiger Wildarten in Slowenien in den Letzen Hundert Jahren Beurteilt nach den Schwankungen des Abschusses]. *Zbornik Biotehniške fakultete Univerze v Ljubljani, Veterina,* **11:** 15-53 (in Slovenian with German summary).

Baruš, V., Bauerová, Z., Kokeš, J., Král, B., Lusk, S., Pelikán, J., Sládek, J., Zejda, J. & Zima, J. (1989). *Červená kniha ohrožených a vzácných druhů rostlin a živočichů ČSSR 2. Kruhoústí, ryby, obojživelníci, plazi, savci.* Praha; Státní zemědělské nakladatelství (in Czech).

Bauer, K. (ed.). (1989). *Rote Listen der gefährdeten Vögel und Säugetiere Österreichs und Verzeichnisse der in Österreich vorkommenden Arten.* Klagenfurt; Österreichische Gesellschaft für Vogelkunde.

Boev, B. & Peschev, C. (Eds.) (1985). [*The Red Data book of NR Bulgaria. Vol. 2 Animals.*] Sofia; B'lgarska Akademija na naukite (in Bulgarian).

Draganović, E. (Ed.) (1994). *Crvena knjiga životinjskih svojti Republike Hrvatske. Sisavci.* Zagreb; Ministarstvo graditeljstva i zaštite okoliša, Zavod za zaštitu prirode (in Croatian).

Gaston, K.J. & David, R. (1994). Hotspots across Europe. *Biodiversity Letters,* **2:** 108-116.

Gaethlich, M. (1988). Otters in Western Greece and Corfu. *IUCN Otter Specialist Group Bulletin,* **3:** 17-23.

Griffiths, H.I. (1991). *On the hunting of badgers.* Brynna; Piglet Press.

Griffiths, H.I. & Kryštufek, B. (1993). Hunting pressure and *badger Meles meles*: patterns and possible futures. *Lutra,* **36:** 49-61.

Griffiths, H.I. & Thomas, D.H. (1993). The status of the badger *Meles meles* (L., 1758) (Carnivora, Mustelidae) in Europe. *Mammal Review,* **23:** 17-58.

Grigorev, G.R. (1986). [Distribution, number and utiliatization of the weasel (*Martes foina* Erxl.), the marten (*Martes martes* L.) and the badger (*Meles meles* L.) in Bulgaria.] *Gorskostopanska Nauka,* **23:** 59-67 (in Bulgarian with English summary).

Karandinos, M. (Ed.) (1992). *The Red Data Book of threatened Vertebrates of Greece.* Athens; Hellenic Zoological Society & Hellenic Ornithological Society.

Kryštufek, B. (1984). Distribution of martens (gen. *Martes* Pinel, 1792, Carnivora, Mammalia) in Slovenia. *Biološki vestnik,* **32:** 21-26.

Kryštufek, B. (1991). *Sesalci Slovenije* [*Mammals of Slovenia*]. Ljubljana; Prirodoslovni muzej Slovenije (in Slovenian with English summary).

Kryštufek, B. (1993). The conservation status of the badger *Meles meles* (L., 1758) in Slovenia. *Small Carnivore Conservation,* **8:** 9-10.

Kryštufek, B. (1996). [Mammals of Slovenia – state and threat status]. In: J. Gregori, A. Martinčič, K. Tarman, O. Urbanc-Berčič, D. Tome & M. Zupančič (eds.), *Narava Slovenije, stanje in perspektive:* 381-386. Ljubljana; Društvo ekologov Slovenije (in Slovenian with English summary).

Kryštufek, B. & Griffiths, H.I. (1999). Mediterranean *vs.* continental small mammal communities and the environmental degradation of the Dinaric Alps. *Journal of Biogeography,* **26:** 167-177.

Kryštufek, B., Griffiths H.I. & Grubešić, M. (1994). Some new information on the distribution of the American and European mink (*Mustela* spp.) in former Yugoslavia. *Small Carnivore Conservation,* **10:** 2-3.

Kurtonur, C., Kryštufek, B. & Özkan, B. (1994). The European polecat (*Mustela putorius*) in Turkish Thrace. *Small Carnivore Conservation,* **11:** 8-10.

Legakis, A. & Kypriotakis, Z. (1994). A biogeographical analysis of the island of Crete, Greece. *Journal of Biogeography,* **21:** 441-445.

Liles, G. & Jenkins, L. (1984). A field survey for otters (*Lutra lutra*) in Yugoslavia. *Journal of Zoology,* **203:** 282-284.

MacDonald, S.M. & Mason, C.F. (1982). Otters in Greece. *Oryx,* **16:** 240-244.

Mitchell-Jones, A.J., Amori, G., Bogdanowicz, W., Kryštufek, B., Reijnders, P.J.H., Spitzenberger, F., Stubbe, M., Thissen, J.B.M., Vohralík, V. & Zima, J. (1999). *Atlas of European mammals*. London; T & AD Poyser.

Milenković, M. (1990). A new find of the steppe polecat, *Mustela eversmannii* Lesson, 1827 in Yugoslavia. *Arhiv bioloških nauka, Beograd*, **42**: 251-257.

Mirić, D. (1970). *Ključi za določevanje živali. V. Sesalci, Mammalia*. Ljubljana; Društvo biologov Slovenije (in Slovenian).

Mirić, D. (1976). [Der Steppeniltis, *Mustela eversmannii* Lesson, 1827 (Mammalia, Carnivora) im südostteil des Pannonischen Beckens.] *Glasnik Prirodnjaćkog muzeja, Beograd (Serija B)*, **31**: 129-157 (in Serbian with German summary).

Mirić, D., Milenković, M. & Tvrtković, N. (1983). [Distribution of marbled polecat (*Vormela peregusna* Gueldenstaedt 1770, Mustelidae, Mammalia) in Yugoslavia]. *Drugi simpozijum o fauni SR Srbije. Beograd*: 185-188 (in Serbian with English summary).

Myrberget, S. (1988). Hunting statistics as indicators of game population size and composition. *Statistical Journal of the United Nations ECE*, **5**: 289-301.

Paunović, M. & Milenković, M. (1996). The current status and distribution of the otter *Lutra lutra* L., 1758 in Serbia and Montenegro. *IUCN Otter Specialist Group Bulletin*, **13**: 71-76.

Peterken, G.F. (1996). *Natural woodland. Ecology and conservation in northern temperate regions*. Cambridge; Cambridge University Press.

Reichstein, H. (1993). *Mustela erminea* Linné, 1758 – Hermelin. In: J. Niethammer & F. Krapp (eds.), *Handbuch der Säugetiere Europas. Band 5: Raubsäuger – Carnivora (Fissipedia). Teil II: Mustelidae 2, Viverridae, Herpestidae, Felidae*: 533-570. Wiesbaden; Aula Verlag.

Ružić, A. (1979). [Decreasing number of the ground squirrel (*Citellus citellus* L.) populations in Yugoslavia in the period 1947 to 1977.] *Ekologija (Beograd)*, **14**: 185-194 (in Serbian with English summary).

Savić, I.R., Paunović, M., Milenković, M. & Stamenković, S. (1995). [Diversity of mammalian fauna (Mammalia) of Yugoslavia, with a review of species of international importance.] In: V. Stevanović & V. Vasić (eds.), *Biodiverzitet Jugoslavije sa pregledom vrsta od međunarodnog značaja*: 517-554. Beograd; Biološki Fakultet & Ecolibri (in Serbian).

Simonič, A. (1976). *Srnjad, biologija in gospodarjenje*. Ljubljana; Lovska zveza Slovenije (in Slovenian).

Spassov, N. & Spiridonov, G. (1993). *Vormela peregusna* (Güldenstaedt) – Tigeriltis. In: J. Niethammer & F. Krapp (eds.), *Handbuch der Säugetiere Europas. Band 5: Raubsäuger – Carnivora (Fissipedia). Teil II: Mustelidae 2, Viverridae, Herpestidae, Felidae*: 817-854. Weisbaden; Aula Verlag.

Spiridonov, G. & Spassov, N. (1998). Large mammals (Macromammalia) of Bulgaria. In: C. Meine (ed.), *Bulgaria's biological diversity: conservation status and needs assessment, Vols I & II*: 467-477. Washington (DC); United Nations Biodiversity Support Program.

Stubbe, M. (1993a). *Martes martes* (Linné, 1758) – Baum., Edelmarten. In: J. Niethammer & F. Krapp (eds.), *Handbuch der Säugetiere Europas. Band 5: Raubsäuger – Carnivora (Fissipedia). Teil I: Canidae, Ursidae, Procyonidae, Mustelidae 1*: 374-426. Weisbaden; Aula Verlag.

Stubbe, M. (1993b). *Martes foina* (Erxleben, 1777) – Haus-, Steinmarten. In: J. Niethammer & F. Krapp (eds.), *Handbuch der Säugetiere Europas. Band 5: Raubsäuger – Carnivora (Fissipedia). Teil I: Canidae, Ursidae, Procyonidae, Mustelidae 1*: 427-479. Weisbaden; Aula Verlag.

Taylor, I.R., Jeffries, M.J., Abbott, S.G., Hulbert, I.A.R. & Virdee, S.R. (1988). Distribution, habitat and diet of the otter *Lutra lutra* in the Drina catchment, Yugoslavia. *Biological Conservation*, **45**: 109-119.

Velichkov, V. & Profirov, L. (1998). Status of the populations of wild animals subject to economic use in Bulgaria. In: C. Meine (ed.), *Bulgaria's biological diversity: conservation status and needs assessment. Vols. I & II*: 601-616. Washington (DC); United Nations Biodiversity Support Program.

Wolsan, M. (1993). *Mustela putorius* Linnaeus, 1758 – Waldiltis, Europäischer Iltis, Iltis. In: J. Niethammer & F. Krapp (eds.), *Handbuch der Säugetiere Europas. Band 5: Raubsäuger – Carnivora (Fissipedia). Teil II: Mustelidae 2, Viverridae, Herpestidae, Felidae*: 699-769. Weisbaden; Aula Verlag.

Youngman, P.M. (1982). Distribution and systematics of the European mink *Mustela lutreola* Linnaeus 1761. *Acta Zoologici Fennici*, **166**: 1-48.

Zimmermann, K. (1949). Die Carnivora von Kreta. *Zeitschrift für Säugetierkunde*, **17**: 58-64.

CHAPTER 19

The on-going decline of riparian mustelids (European mink, *Mustela lutreola*, polecat, *Mustela putorius*, and stoat, *Mustela erminea*) in eastern Europe: a review of the results to date and an hypothesis.

Vadim E. Sidorovich

Abstract

Evidence is provided for a decline in riparian mustelid species (European mink, European polecat and stoat) in Belarus and several adjacent areas of eastern Europe. After analysis of data on feeding ecology, population structure, habitat use, inter-specific relationships and prey abundance, the decline of these species is discussed in the context of the recent naturalisation of two new, exotic vertebrate predators: the American mink and the raccoon dog. Both new species are present in these areas either after escaping from fur farms, or being deliberately introduced by hunters. The hypothesis is presented that the decline in riparian mustelid species has been caused by these naturalised species.

Introduction

Between 1950 and 1970 the European mink, *Mustela lutreola*, disappeared very rapidly from many eastern European countries, notably Russia, Belarus, Ukraine, Latvia, Lithuania and Estonia (Danilov & Tumanov, 1976; Tumanov & Zverev, 1986; Tumanov, 1992, 1996; Sidorovich, 1992a, 1997; Sidorovich *et al.*, 1995; Maran & Hentonen, 1995; Maran *et al.*, 1998). At the same time, European polecat, *Mustela putorius*, population numbers also declined in Belarus (Sidorovich, 1997), Russia (I. Tumanov, pers. comm.), Latvia (J. Ozoliņš, pers. comm.) and Lithuania (A. Ulevichus, pers. comm.), although this decline was gradual and less dramatic. In the main, the polecat became rare in riparian habitats and forest ecosystems, but polecats are still common in the mostly open areas of anthropogenic landscapes (Sidorovich, 1997; Sidorovich *et al.*, unpubl.). In the case of the Eurasian otter, *Lutra lutra*, only a temporary decline has been recorded in its population in Belarus, and this was due to over-exploitation (Sidorovich, 1991, 1992b, 1997). Furthermore, since 1950-1970, there is substantial evidence that stoat, *Mustela erminea*, densities also have decreased markedly in Belarus. Despite this, the stoat remained common in various parts of Belarus until 1993-1997 (Sidorovich, 1997) and also in adjacent parts of eastern Poland (Sidorovich *et al.*, 1996). Stoats mainly inhabit riparian habitats such as river valleys, lake shores and

Mustelids in a modern world
Management and conservation aspects of small carnivore: human interactions
edited by Huw I. Griffiths, pp. 295–317
© 2000 Backhuys Publishers, Leiden, The Netherlands

marshes but, in both Belarus and eastern Poland, stoat population numbers have become reduced to very low densities in the last few years (Sidorovich, unpubl.; W. Jedrzejewski, pers. comm.). Furthermore, stoats have become rare in large expanses of neighbouring countries such as Russia (I. Tumanov, pers. comm.; M. Vaisfeld, pers. comm., Sidorovich et al., unpubl.), Latvia (J. Ozolinš, pers. comm.) and Lithuania (A. Ulevichus, pers. comm.).

In contrast, the numbers of naturalised American mink, Mustela vison, have increased rapidly (Tumanov & Zverev, 1986; Tumanov, 1992, 1996; Sidorovich, 1992b, 1997; Sidorovich et al., 1995; Maran & Hentonen, 1995; Maran et al., 1998). Also, in Belarus in the period 1989-1996, an introduced canid, the raccoon dog, Nyctereutes procyonoides, again attained high densities (Sidorovich, unpubl.), although local hunters had reported very low population levels for more than a decade. According to the information available, the earlier raccoon dog population crash may have been caused by an epidemic disease that became widespread during the species' period of naturalisation.

There is little evidence to suggest that in eastern Europe, where large-scale wilderness conditions prevail, that native riparian mustelid species could have been sufficiently affected by human activities to cause declines such as these. So, why have native riparian mustelid populations declined in Belarus, and also more widely in eastern Europe as a whole? It seems probable that natural causes, such as declines in prey abundances and competition for food and habitats, could have led to these declines in native riparian predators. But what actually has change to cause such a marked effect? A possible answer lies with the naturalised populations of American mink and raccoon dog - introduced predatory species that are new to the area and have similar diets and a preference for riparian habitats. Moreover, both American mink and raccoon dog are characterised by well-developed feeding plasticity, both in their use of a broad spectrum of food types, and by feeding on the most common and available prey in any habitat in any season (Gerell, 1967; Eberhardt & Sargeant, 1975; Jenkins & Harper, 1980; Arnold & Fritzell, 1987; Kyne et al., 1989; Kauhala et al., 1992; Dunstone, 1993; Sasaki & Kawabata, 1994; Sidorovich, 1997; Jedrzejewska & Jedrzejewski, 1998; Sidorovich et al., 1998). So, competition with these additional and numerous predators could have affected native riparian mustelid species. To test this hypothesis, between 1986-1998 we studied the feeding ecology, inter-specific interactions, habitat selection and demography of riparian predator species at two study areas in Belarus and at one in an adjacent region of Russia.

Study areas, materials and methods

All the study sites are located in an area of mixed forest in the middle of the temperate forest zone, and lie between more southern deciduous forest and boreal coniferous forest. Here spruce, Picea spp., and pine, Pinus spp., are abundant amongst the conifers. Black alder, Alnus glutinosus, grey alder, Alnus incana, birch, Betula spp., and aspen, Populus tremula, are the most common deciduous trees, whilst oak, Quercus spp., maple, Acer sp., lime, Tilia sp., elm, Ulmus sp., and ash, Fraxinus sp., which produce many nourishing seeds for rodents, are rare in the mixed forest. All the study sites are characterised by semi-undisturbed conditions, with a network of rivers and wetlands, as well as large-scale forest ecosystems. In northern Belarus, where our main data on the decline in riparian mustelids were obtained, only 12-31% of the landscape is agricultural. Other effects of human activities (including pollution) which could lead to a substantial deterioration in these natural ecosystems are unimportant in the study areas. In Belarus, dangerous concentrations of contaminants (heavy metals, organochlorine pesticides and radionuclides) have not been found either in the habitats or animals studied - the exceptions being the area of the city of Minsk, and the zone contaminated by radionuclide fallout from Chernobyl (Savchenko & Sidorovich, 1994; Sidorovich, 1997; Sidorovich & Maran, 1997; Sidorovich *et al.*, 1997a,b). PCBs have not been found in either body tissue samples or habitats at a detection limit of 0.01 mg/kg$_{(wet\ weight)}$. As to acid deposition, only a small proportion of the glacial lakes is characterised by naturally slightly acidic water, and substantial acid contamination is still uncommon in Belarus (Jakushko *et al.*, 1988, 1995). In Belarus and Russia fur trapping has gradually decreased during the time of our study because of the economic crisis: fewer people are buying furs, and the cost of trapping has become increasingly expensive. So, in the study areas and in all of Belarus (at least), human impacts cannot have been responsible for the decline in riparian mustelids.

The Belarussian study areas are in the north of the country, where American mink and raccoon dog reached high densities quite recently. The main study area, where the most detailed work has been carried out, is an area of *c.* 20 x 40 km at the head of the River Lovat, Gorodok district, Vitebsk region (hereafter called the Gorodok Study Area). Here habitats consist of dense, mixed and coniferous forests on rough glacial terrain, interspersed by fields and a few small villages. Small rivers, glacial lakes and marshes are abundant. Aquatic habitats in the area may be categorised broadly as small rivers (either slow or fast flowing), small streams and glacial lakes. The slow flowing rivers are between 7-25 m wide and 1.0-2.5 m deep, with wide (200-1,000 m), swampy floodplains of 60-100% marshland. They support a considerable diversity of fishes (*c.* 16 species), variable abundances of crayfish, *Astacus astacus*, and voles (bank vole, *Clethrionomys glareolus*, field vole, *Microtus agrestis*, root vole, *Microtus oeconomus*, common vole, *Microtus arvalis*, and water vole, *Arvicola terrestris*) are rather abundant but species composition is very variable. Semi-aquatic and other birds are abundant, and frogs, *Rana* spp., are common on the flood plains. In winter access to these rivers may be limited, and large-scale flooding occurs in spring. The fast flowing rivers are between 5-8 m wide and 0.5-1.5 m deep, and have high, steep, wooded banks but little floodplain. Fish diversity is low in these rivers (only five species are common, and there are no salmonids), and crayfish may be moderately abundant or absent. The bank vole is the main vole species present - others being either rare or absent. Small birds are abundant in the warm season, and there are many common frogs, *Rana temporaria*, and other frog species (e.g. *R. arvalis*, *R. esculenta* complex) are plentiful too. Small streams (between 1-10 km long) are usually 0.5-2.0 m wide and 0.1-0.8 m deep, and tend to be shallow, often drying out in summer. As a consequence, small streams only contain between one and five fish species for part of the year, but some do have crayfish, and common frogs are abundant. Bank voles are the main vole present and other voles are less common; small birds are abundant in the warm season. The glacial lakes generally have high densities and diversities of fish (Zhukov, 1965, 1988). In the study area glacial lakes are inhabited by nine to 18 fish species, but crayfish numbers fluctuate between zero and being very common. Voles (*C. glareolus*, *M. agrestis*, *M. oeconomus*, *M. arvalis*, *A. terrestris*) are rather abundant but their species composition is very variable, however, both birds and frogs are very common. There is no access to the water in winter.

Our work in the study area started in 1986. Prior to 1992, European mink were common in all types of aquatic habitats, and the American mink has been common in the study area since its arrival in 1988 (Sidorovich, 1992b). Raccoon dog numbers only reached a high density a few years ago (in 1995-1996) following more than a decade at very low population densities.

Another study area in northern Belarus is *c.* 40 x 60 km, completely forested and located between three medium-sized rivers: the R. Drissa, R. Nischa and R. Svolna in Rossony district, Vitebsk region (hereafter called the Rossony Study Area). Here environmental conditions are similar to those in Gorodok but there are many more glacial lakes and the rivers are larger. In the Rossony Study Area the European mink had disappeared by 1990-1992. American mink entered the area between 1973 and 1978, but the raccoon dog only became abundant in 1989-1990 (again after a decade-long population crash).

The study area in Russia (Loknja district, Pskov region) was used in order to continue Tumanov's work on riparian mustelids (Danilov & Tumanov, 1976). It also provides a good opportunity for comparison of our results with a large dataset from the period before the naturalisation of these new predators. Furthermore, at the beginning of our study in 1991, only native mink inhabited the Loknja river catchment area, so we could observe all the changes in the native riparian mustelid community in relation to the expansion of American mink, as had been done a few years previously in the upper reaches of the River Lovat (Belarus).

Otter, polecat, stoat and the two species of mink were censused in winter in wetland areas and along the banks of small rivers, streams and lakes. The census was carried out by searching the banks, shores and particular wetland areas for tracks and other signs of species activity. The census methods used have been described elsewhere (see Teplov, 1952; Danilov & Tumanov, 1976; Sidorovich, 1992a,b, 1997, 1999; Sidorovich *et al.*, 1995, 1996). Fresh tracks of individual mink, otter, polecat and stoat usually formed concentrations along the river or in the wetlands, and were separated by variable distances either without tracks or where only old tracks were found. We aimed thus to determine the number of individual mustelids inhabiting the survey areas, using the assumption that concentrations of fresh tracks found in mid-winter belonged to single animals. Winter conditions are characterised by low prey availabilities so predators disperse to raise their survival potential. We believe that this is a valid assumption, as extensive winter trapping has shown that the removal of an individual animal usually was followed by an absence of fresh tracks (14/14 cases for European mink, 93/97 for American mink, 19/20 for polecat, and 23/23 for stoat). Wherever possible, the sex of individual animals was determined by examining the positioning of fresh marks: males leave urine marks on the snow in front of the scat, whereas females deposit both the scat and urine in the same place or sprinkle urine behind the scat (Teplov, 1952; Danilov & Tumanov, 1976). This allowed further assessment of our assumption; it is extremely unlikely that two individuals of the same sex would be found in the same place at the same time in winter - such intra-sexual range overlap has never been recorded during our long experience of winter trapping in the area. The tracks of the two mink species were distinguished following the keys of Sidorovich (1994, 1999). Observations made in the field and in captivity (at Tallinn Zoo, Estonia) suggest that incorrect identifications probably account for <10% of all observations, which we consider acceptable. Differences of >1 cm in the measurements of single otter foot prints were accepted as a criterion for differentiating individual animals, and their sex was determined by the examination of fresh marks.

Each winter, the main study area on the upper reaches of the R. Lovat was surveyed for the presence of all species: 20-43 km of small rivers were surveyed, 12-61 km of small streams and between one and eight glacial lakes. Between December, 1995 and June, 1999, 12 European mink, 47 American mink, nine polecats, two stoats and four raccoon dogs were radio-tracked. The total number of radio-locations taken was >19,000, with each radio telemetric "fix" lasting for *c.* 15 minutes, but sometimes less. Independent data were obtained by randomly choosing an "active" fix and one "inactive" fix each day for each radio-tagged animal.

In addition, to analyse differences in the densities of European mink and American mink in more detail, we compared data from other study sites: the R. Lovat (Pskov region, Russia), the eastern Berezina river basin and its surrounding area (Berezinsky Reserve, Vitebsk and Minsk regions, Belarus), and the western Berezina river basin and its surrounding area (Naliboky Reserve, Minsk and Grodno regions, Belarus).

Scats of both mink species were collected on a regular basis from main dens at which the identity of the occupant was known from live capture, radio-tracking, trapping or from visual observation. Furthermore, during the winters large numbers of scats were taken from mustelid tracks, or from the fresh tracks of radio-tagged individuals under our observation. Otter scats were only collected from otter tracks. The total numbers of scats collected in the study areas were: 2,347 (European mink), 2,543 (American mink), 2,934 (otter), 841 (polecat), 72 (stoat) and 420 (raccoon dog) (Sidorovich, 1997, unpubl.; Sidorovich *et al.*, 1998). Scats were analysed using both species identifications and size differences to identify as many different prey items as possible. Scat contents were identified microscopically using published keys for vertebrate remains (Galkin, 1953; Zhukov, 1965, 1988; Böhme, 1977; Pucek, 1981, Debrot *et al.*, 1982, Marz, 1987; Steinmetz & Muller, 1991) whilst insects, crayfish and molluscs were distinguished from the remains of shells or exoskeletal elements. To compare the overall dietary diversity of the four riparian mustelid species, Levins' Index (Levins, 1968) was calculated for the occurrences of eight prey categories, and Pianka's Index (Pianka, 1973) was used to evaluate dietary overlap.

In the warm seasons of 1995-1998, the abundances of various prey categories were estimated in the main study area. Frogs were censused at one metre intervals along a ten metre transect. Crayfish abundances were estimated with a special net (Budnikov & Tretyakov, 1952; Rumyantcev, 1974) fitted with a lure (a fried frog) and set for one night. Snap traps were used to estimate the abundances of small mammals. Snap traps were baited with carrot and bread fried in oil and set at five metre intervals. Normally 80-120 snap traps were set for three days and checked and rebaited daily.

Review of results on the decline of riparian mustelids

The decline of native riparian mustelids in relation to the naturalisation of the American mink and the raccoon dog

1. European mink

In the Rossony Study Area, where both the dense river network and the numerous glacial lakes are in nearly pristine condition, European mink disappeared in 1990-1992. When we began our study in 1986, we found a very low density of European mink (about 0.5 individuals/10 km stretch of river). However, after the decline occurred it was nearly impossible to discern its cause. Raccoon dogs only became abundant in the area in 1989-1990, so this naturalised predator could not be responsible for the European mink's decline here. American mink entered the area between 1973 and 1978. It is natural to assume that the American mink's expansion caused the European mink's decline and, using this hypothesis, in 1986 we began an intensive study of European mink in the upper reaches of the R. Lovat, Gorodok district, Belarus. American mink had never been recorded here before. However, within a few years American mink reached their maximum level and, because they were already common in the neighbouring river catchment area, we were waiting for them.

In the R. Lovat's upper reaches before the arrival of the American mink (in 1986-1989) the European mink population appeared to be both relatively stable and at a high density (Fig. 1). On small rivers, the density of the native mink ranged between 4-10 inds./10 km of water course (mean = 7.3, SD = 2.0, n = 10) and was habitat-type dependant (Sidorovich *et al.*, 1995); these values are high for European mink generally (Novikov, 1939; Danilov & Tumanov, 1976). Annual variation in density was high, varying by an average of 11.5% (range = 5-25%) within particular habitats. Sex ratio did not differ from one male: one female (χ^2 = 0.2, P >0.1; *i.e.* 29 males: 25 females, 53.7%: 46.3%) - similar sex ratios have been recorded in European mink populations in the north-western regions of Russia (Danilov & Tumanov, 1976). However, sexual differences in habitat use were found: females preferred to inhabit aquatic ecosystems larger than small streams (*i.e.* up to 10 km long) (20 and five individuals, respectively; χ^2 = 5.0, P = 0.03), whereas males demonstrated no preference for either habitat type (17 and 12 individuals, respectively; χ^2 = 0.4, P >0.1).

The first American mink was trapped in the study area at the head of the R. Lovat in the middle of December, 1988. As trapping intensity had been high we assume that this was genuinely the first year that American mink were present. By the spring of 1990 American mink had became a common species in the study area (Sidorovich 1992b; Sidorovich *et al.*, 1995). Figure 1 shows that, in the upper reaches of R. Lovat, European mink densities decreased from a rather high level to near extinction at the same time as the American mink's expansion (r_s = -0.96, P <0.01).

In the Gorodok Study Area, raccoon dogs reached high densities only a few years ago (in 1995-1996). So, once more, this naturalised carnivore could not be responsible for the European mink's decline in the R. Lovat's upper reaches. Again it was reasonable to assume that the expansion of American mink led to the decline of European mink, especially when one takes into account their similar feeding

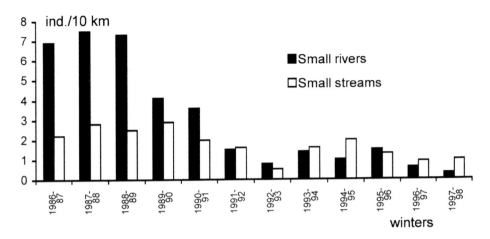

Fig. 1. Dynamics of European mink density (individuals/10 km stretch of stream) on the upper reaches of the River Lovat in the winters of 1986-1998.

ecology, and the greater physical strength and high reproductive rate of expanding American mink populations (Sidorovich, 1992c, 1993).

Amongst the demographic results, it is especially important to emphasise the increase in reproduction in expanding American mink populations, as recorded on the upper reaches of the R. Lovat by Sidorovich (1993, 1997). There, in the spring of 1991, American mink fertility was very high and varied between six and eight unresorbed embryos per pregnant female (mean = 7.6) and all females trapped were pregnant. In the spring of 1992, all three female American mink trapped were pregnant, each having seven or eight embryos (mean = 7.3). The differences between the fertilities of American mink on the Lovat's upper reaches and in the Drissa catchment area were highly significant (U_s = 135.5, P < 0.01). The Drissa catchment has a high-density mink population in which fertility ranges from one to six embryos per pregnant female (mean = 3.3 in one year old females, 4.3 in two year olds). This was also the case when the over-exploited, low density Drissa population (fertility = two to six embryos per pregnant female, mean = 4.2 in one year old females and 6.0 in two year olds) was compared to the population in the Lovat's upper reaches (U_2 = 227, P <0.01). Thus, the high fertility of the American mink allowed this species to occupy its new range successfully.

The reduction in European mink density (Figs. 1-3) was greatest on small rivers (t = 11.3, P <0.001) whereas the change on small streams was less, although still statistically significant (t = 4.9, P = 0.001). In conditions of high American mink density, European mink used small streams (<2 km long in 20% of all radiolocations, 2-10 km long in 19.8%) more frequently than did naturalised mink (1.7 and 7.0%, respectively; G ≥6.4, P ≤0.03). One notable difference between male and female European mink lay in their use of rivers and small streams: females inhabited small streams less frequently than males (21.5% *vs.* 51.0%; G = 12.4, P <0.01) and fast flowing, small rivers more often than males (60.7 *vs.* 20.2%; G = 21.2, P <0.01). This preference for fast-flowing, small rivers in female native mink was noted for both "active" (64.4%) and "inactive" individuals (55.8%).

Table 1. Differences in habitat use (% of radio-locations, males + females, active + inactive) between the two mink species and the polecat in the presence of a high density population of American mink on the upper reaches of the R. Lovat, Belarus, 1995-1997 (based on data obtained by radio-tracking).

Type of habitat	*M. lutreola*[a] (n=7267/609)	*M. vison* (n=4583/786)	*M. putorius* (n=2295/310)
Small streams (<2 km long)	20.0/19.5[b]	1.7/1.4	2.6/4.8
Small streams (2 -10 km long)	19.8/26.8	7.0/8.3	3.1/4.8
Fast or moderately flowing, small rivers without a floodplain or with somewhat swamped floodplains	35.6/31.0	27.3/28.8	9.1/8.7
Slowly flowing, small rivers with active floodplains	5.8/9.4	24.2/24.7	0.4/0.3
Glacial lakes	7.0/7.7	11.3/9.7	13.2/10.0
Pools	2.1/2.5	8.6/9.5	11.2/11.6
Swamped forest	2.9/1.1	6.5/5.0	8.5/10.6
Non-swamped forest	7.1/1.9	2.6/1.9	17.7/17.1
Fields	0.4/0.2	0.2/0.0	7.4/6.1
Swamped meadows and marshes	0.2/0	10.5/10.4	3.1/4.5
Non-swamped meadows	0/0	0.1/0.3	7.4/6.1
Villages	0/0	0/0.1	16.4/15.2

[a] is the number of radiolocations. The first number is the total number of fixes, the second is the number of independent fixes.
[b] The first percentage was calculated from the total number of fixes, the second from independent data alone.

When considering the use of small streams by European mink, an important feature relating to their decline should be emphasised. There were substantial differences in the occupation of habitat type between the sexes. According to our trapping data (and that of local trappers) from 1986-1997, of a total of 206 individuals taken, of those captured on small streams, 76 were male and only three were female. This difference between the sexes was apparent both before and after the arrival of American mink: one female to 27 males in 1986-1991 (before and during the species' expansion) and two females to 49 males in 1992-1997 (in the presence of a high density population). During the radiotracking study, male European mink inhabited small streams for 60% of the time, while females used this type of habitat less frequently (22% of the time; G = 18.3, P <0.01). Furthermore, we have never found a European mink litter on a small stream, whereas 33 litters were found on small rivers or glacial lakes. It is possible that females are not able to inhabit small streams continuously as these hold insufficient resources to allow them to raise a litter.

Naturalised American mink population densities varied with habitat type (Table 2) and were lowest on small streams (approximately one third of streams <2 km long were inhabited by only a single American mink [n = 48]), and on small, fast-flowing rivers (mean = 2.9 inds./10 km). In contrast to European mink, the density of naturalised mink was highest and most variable on large and medium-sized rivers. Here numbers ranged from 3.3-38.9 inds./10 km of river bank, and reached 4 inds./km^2 in the river valley. American mink inhabited the same rivers and glacial lakes in the Lovat river basin, but at a significantly higher density than European

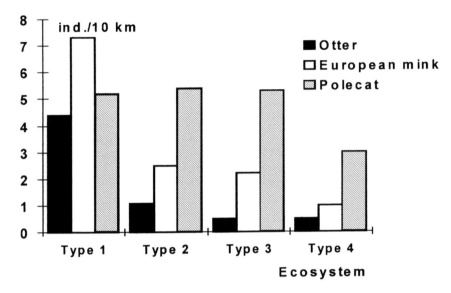

Fig. 2. Density of semi-aquatic mustelids and polecats (inds./10km) on the upper reaches of the River Lovat, NE Belarus, before the expansion of the American mink (winter 1986-89). **NB:** Ecosystem type 1 = small rivers, type 2 = small streams, type 3 = glacial lakes, type 4 = drainage canals.

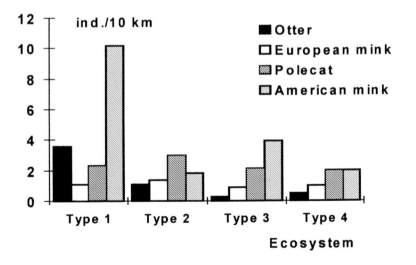

Fig. 3. Density of semi-aquatic mustelids and polecats (inds./10 km) in the presence of high density population of American mink on the upper reaches of the River Lovat, NE Belarus, winter 1992-95. **NB:** Ecosystem type 1 = small rivers, type 2 = small streams, type 3 = glacial lakes, type 4 = drainage canals.

mink (t ≥ 3.6, P ≤0.003) and, throughout Belarus, they inhabit almost all aquatic ecosystems (except small, fast- or moderately-flowing rivers) at a higher density than do European mink (Table 2).

Table 2. Densities of European mink and American mink in various habitat types. Three different river systems were surveyed: the Lovat river basin (Belarus and Russia) (1986-1998); the eastern Berezina river basin (Belarus) (1985-1989) and the western Berezina river basin (Belarus) (1983-1992). Data on European mink are from the Lovat river basin only, but data on American mink are from all three sites. Densities are expressed as min.-max./mean ± SD per 10 km of river bank or shore (number of stretches surveyed, total km surveyed). See text for details of census methods.

Habitat type	Density	
	M. lutreola	*M. vison*
Large and medium-sized rivers > 100km long	2.0-6.1 (8, 148)	3.3-38.9 (9-24, total 84, 1344)
	3.6 ± 1.3	5.8 ± 0.9 - 22.4 ± 3.9
Fast flowing, small rivers (10-100km long) without floodplains or with narrow slightly swamped floodplains[a]	5.8-8.2 (9, 143)	2.4-6.2 (13, 247)
	6.9 ± 0.9	2.9 ± 1.0
Moderately flowing, small rivers (10-100 km long) with moderately swamped floodplains[a]	5.9-10.0 (8, 151)	4.2-9.4 (24, 336)
	7.3 ± 1.5	6.3 ± 0.7
Slow flowing, small rivers (10-100 km long) with wide active floodplains[a]	1.9-5.6 (7, 113)	8.2-14.3 (19, 228)
	4.3 ± 1.4	10.7 ± 1.2
Small streams 2-10 km long	0-4.0 (7, 56)	2.2-4.9 (34, 238)
	2.5 ± 1.4	2.8 ± 0.6
Glacial lakes	0-6.0 (6, 25)	3.5-11.3 (18, 72)
	3.1 ± 1.9	7.2 ± 1.3

[a] a 'slightly swamped' floodplain is defined as a floodplain consisting of 0-30% marshland, a 'moderately swamped' floodplain as 30-60% marshland, and an 'active' floodplain is 60-100% marshland.

On the upper reaches of the R. Lovat during the American mink's expansion in 1991-1997, male European mink were found in higher numbers than females: 13/19 of the kits inspected in nests were male (68%), as were 8/14 trapped juveniles (57%), 24/35 trapped adults (69%) and 56/67 live-trapped individuals (84%). Only the last ratio differs significantly from 1:1 (χ^2= 17.3, P <0.01), whereas the sex ratio of European mink populations prior to the arrival of the American mink approximated 1:1.

The proportion of juveniles in the European mink population was very low (28.6%) (Fig. 4). As a result, the average age within the population was fairly high (males = 2.2 years, females = 1.6 years), and the ratio of juveniles: adults was 0.4. However, in an expanding American mink population, the proportion of juveniles and the juvenile:adult ratio were significantly higher: 83.0% and 4.0, respectively (G = 27.1, P <0.01).

Nine female European mink were caught within the study area and in adjacent areas of north-eastern Belarus in May, 1990-1995 when naturalised mink density was rather high. All were pregnant and fertilities ranged between 3-6 embryos/female (mean = 4.0). Although one embryo was resorbing, the rest (n = 36) were well developed. All the pregnant females inhabited small rivers densely populated by American mink, and the density of European mink was very low (*c.* 0.5-2.0 inds./10 km).

A similar situation relating to European mink decline and American mink expansion was observed in the adjacent Pskov region of Russia in the Loknya river basin (part of the R. Lovat's catchment area). Between 1968-1972 the catchment area was inhabited by a stable European mink population with a nearly equal sex

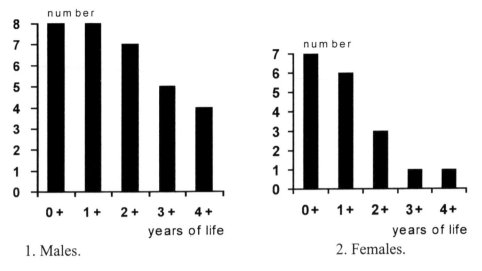

1. Males.   2. Females.

Fig. 4. Age structure of the declining European mink population on the upper reaches of the R. Lovat, NE Belarus.

ratio (Danilov & Tumanov, 1976). In the winters of 1991-1993 the density of this population was high: 2.7-6.2 inds./10 km (mean = 4.2), and snow-tracking and data from local trappers show a nearly equal sex ratio (13 males:11 females; χ^2= 0.1, P > 0.1, and 27 males: 23 females; χ^2= 0.2, P >0.1, respectively). American mink were absent at the time. During 1994-1996 American mink expanded into the area. Simultaneously, the density of European mink decreased to 1.1-2.3 inds./10 km (mean = 1.8) and examination of skins taken by local trappers demonstrated a changed sex ratio (18 males: one female; χ^2= 9.5, P <0.01).

2. Eurasian river otter

No changes in otter habitat use were found after the American mink's expansion (Figs. 2, 3). In several regions of Belarus only a temporary decline in otter populations was recorded, this being due to over-exploitation (Sidorovich, 1991, 1992b, 1997).

3. European polecat

In 1986-1989, when we began our study in the Rossony Study Area, there was a rather low polecat density in the natural landscape, whereas the density of American mink was very high (7-18 inds./10 km of river stretches, mean = 13.3). Here the polecat population inhabited pine bogs (1-6 inds./10 km², average = 3.1) and forest ecosystems (c. 2 inds./10 km²). In addition, polecats (mainly males; 93.2%, n = 44) lived in river valleys at a density of 1-4 inds./10 km² (average = 2.2 inds./10 km²). These densities were approximately two to three times lower than in similar ecosystems at the head of the R. Lovat (annual means = 6.1, 3.0, 5.2, respectively; t ≥ 3.2, P <0.01) where there were no American mink. Then, in 1991-1993, in the Rossony

Study Area, polecats became rare (<1 ind./10 km² of natural landscape) and all of the 11 animals captured were males. Just before this next step in the polecat's decline (in 1989-1990) raccoon dogs had reached a high density. Taking into account the dietary similarity of these predators, their very similar habitat use, and the high density of raccoon dogs (Sidorovich, 1997; Jedrzejewska & Jedrzejewski, 1998; Sidorovich *et al.*, in press a), competition with this naturalised carnivore could have led to a polecat decline in the Rossony Study Area. The polecat remained common in the farmlands of Rossony, where it could not be affected substantially by either of the naturalised carnivore species.

In the Gorodok Study Area at the Lovat river head, the average polecat density was 5.2 inds./10 km, independent of riparian habitat type (Fig. 1). Following the American mink's expansion in the river's upper reaches, the polecat population on banks and lake shores was reduced by approximately half (mean = 2.4; t = 5.4, P <0.01). Since 1992, when American mink population density has been high, changes also have been observed in the sex ratio of polecat inhabiting river banks. Prior to the arrival of the American mink the polecat sex ratio was 1.5: 1 (*i.e.* 42 males: 29 females; $\chi^2 \geq$ 4.8, P $\leq$0.03) yet in recent years this has been reduced to 1: 3.5 (in 1992-1993), 1: 10 (1994-1996) and 1: 18 (1997-1998). In other types of habitat we did not record a statistically significant reduction in polecat numbers. As for the possible impact of the raccoon dog, this species reached a high density in the area in 1995-1996, and we have started to observe a further, on-going decline in polecat. Now polecat have became rare in natural landscapes (<1 ind./10km²) and 19 males but no females were captured in 1997-1998 - this is also the case in the natural landscape of the Rossony Study Area. In the farmlands (villages and their surroundings) of the Gorodok Study Area, polecats are still common.

A similar situation was recorded on the rivers in the Loknja Study Area. Before the American mink's expansion in 1991-1993, local trappers caught *c*. one polecat for each European mink, and at least half of the polecats trapped were female. During the period 1994-1996 American mink expanded into the area of the R. Loknya and, in 1996-1998, local trappers caught *c*. one polecat for between four and seven mink (both species); most of the trapped polecats (at least eight out of ten) were male.

4. Stoat

There is a high probability that stoat populations also were affected by these naturalised carnivore species. In this case, we have both our own data and information from local trappers, however, these are not as complete and consistent as those on European mink and polecat population declines.

In the period 1930-1960, before the expansion of the American mink in Belarus, there were many trappers who specialised on stoats (*i.e.* on ermine) and normally each caught 40-100 stoats every winter. However, at present almost no-one traps stoats because their densities are much lower, even though stoats were still common only a few years ago.

In the Gorodok and Loknja Study Areas, before the American mink's expansion, trappers who caught European mink usually also by chance caught *c*. one stoat for eight or ten European mink, whereas under current conditions (*i.e.* with a dense American mink population) the ratio between trapped stoat and mink is *c*. one stoat to 90-120 mink. In the Gorodok Study Area at the R. Lovat head, in the winters of 1986-1990 and before 1992 (since when American mink populations have been at a high level) the density of stoats recorded was 8-13 stoats/km^2 of active floodplain (average = 11.5 inds./km^2), whilst 5-9 stoats/km^2(average = 6.9 stoats/km^2) were found in the same habitats in 1993-1995. In the winter of 1997-1998 we found only ≤4 stoats/km^2 (average = 1.8; t >5.5, P <0.01). The notable result is that in the Rossony Study Area in the same years (1986-1990), where there already was a high density of American mink, we censused 5-7 stoats/km^2 of active floodplain (average = 5.9 stoats/km^2; t > 6.1, P <0.01). This difference suggests that the cause of the decrease in the stoat population in the Gorodok Study Area could not possibly be changes in rodent abundance, but could be due to the impact of naturalised mink.

The data obtained in the Rossony Study Area suggest that the decline in stoats could be, in part, due to the naturalisation of the raccoon dog. We can substantially support this idea only from observations based on the peculiarly changeable situations in two marshes with areas of *c.* 1.0 km^2 and 2.1 km^2. In the Rossony Study Area, the raccoon dog attained a high density in 1989-1990. Before this, stoats inhabited these marshes at a very high density (*c.* 7.6 and 9.0 stoats/km^2, respectively). After the raccoon dogs' expansion (in winter, 1995) the stoat population was reduced in number to 1.4 and 1.0 stoats/km^2, respectively. Then in January, 1998 we found no stoats there, whilst family groups of raccoon dog and American mink were common in early summer in 1997 and 1998 (Table 3).

Table 3. Numbers of family groups of naturalised carnivore species in the marshes of the Rossony Study Area, 1997-1998.

Period	Species (*c.* 1.0 km^2)	Small marsh (*c.* 2.1 km^2)	Larger marsh
Early June, 1997	Raccoon dog	2	5
Early June, 1997	American mink	2	4
Mid June, 1998	Raccoon dog	3	3
Mid June, 1998	American mink	2	5

Table 4. Frog densities in different habitats within the study areas, summers of 1995-1998:
Min. – max. (n)
Mean ± SD (SE)

Ecosystem	Gorodok Area	Rossony Area	Loknja Area
River valleys	0 - 18 (3567) 0.41 ± 1.10 (0.02)	0 - 24 (623) 0.32 ± 1.69 (0.07)	0 - 8 (175) 0.97 ± 1.60 (0.12)
Shore	0 - 8 (604) 0.64 ± 0.75 (0.03)	0 - 10 (169) 0.79 ± 1.84 (0.14)	?
Marshes with pools	0 – 40 (438) 1.31 ± 4.05 (0.19)	0 - 3 (156) 0.35 ± 0.94 (0.08)	?
Dry land forest	0 - 9 (3468) 0.33 ± 0.80 (0.01)	0 - 7 (1114) 0.14 ± 0.52	(0.02) 0 - 8 (201) 1.55 ± 1.82 (0.13)
Swamped forest	0 - 7 (968) 0.40 ± 0.87 (0.03)	0 - 18 (3567) 0.41 ± 1.10 (0.02)	?
Dry land meadows	0 - 6 (723) 0.19 ± 0.64 (0.03)	0 - 2 (81) 0.06 ± 0.29 (0.03)	0 – 4 (35) 0.54 ± 1.17 (0.20)

Dietary overlap and competition for prey between native riparian mustelids and naturalised carnivore species in relation to prey abundance and availability

Many different studies of native riparian mustelids and naturalised carnivores have been carried out and published (e.g. Sidorovich, 1992a,b,c, 1997, in press; Sidorovich *et al.*, 1998 & unpubl.; Pikulik & Sidorovich, 1991; Macdonald *et al.*, unpubl.). Therefore, in this review my intention is to present either more general statements, or more substantial results, to help clarify the causes of the declines of riparian mustelids.

The data obtained suggest that native semi-aquatic predator species, *i.e.* otter and European mink, utilise streams as their main habitats and, as they have become evolutionarily separated in terms of prey consumption, they do not compete significantly for food (Sidorovich, 1997; Sidorovich *et al.*, 1998). Inhabiting fairly large aquatic ecosystems with sufficient fish abundance, otters specialise in feeding on fish, whereas European mink are a generalist predator of land-water ecotones such as stream banks and glacial lake shorelines. Nevertheless, European mink are characterised by their rather specialised feeding upon frogs (Sidorovich *et al.*, unpubl.). Crayfish are an important prey item for both native semi-aquatic mustelids. In our study areas, crayfish abundances varied a lot both from year to year and between habitats. In the R. Lovat's upper reaches, captures of crayfish varied between 0-8 crayfish/net-night, with an average of ≤1.7 at particular places in certain aquatic ecosystems (rivers, glacial lakes, brooks). In small rivers, no crayfish were captured on 62% of net-nights (n = 42), on 39% in glacial lakes (n = 28) and 94% in small streams (n = 64). In years of crayfish population peaks or in habitats where crayfish survived in fair numbers during population crashes, both European mink and otter fed on crayfish a lot (Kolbin, 1958; Zharkov *et al.*, 1977; Sidorovich, 1997; Sidorovich *et al.*, unpubl.). In contrast, in crayfish population crash years, European mink consumed many more frogs, whereas otter fed mostly on fish - a shortage of this prey item forced them to supplement their diet with frogs (Sidorovich, 1997). So, as frogs (a substitute prey item) are plentiful in Belarus and adjacent regions of Russia (Pikulik, 1985; Sidorovich *et al.*, 1997c; Pikulik & Sidorovich, unpubl.) this may have caused our studies not to show any influence of crayfish population density crashes on either otter or European mink.

The dietary differences between European mink and otter partly separate these semi-aquatic predators. In this respect, the important feature is that European mink mainly live on small rivers and the smaller streams, whereas otters inhabit larger rivers with a higher prey density (Sidorovich, 1992b, 1997). Such patterns of habitat use increase the extent of evolutionarily-determined resource sharing between native semi-aquatic mustelids, and should maintain stable co-existence between otters and European mink. Polecats feed mainly on small mammals, amphibians and birds (Sidorovich, 1992c, 1997; Sidorovich *et al.*, 1998), so this terrestrial predator basically uses another ecological carrying capacity and does not compete with native semi-aquatic mustelids. There is much support for the contention that in Belarus and adjacent regions of Russia, frog densities cannot act as a limiting factor on the densities of their main consumers (European mink and polecat), simply because frogs are really plentiful (Pikulik, 1985). In our study areas we counted up to 39 frogs (mainly *Rana temporaria*)/10 m² of stream bank (average = 0.4-5.6

frogs/10 m²; Pikulik & Sidorovich, unpubl.). Also, common frogs concentrate in streams to over-winter and this leads to a marked increase in the total prey biomass available there (Pikulik & Sidorovich, 1991). For instance, during the winter of 1995-1996 in the Lovat's upper reaches, the average common frog biomass was *c.* 395 kg/km of river. So, high frog biomass actually determines the demographic success of semi-aquatic mustelids by, for example, providing successful autumn breeding conditions for otters (Sidorovich *et al.*, 1997c).

In Belarus, in comparison with the native riparian mustelid species, American mink have many competitive features as a predator on land-water ecotones (Sidorovich, 1997, in press). In seasonally changing conditions the feeding habits of naturalised mink are characterised by a well-developed opportunism. This has been found for the American mink in many areas of North America (Eberhardt, 1974; Eberhardt & Sargeant, 1975; Arnold & Fritzell, 1987) and in naturalised populations throughout Europe (Gerell, 1967; Jenkins & Harper, 1980; Chanin & Linn, 1980; Kyne *et al.*, 1989; Pikulik & Sidorovich, 1991; Dunstone, 1993; Sidorovich, 1997; Sidorovich *et al.*, 1998; Jedrzejewska & Jedrzejewski, 1998). This is highly adaptive and allows a semi-aquatic predator to survive in unfavourable or changeable habitat conditions in land-water ecotones. Therefore, American mink appear to be more competitive as a semi-aquatic predator when compared with native mink in the seasonally dynamic conditions of riparian habitats (Sidorovich, in press). European mink are much less opportunistic, and maintain a narrow diet despite decreases in the abundance and availability of their prey. For instance, in dry and hot summers, fish and crayfish are quickly extirpated by various predators. After that, the most readily abundant and available prey for a riparian mustelid become frogs, small mammals and birds. Nevertheless, European mink maintain their typical diet, whereas American mink switch to feeding upon the small mammals concentrating in riparian habitats (Sidorovich, 1997, in press). In conditions where ice cover limits access to aquatic ecosystems, access to prey is very limited and air and water temperatures are low. Here American mink change from their typical diet and specialise in feeding on small mammals too. At the same time, despite the unfavourable prey conditions in the water, this trend is much less typical of native mink (Sidorovich, 1997, in press; Sidorovich *et al.*, 1998).

Nevertheless, detailed analysis of the feeding relationships of the two mink species (Sidorovich, 1997, in press; Sidorovich *et al.*, 1998) suggests that there is little support for the contention that competition for prey could lead to the European mink's disappearance. Resource competition with American mink could affect native mink populations. However, this takes time, and European mink populations have declined too quickly to be responding to resource competition (Sidorovich, 1997; Sidorovich *et al.*, 1995).

There is an important feature of the feeding ecology of the American mink that perhaps has affected polecats and stoats substantially and should be emphasised. Annually, American mink prey more upon small mammals than do native mink, and many naturalised mink specialise in feeding on small mammals, especially in the warm period (Sidorovich, 1997; Sidorovich *et al.*, unpubl.). In river valley habitats in the Lovat's upper reaches, small mammals occurred in 32% of American mink scats (n = 1,930) and 14.5% of European mink scats (n = 1,474; G = 6.8, P <0.01). In the winters these differences were much higher, and the occurrence of small mammals in the diets of the two species were 83% and 24.3%, respectively (G = 33.9, P <0.01). In the upper reaches of the R. Lovat in 1996-1997, at least three of ten radio-tagged American mink fed largely on small mammals (72-98%, n = 92-212 prey) and scats from 147 American mink latrines, each containing *c*. 40-200 faeces (all probably originating from a single individual) suggested that, during the periods over which these scats had accumulated, 22% (7/32) of American mink fed heavily on small mammals (at least 70% of the scats in a latrine contained small mammal remains). Eight of ten American mink specialising on small mammal prey mainly inhabited marshes. The differences in the proportions of small mammals consumed annually in riparian habitats by American mink is much higher when compared with native mink, taking into account that naturalised mink inhabit most aquatic ecosystems at a much higher density than do European mink (Table 2). Furthermore, in the warm season American mink inhabit marshes and pools, even ones far from the nearest river bank or glacial lake shore; here they specialise in feeding on small mammals (Macdonald *et al.*, unpubl.; Sidorovich *et al.*, unpubl.). Native mink prefer to inhabit land-water ecotones throughout the year. The use of radio-tracking allowed detailed analysis of inter-specific differences in habitat in the R. Lovat upper reaches and showed that remote pools were visited more frequently by American mink (<40.3% , average = 7.2% of radiolocations) than European mink (<20.9%, average = 2.4% of radiolocations; G = 2.2-24.5, P = 0.001-0.16). Furthermore, during summer naturalised mink often visited willow marshes and swampy meadows (<33.8%, average = 4.9% of radiolocations) and black alder swamps (<9.3%, average = 1.0% of radiolocations) which often were remote from the nearest bank or shoreline. Long stays, feeding, marking behaviour and self-made American mink burrows were also recorded in these habitats. These all suggest that naturalised mink used these habitats regularly and stayed there for quite long periods. In contrast, native mink less often visited willow marshes and swampy meadows (<0.7%, average = 0.08% of radiolocations; G = 6.1-32.2, P = 0.001-0.03) or black alder swamps (0%; G = 1.4-9.1, P = 0.007-0.19). Marshes on banks, shores and floodplains, and fragmented marshes amongst dry land, are important habitats for polecats and stoats, allowing them to prey upon small mammals, mainly voles (Sidorovich, 1997).

Moreover, small mammal numbers varied a lot for a very important prey item, both annually and seasonally (Fig. 5). According to the data obtained, a substantial recent decrease in small mammal abundances was recorded (Sidorovich *et al.*, in press b); the main rodent prey of stoats are *Microtus* voles and water voles (Sidorovich, 1997) whose numbers declined most substantially (Table 5). The trend in microtine rodents could be connected with population cycling in these species as typically recorded in other areas (Pucek *et al.*, 1993; Jedrzejewska & Jedrzejewski, 1998). Also, there is abundant evidence from northern Belarus (Macdonald *et al.*, unpubl.; Sidorovich *et al.*, unpubl.) that riparian small mammals (*A. terrestris*, *M. oeconomus* and water shrews, *Neomys fodiens*) have been affected substantially by an abundant, additional predator - the naturalised American mink. These riparian small mammals are gradually replaced by other species (mainly *C. glareolus*, *M. agrestis*, *M. arvalis* and common shrew, *Sorex araneus*) which inhabit dry areas (dry habitats are much less limited in area than wetlands). This trend leads to a greatly reduced prey biomass for vertebrate predators in wetlands - riparian vole species are bigger, and their populations are characterised by higher densities due to the higher

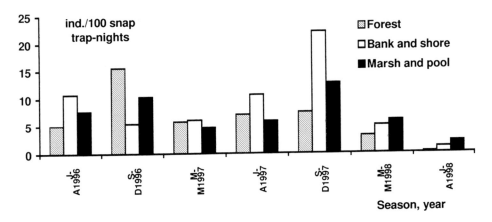

Fig. 5. Changes in small mammal abundances (trapped inds./100 snap trap-nights) in different ecosystems of north-eastern Belarus (the Gorodok Study Area) in 1996-1998. **NB:** M-M = March to May, J-A = June to August, S-D = September to December.

Table 5. Abundances (as numbers of individuals captured/100 snap traps) of *Microtus* voles (*M. oeconomus, M. agrestis, M. arvalis*) in the wetlands of the Gorodok Study Area, 1996-1998; mean ± SE (n).

Ecosystem	1996		1997			1998	
	J-A	S-D	M-M	J-A	S-D	M-M	J-A
River valleys and shores	2.9±1.1	1.6±0.6	0	0.2±0.2	0		0
	(24)	(17)	(11)	(6)	(3)	(3)	(5)
Marshes with pools outside	0.6±0.3	0.6±1.3	1.7±1.1	0.2±0.2	0		0.2±0.1
of floodplain	(9)	(8)	(3)	(7)	3)	(3)	(24)

NB: M-M = March to May, J-A = June to August; S-D = September to December.
n = number of places at which small mammals were censused.

grass productivity and nutrient status of wetlands. Moreover, for the majority of flooded sedge marshes this process stops after a decline in riparian small mammals - these probably cannot be replaced by small mammals from dry valley habitats.

In the main study area on the Lovat river head, a comparative analysis of the twenty four hour activities of polecat and the two mink species has been undertaken in relation to either possible competition for prey or resource-sharing (Sidorovich, 1997). In the main, polecats were inactive during daylight hours, whereas mink were active both day and night. European mink spent more time foraging and in other types of activity than did naturalised mink: 59 *vs.* 41% of their time (χ^2= 47, P <0.01). Considering the similar daily food intakes of the two mink species and the polecat (Tumanov & Smelov, 1980) the data obtained suggest that American mink are a more effective predator than are native mink, whereas the polecat is a more effective predator than either of them: polecats spent only 34% of their time in foraging and other types of activity (χ^2= 12-72, P <0.01).

As for competition for food between the riparian mustelid species and the raccoon dog, several notable features should be mentioned. Amongst vertebrate predators in Belarus and eastern Europe as a whole, the raccoon dog has one of the most catholic diets (Kauhala *et al.*, 1992; Sidorovich, 1997; Jedrzejewska & Jedrzejewski, 1998; Sidorovich *et al.*, in press a). This generalist predator consumes a high diversity of food types including even wild boar, *Sus scrofa*, scats or herbs as a last resort. Several food resources that are consumed substantially by raccoon dogs are definitely not limiting in Belarus. These include molluscs (occurrence in the raccoon dog scats analysed = 12.3%, n = 848 scats), amphibians (20.9%), herbs (14.0%) and fruits (48.5%). In addition, raccoon dogs consume a great deal of wild ungulate carrion (occurrence in scats = 41.6%, but rising in late winter to 88.4%, n = 121 scats). Carrion is a very important and limiting food resource for many vertebrate predators (including both polecat and stoat). In the harsh habitat conditions of late winter, when other food sources have failed, carrion-feeding provides many vertebrate predators with a way to survive (Sidorovich *et al.*, in press a). In the forested area during this unfavourable period, the occurrence of wild ungulate carrion in polecat scats was 80.6% (n = 98). Although in late winter carrion comprised only 25.6% in stoat scats (n = 43), wild ungulate carcasses seem to play a greater role as a food resource than suggested by scat analyses. By late winter, stoat tracks and feeding were recorded at 99/121 of the wild ungulate carcasses inspected.

A special survey to find all wild ungulate carcasses and estimate the abundance of carrion as a food resource in particular areas (5-7 km^2 each winter) showed that carrion was scarce. Usually, in one such area we found one or two (up to four) elk, *Alces alces*, carcasses and one to four (up to nine) carcasses of wild boar. Only six of those carcasses (one elk and five wild boar) out of 98 (*i.e.* 6.1%) had been partly eaten, and 32 carcasses (32.7%) contained a substantial amount of carrion, however, the majority of them (60/98, *i.e.* 61.2%) had been nearly completely consumed and retained only the skull, the larger bones and the remains of the skin. Nevertheless, all such poor remnants of wild ungulate carcasses were visited by generalist carnivores such as raccoon dog, red fox, *Vulpes vulpes*, pine marten, *Martes martes*, polecat and others, and it was evident that they tried to consume the carrion. This also gives much support to the idea that this important food resource for predators (including polecat and stoat) was limited in the harshest period. After raccoon dogs reached a high density, carrion feeding appeared to cause serious competition for food by late winter, and this affected native predators, including polecats and stoats.

Interference between native riparian mustelids and naturalised carnivores

During an intensive radio-tracking study made in 1995-1997 and a further, less intensive radio-tracking study in 1998-1999 on the head of the R. Lovat, it has been revealed that aggressive encounters between naturalised mink and native mink are common, and the data obtained suggest that simply attacks by naturalised mink could lead to the rapid disappearance of European mink (see Table 6; Sidorovich, 1997; Sidorovich *et al.*, unpubl.). These aggressive encounters were mostly (12/14 encounters recorded) initiated by male American mink, and directed towards European mink of either sex. Only once was an aggressive attack from a female American mink towards a female native mink recorded. Following such attacks the European mink left the river area and sheltered for up to 22 hours in the forest or fields, e.g. under a fallen spruce. The European mink did usually attempt to return to the river, sometimes within 15 minutes, in which case they were normally subjected to repeated attacks. (Most often they returned within 30 minutes to two hours.) The data suggest that, if a male American mink came within a distance 200 m of a European mink, the naturalised mink male would chase and drive away the European mink. Moreover, according to observations obtained within European mink territories (Sidorovich *et al.*, unpubl.), American mink tended to use fresh tracks to search for European mink and then drove them off. Considering these results it becomes clear why the European mink declined so quickly from a dense population to near extinction (Sidorovich, 1997; Sidorovich *et al.*, 1995).

Single aggressive encounters between male American mink and male polecats have been recorded, after which the polecat ran away, but without being pursued by the mink. Also, mutual avoidance behaviour (nine cases) by males of these two species was rather common. A single aggressive behaviour (quite a severe encounter) between two male European mink has been observed, whereas American mink seem to be a more social species, and intra-specific aggressive behaviour has never been recorded. Moreover, we observed two peaceful contacts between two male American mink and nine peaceful contacts between males and females of this species. At the same time, peaceful behaviour such as this was common in European mink, too (Table 6).

Changes in body size in European mink and female polecats in relation to the expansion of American mink

During the first two years of the American mink's expansion (in comparison with European mink and polecat) the markedly bigger size and weight of naturalised mink were statistically significant (Table 7; Sidorovich *et al.*, 1999). In the course of several years following the American mink's arrival, there were striking changes in the weights and sizes of European mink as well as female polecats. In subsequent years, both sexes of this native species became larger and larger; the trends are statistically significant. Now, when European mink are near extinction in an area, their body weight and size are almost the same as those of American mink. The same is true of female polecats, but there was no weight change in males (Table 7). This was quite the opposite of what was expected: if there had been competition for food, then the body weights should have diverged from each other after the American mink's arrival. It seems that the most likely explanation is aggression – *i.e.* direct attacks by American mink on European mink and female polecats.

An hypothesis for the decline of riparian mustelids

The decline in European mink populations is thought to be the result of direct competition - in the form of aggressive encounters with American mink - accentuated by rapid American mink population expansion and high reproductive rates (Sidorovich, 1993). There is no evidence that the decline in European mink is due either to a decline in prey availability, or to competition for prey (Sidorovich, 1997; Sidorovich *et al.*, 1998, in press a, unpubl.). Taking into account that naturalised

Table 6. Registered contacts between radio-tagged American mink, European mink and polecats as numbers of observations (total radiolocations = 19,217) in the upper reaches of the River Lovat, NE Belarus, 1995-1999

Species, sex	Distances between radio-tagged mustelids (m)			Pattern of behaviour at short distances		
	200 1000	<200	Very close	Aggressive encounter	Avoidance	Nothing happened-probably a peaceful contact
M.l. m-m	14	4	2	1?	4	1
M.l. f-f	2	1	0	0	1	0
M.l. m-f	17	7	5	0	1	5
M.l. f - *M.v.* m	16	6	6	5	5, after the encounter *M.l* avoided *M.v.*	1?
M.l. m - *M.v.* m	25	8	8	8	7, after the encounter *M.l* avoided *M.v.*	0
M.l. f - *M.v.* f	7	1	1	1	1, after the encounter *M.l* avoided *M.v.*	0
M.l. m - *M.v.* f	8	1	1	0	0	1?
M.v. m-m	22	4	2	0	0	2
M.v. f-f	4	0	0	0	0	0
M.v. m-f	47	12	9	0	0	9
M.l. m - *M.p.* m	10	5	0	0	5	0
M.l. f - *M.p.* m	8	2	0	0	2	0
M.v. m - *M.p.* m	21	4	1	1	4	0
M.v. f - *M.p.* m	7	1	0	0	1	0
M.p. m-m	8	3	0	0	2	1

NB: *M.l.* = European mink, *M.v.* = American mink; *M.p.* = polecat, m = male, f = female.

Table 7. Mean weights and body lengths of European mink, American mink and polecat in the Gorodok Study Area, NE Belarus. Measurements of European mink and polecat are from before and after the arrival of large numbers of American mink (July, 1990). Data shown include weights (g), snout-vent lengths (cm), standard errors, number of observations (in brackets), and Coefficients of Variation (cv).

Species	Sex	Weight before (g)	Weight after (g)	Length before(cm)	Length after (cm)
M. vison	Male	-	1325±36.9 (42) cv=18.0	-	42.9±0.3 (42) cv=4.8
M. vison	female	-	781±21.0 (23) cv=12.9	-	37.0±0.2 (23) cv=3.1
M. lutreola	male	851±24.2 (16) cv=11.4	990±20.5 (22) cv=9.7	39.2±0.3 (16) cv=3.3	40.7±0.3 (22) cv=3.0
M. lutreola	female	534±12.7 (8) cv=6.7	646±64.9 (6) cv=24.6	35.1±0.3 (8) cv=2.7	36.5±0.1 (6) cv=0.9
M. putorius	male	1093±36.7 (9) cv=10.1	1165±34.3 (20) cv=13.1	40.6±0.6 (9) cv=4.1	41.1±0.5 (20) cv=5.1
M. putorius	female	507±8.8 (3) cv=3.1	634±56.5 (7) cv=23.6	31.7±0.7 (3) cv=3.7	34.0±0.5 (7) cv=4.9

mink seem to be a more competitive species, resource competition with American mink could affect native mink populations. However, this takes time, and European mink populations have declined too quickly for this to be a response to resource competition (Sidorovich, 1997; Sidorovich *et al.*, 1995). The aggressive attitude of American mink towards native mink occurs before resource competition, and is the main factor in the decline of European mink. Raccoon dog naturalisation also could partly affect European mink populations; raccoon dogs are much bigger, more numerous, and tend to inhabit wetlands. Nevertheless, it seems that this could not have contributed substantially to the European mink's disappearance because, in our studies, the marked decline in native mink occurred when the raccoon dog population density was fairly low.

Ternovsky (1977, 1994) assumed that the decline in the European mink was determined by a decrease in reproduction - a result of interbreeding between male American mink and female European mink, and the abnormal development of the resulting hybrid embryo. Abnormal hybrid embryos have been recorded in captivity (Ternovsky, 1977) but may be unusual in wild European mink populations. We found a very high proportion of well developed, normal embryos (36/37 observed in nine pregnant females) under conditions of high naturalised mink density (Sidorovich, 1997). Also, there is no recorded evidence that can confirm this hypothesis in wild European mink. So, this hypothesis is probably an unlikely explanation for the decline of European mink populations.

Gradually, during the American mink's expansion, European mink become rare on rivers. However, on brooks up to 10 km long (which are used less frequently by American mink) there was less change in European mink densities. Radio-tracking data show that American mink drive European mink away from rivers, and that these European mink then move onto small streams that are usually a poorer quality habitat. However, brooks are used more frequently by European mink males than females; females clearly prefer small rivers which offer more food to a semi-aquatic predator. It is possible that female native mink are unable to inhabit small streams continuously as these have insufficient resources to allow them to raise a litter.

The data suggest that declining European mink populations are characterised by an altered population structure, low reproductive rate and high mortality. A possible explanation is interference from American mink - females appear to be more vulnerable than males. This situation is accentuated by the female's apparent inability to raise a litter in poor quality habitats. In effect, the native mink are being eliminated from favourable habitats, which then are occupied by the expanding American mink population. Such habitat loss, and particularly its effect on female European mink, may offer an explanation for the observed decrease in reproductive rate and increase in mortality.

Although polecats can co-exist with European mink, the naturalised mink feeds on small mammals more frequently than do native mink, so there is substantial dietary overlap between polecat and American mink, especially during harsh severe winter conditions (Sidorovich, 1997; Sidorovich *et al.*, 1998). American mink are well adapted to foraging in both aquatic and terrestrial ecosystems (Dunstone, 1993). Perhaps American mink are more competitive in aquatic ecosystems than polecats and, as a result, polecat populations tend to decline on rivers and glacial lakes and wetlands. Furthermore, as with European mink, polecat females are at an even greater competitive disadvantage due to their smaller body size, so they are driven away from river valleys (a high quality habitat) by the physically stronger American mink. Also, there is some support for the idea that in all natural ecosystems, and especially in wetlands, polecat populations were affected by the raccoon dog because of their markedly similar diets and habitat use, and the much greater strength of the latter. Raccoon dogs consume a great deal of wild ungulate carrion which, by late winter, is a very important and limiting food resource for polecats.

Body measurements show that on the way to extinction there is a substantial increase in body size and relative weight (*i.e.* overall condition) in European mink, and that this coincides with the arrival of the larger American mink (Sidorovich *et al.*, 1999). Female polecats also display the same trend. The most likely explanation for this size increase is increased survival of larger individuals, perhaps because of the direct aggression of American mink - seen both in the wild (Sidorovich, 1997; Sidorovich *et al.*, unpubl.) and in captivity (Maran, 1989). This trend is significant only for the survival of male European mink, and mainly males were recorded in the declining European mink populations at the head of the R. Lovat. Thus, on a river where the American mink is expanding, these data suggest that, despite an increase in European mink body size, it is much more difficult for female European mink to survive than males. In such a situation, European mink populations will decrease rapidly because of their low reproductive rate (the density of females having become extremely low). As for female polecats, which also become larger, most of them are forced to stay away from the banks by the stronger American mink.

A possible explanation for the decline in stoat numbers could be as follows. At first, most wetlands that formerly were inhabited by a high density of stoats, were densely inhabited by naturalised American mink and raccoon dogs, both of which have substantially higher physical strength. Perhaps this leads to aggressive encounters between the bigger species and stoats, especially in the breeding season and in winter, where there is competition for favourable habitat. Secondly, both naturalised predators act to reduce food resources that are very important to stoats (riparian voles throughout the year and wild ungulate carrion in late winter). The American mink substantially affects riparian small mammals (*A. terrestris*, *M. oeconomus*, *N. fodiens*) which either are gradually replaced by other species from dry areas, or simply disappear. This trend leads to much lower prey biomass in wetlands, because riparian voles are bigger and their populations are characterised by higher densities. Because of the stoat's high energy expenditure (King, 1989) this is very unfavourable to them as they require a high small mammal biomass. By late winter raccoon dogs consume a lot of carrion and so limit another very important food resource for stoats. Thirdly, the recent reduction in stoat numbers can be explained by the substantial, recent decreases in the abundance of rodents (and especially microtine voles) – possibly connected with the normal population cycles of these rodents.

Acknowledgements

This review is based on both my own and joint studies, and those undertaken with my colleagues, notably Dr. David Macdonald (Wildlife Conservation Research Unit, Oxford University, UK), Dr. Hans Kruuk (Institute for Terrestrial Ecology,

Banchrory, Scotland), Prof. Dr. Michael Pikulik (Institute of Zoology, National Academy of Sciences of Belarus), and Dr. Helena Anisimova, Dmitry Krasko and Alexey Polozov (Vertebrate Predation Research Group, Institute of Zoology, National Academy of Sciences of Belarus). Larisa Tihomirova, Svetlana Adamovich and Nikolai Jakovets also helped. These studies were supported financially by several bodies. The Institute of Zoology of the National Academy of Sciences of Belarus supported the study in its entirety between 1986-1993, and in part between 1994-1998. In addition, partial support (1994-1996) was provided by the Soros Foundation. Special acknowledgement is made of the substantial financial support (1995-1997) provided by the British Government's Darwin Initiative Foundation. Some of the results of these researches have been published in a book about mustelids in Belarus (Sidorovich, 1997) in which individual authorship is given for different chapters. Further joint publications with my colleagues are either in preparation or "in press" (e.g. Sidorovich *et al.*, unpubl.; Macdonald *et al.*, unpubl.). Therefore, this paper represents an extended review of the results obtained in order to consider the decline of all the riparian mustelid species together - there being much support for the contention that the declines of these species have a similar set of causes.

References

Arnold, T.N. & Fritzell, E.K. (1987). Food habits of prairie mink during the waterfowl breeding season. *Canadian Journal of Zoology*, **65**: 2322-2324.

Böhme, G. (1977). Zur Bestimmung quartärer Anuren Europas an Hand von Skelettelementen. *Wissenschaftliche Zeitschrift der Humboldt-Universitat zu Berlin (Mathematisch-Naturwissenschaften Reihe)*, **26**: 283-300.

Budnikov, K.N. & Tretyakov, F.F. (1952). [*Crayfish and their capturing.*] Moskow; Pischepromizdat (in Russian).

Danilov, P.I. & Tumanov, I.L. (1976). [*Mustelids of north-eastern of SSSR.*] Leningrad; Nauka (in Russian).

Day, M.G. (1966). Identification of hair and feather remains in the gut and faeces of stoats and weasels. *Journal of Zoology*, **148**: 201-217.

Debrot, S., Fivaz, G., Mermod, C. & Weber, J.-M. (1982). *Atlas des poils de mammifères d'Europe.* Neuchâtel: Editions d'Institute de Zoologie, Université de Neuchâtel.

Dunstone, N. (1993). *The mink.* London; T & AD Poyser Ltd.

Eberhardt, L.E. (1974). *Food habits of prairie mink (Mustela vison) during the waterfowl breeding season.* MS thesis. St. Paul (Minnesota); University of Minnesota.

Eberhardt, L.E. & Sargeant, A.B. (1975). Mink predation on prairie marshes during the waterfowl breeding season. In: *Proceedings of the Predator Symposium, Missoula, USA*: 33-43.

Galkin, G.G. (1953). [*Atlas of scales of freshwater fishes.*] *Publications of the Research Institute of River and Lake Economy*, **16**: 1-167 (in Russian).

Gerell, R. (1967). Food selection in relation to habitat in mink (*Mustela vison*, Schreber) in Sweden. *Oikos*, **18**: 233-246.

Gorner, M. & Hackethal, H. (1988). *Säugetiere Europas.* Leipzig; Neuman Verlag.

Jakushko, O.F., Myslivets, I.A. & Rachevsky, A.N. (1988). [*Lakes of Belarus.*] Minsk; Urodzhai (in Russian).

Jakushko, O.F., Vlasov, B.P. & Bogdanov, S.V. (1995). [*Biological and economy classification of glacial lakes in Belarus.*] Minsk; Urodzhai (in Russian).

Jedrzejewska, B.& Jedrzejewski, W. (1998). *Predation in vertebrate communities. The Białowieża primeval forest as a case study.* Berlin; Springer Verlag.

Jenkins, D. & Harper, R.J. (1980). Ecology of otters in Northern Scotland. II. Analyses of otter (*Lutra lutra*) and mink (*Mustela vison*) faeces from Deeside, N.E. Scotland in 1977-78. *Journal of Animal Ecology*, **49**: 737-754.

Kauhala, K., Kaunisto, M. & Helle, E. (1992). Diet of raccoon dog, *Nyctereutes procyonoides*, in Finland. In: *Ecological characteristics of the raccoon dog in Finland*. Academic dissertation. Helsinki; University of Helsinki, Department of Zoology.

King, C.M. (1989). *The natural history of weasels and stoats*. London; Christopher Helm.

Kolbin, L.V. (1958). [Relationships beavers and otters in Belarus.] *Publications of the hunting reserve "Belovezhskaja Puscha", Minsk*, **1:** 139-150 (in Russian).

Kyne, M.J., Smal, C.M. & Fairley, J.S. (1989). The food of otters *Lutra lutra* in the Irish Midlands and a comparison with that of mink *Mustela vison* in the same region. *Proceedings of the Royal Irish Academy (Series B)*, **89:** 3-46.

Maran, T. (1989). Einige Aspekte zum gegenseitigen Verhalten des Europäischen *Mustela lutreola* und Amerikanischen Nerzes *Mustela vison* sowie zu ihrer Raum- und Zeitnutzung. In: M. Stubbe (ed.), *Populationsökologie marderartiger Säugetiere*: 321-333. Halle (Saale); Martin-Luther-Universität Halle-Wittenberg.

Maran, T. & Henttonen, H. (1995). Why is the European mink (*Mustela lutreola*) disappearing? - A review of the process and hypotheses. *Annales Zoologici Fennici*, **32:** 47-54.

Maran, T., Macdonald, D.W. Kruuk, H., Sidorovich, V.E. & Rozhnov, V.V. (1998). The continuing decline of the European mink *Mustela lutreola*: evidence for the intraguild aggression hypothesis. In: N. Dunstone & M.L. Gorman (eds.), *Behaviour and ecology of riparian mammals*: 297-324. Cambridge; Cambridge University Press.

Marz, R. (1987). *Gewoll-und Rupfungskunde*. Berlin; Akademie Verlag.

Pikulik, M.M. (1985). [*Amphibians in Belarus.*] Minsk; Nauka & Tekhnika (in Russian).

Pikulik, M.M. & Sidorovich, V.E. (1991). [Estimation of structural and functional inter-population relationships of semi-aquatic mustelids and amphibians in Belarus.] *Ekologija (Sverdlovsk)*, **6:** 28-36 (in Russian).

Pucek, Z. (1981). [*Keys to vertebrates of Poland: Mammals.*] Warszawa; Panstowowe Wydawnictwo Naukowe (in Polish).

Pucek, Z., Jedrzejewski, W., Jedrzejewska, B. & Pucek, M. (1993). Rodent population dynamics in a primeval deciduous forest (Białowieża National Park) in relation to weather, seed crop, and predation. *Acta Theriologica*, **38:** 199-232.

Rumyantcev, V.D. (1974). [*Crayfish of Volga-Caspia (biology and capturing).*] Moskow; Pischevaya promyshlennost (in Russian).

Sasaki, H. & Kawabata M. (1994). Food habits of the raccoon dog *Nyctereutes procyonoides viverrinus* in a mountainous area of Japan. *Journal of the Mammal Society of Japan*, **19:** 1-8.

Savchenko, V.V. & Sidorovich, V.E. (1994). [Comparative analysis of water pollution and semi-aquatic mammal distribution in Belarus. In: *Problems of biology, conservation and exploitation of animal diversity* (*Proceedings of the 7th Zoological Conference of Belarus, Minsk, 1994*)]: 261-262 (in Russian).

Sidorovich, V.E. (1991). Structure, reproductive status and dynamics of the otter population in Byelorussia. *Acta Theriologica*, **36:** 153-161.

Sidorovich, V.E. (1992a). Gegenwärtige Situation des Europäischen Nerzes (*Mustela lutreola*) in Belorußland. Hypothese seines Verschwindens. In: R. Schröpfer, M. Stubbe & D. Heidecke (eds.), *Semiaquatische Säugetiere*: 316-328. Halle (Saale); Martin-Luther-Universität Halle-Wittenberg.

Sidorovich, V.E. (1992b). [Otter (*Lutra lutra*) population structure in Belarus.] *Biulletin Moskovskogo Obshchestva Ispytatelei Prirody, Otdel Biologicheskii*, **97**(6): 43-51 (in Russian).

Sidorovich, V.E. (1992c). Comparative analysis of the diets of European mink (*Mustela lutreola*), American mink (*M. vison*) and polecat (*M. putorius*) in Byelorussia. *Small Carnivore Conservation*, **6:** 2-4.

Sidorovich, V.E. (1993). Reproductive plasticity of the American mink (*Mustela vison*) in Belarus. *Acta Theriologica*, **38:** 175-183.

Sidorovich, V.E. (1994). How to identify the tracks of the European mink (*Mustela lutreola*), the American mink (*M. vison*) and the polecat (*M. putorius*) on waterbodies. *Small Carnivore Conservation*, **10:** 8-9.

Sidorovich, V.E. (Ed.) (1997). *Mustelids in Belarus. Evolutionary ecology, demography and interspecific relationships*. Minsk; Zolotoy uley.

Sidorovich, V.E. (1999). How to identify mustelid tracks. *Small Carnivore Conservation*, **20:** 22-27.

Sidorovich V.E. (in press). Seasonal feeding habits of riparian mustelids in river valleys of NE Belarus. *Acta Theriologica*.

Sidorovich, V.E. & Maran T. (1997). Pollutant concentrations in the European mink and rivers with implications for the decline of its populations in Belarus. In: V.E. Sidorovich (ed.), *Mustelids in Belarus. Evolutionary ecology, demography and interspecific relationships*: 244-247. Minsk; Zolotoy uley.

Sidorovich, V.E., Savchenko, V.V. & Budny, V.B. (1995). Some data about the European mink *Mustela lutreola* distribution in the Lovat river basin in Russia and Belarus: current status and retrospective analysis. *Small Carnivore Conservation*, **12**: 14-18.

Sidorovich, V.E., Jedrzejewska, B. & Jedrzejewski, W. (1996). Winter distribution and abundance of mustelids and beavers in the river valleys of Bialowieza Primeval Forest. *Acta Theriologica*, **41**: 155-170.

Sidorovich, V.E., Savchenko, V.V. & Lauzhel G.O. (1997a). Pollutants in an organism of the semi-aquatic mustelids: accumulation and removal. Heavy metals. In: V.E. Sidorovich (ed.), *Mustelids in Belarus. Evolutionary ecology, demography and interspecific relationships*: 231-237. Minsk; Zolotoy uley.

Sidorovich, V.E., Denisova, A.V. & Lauzhel, G.O. (1997b). Pollutants in an organism of the semi-aquatic mustelids: accumulation and removal. Organochlorine pesticides. In: V.E. Sidorovich (ed.), *Mustelids in Belarus. Evolutionary ecology, demography and interspecific relationships*: 237-240. Minsk; Zolotoy uley.

Sidorovich, V.E., Pikulik M.M. & Tumanov I.L. (1997c). Analysis of the non-cyclic breeding of otters in relation to prey abundance and availability. In: V.E. Sidorovich (ed.), *Mustelids in Belarus. Evolutionary ecology, demography and interspecific relationships*: 158-162. Minsk; Zolotoy uley.

Sidorovich, V.E., Kruuk, H. Macdonald, D.W. & Maran, T. (1998). Diets of semi-aquatic carnivores in northern Belarus, with implications for population changes. In: N. Dunstone & M.L. Gorman (eds.), *Behaviour and ecology of riparian mammals*: 177-190. Cambridge; Cambridge University Press.

Sidorovich, V.E., Kruuk, H. & Macdonald, D.W. (1999). Body size, and interactions between European and American mink (*Mustela lutreola* and *M. vison*) in Eastern Europe. *Journal of Zoology* (in press).

Sidorovich, V.E., Krasko, D.A., Lauzhel, G.O. & Polozov, A.G. (in press a). Feeding habits and dietary overlaps of the forest generalist carnivores in the northern Belarus. In: *Proceeding of the IV Baltic Theriological Conference, 1999*.

Sidorovich, V.E., Anisimova, E.I., Sidorovich, N.V., Lauzhel, G.O. & Tihomirova, L.L. (in press b). [Structure of small mammal community (Rodentia, Insectivora) as prey of vertebrate predators in various ecosystems of northern Belarus.] *Journal of the National Academy of Sciences of Belarus, Biological Series*, **1999** (in Russian).

Teplov V.P. (1952). [Census methods of otters, martens and small mustelids. In: *Methods of census and study on distribution of terrestrial vertebrate mammals*]: 165-172. Moscow; Nauka Publisher (in Russian).

Ternovsky, D.V. & Ternovskaja, U.G. (1994). [*Ecology of mustelids.*] Novosibirsk; Nauka Publisher (in Russian).

Tumanov, I.L. (1992). The number of European mink (*Mustela lutreola* L.) in the eastern area and its relation to American mink. In: R. Schröpfer, M. Stubbe & D. Heidecke (eds.), *Semiaquatische Säugetiere*: 329-335. Halle (Saale); Martin-Luther-Universität Halle-Wittenberg.

Tumanov, I.L. (1996). [A problem of *Mustela lutreola*: reasons of disappearance and conservation strategy.] *Zoologichesky Zhurnal*, **75**: 1394-1403 (in Russian with English abstract).

Tumanov, I.L. & Smelov, V.A. (1980). [Feeding relationships of mustelids in north-eastern of USSR]. *Zoologichesky Zhurnal*, **59**: 1536-1544 (in Russian).

Tumanov, I.L. & Zverev E.L. (1986). [Current distribution and abundance of the European mink (*Mustela lutreola*) in USSR.] *Zoologichesky Zhurnal*, **65**: 426-435 (in Russian).

Zharkov, I.V., Gatih, V.S. & Rodikov, V.P. (1977). [Otters in area of the Pripjat reserve. In: *Reserves of Byelorussia. Researches (vol. 1)*]: 118-126. Minsk; Urodzhai (in Russian).

Zhukov, P.I. (1965). [*Fish in Belarus.*] Minsk; Nauka & Technika (in Russian).

Zhukov, P.I. (1988). [*Reference book on freshwater fish ecology.*] Minsk; Nauka & Technika (in Russian).

CHAPTER 20

The marbled polecat, *Vormela peregusna* (Güldenstaedt, 1770), in FR Yugoslavia and elsewhere

Miroljub Milenković, Milan Paunović*, Helen E. Abel & Huw I. Griffiths*

Abstract

The marbled or tiger polecat is one of only two European mustelid species featured in the IUCN Red List (Groombridge, 1996). Although widespread throughout the southern Palaearctic, in Europe the species only occurs in the south-east (the Balkans) where its status is poorly understood. We here report new records of the marbled polecat from Yugoslavia, and place these within the context of other recent researches into this unusual and little-known species.

Introduction

The marbled polecat (also known as the tiger polecat) is one of very few Palaearctic mustelids thought to be of conservation concern. This stems from the listing of the European subspecies, *Vormela peregusna peregusna*, as Vu (Vulnerable) because of presumed population reductions through range regression and/or exploitation (Groombridge, 1996). There have been two recent reviews of the species in Europe, notably those of Spassov & Spiridonov (1993) and Mitchell-Jones *et al.* (1999) although some of the records cited in both require further evaluation. The only other detailed studies of the marbled polecat in Europe are those of Mirić *et al.* (1983) who discuss the species' status within the former Socialist Federal Republic of Yugoslavia (SFRY), and an older work by Atanassov (1966) detailing the species' occurrence in the Balkans.

Within Europe itself, marbled polecats are present in the Federal Republic of Yugoslavia (hereafter Yugoslavia, *i.e.* Serbia and Montenegro), Macedonia, Bulgaria, southern Romania, north-eastern Greece, Turkish Thrace and possibly Albania. Elsewhere, the species occupies a wide, poorly defined range spreading across the southern margins of the Palaearctic Region, and generally occupying steppic and semi-desert habitats. Various subspecies have been described, but no consensus exists over which (if any) are valid or what their geographical distributions are (see Abel & Griffiths, 1999). However, broader-scale regional, species-based distributions have been reported by several authors (e.g. Ognev, 1935; Vereshchagin, 1959; Harrison & Bates, 1991; Qumsiyeh, 1996; Zhang Yongzu *et al.*, 1997) and

---

* Corresponding authors.

Mustelids in a modern world
Management and conservation aspects of small carnivore: human interactions
edited by Huw I. Griffiths, pp. 321–329
© *2000 Backhuys Publishers, Leiden, The Netherlands*

Chotolchu *et al.* (1989) attempt a global review. Despite this, few of these accounts offer information on population status and, moreover, many simply restate older records which give no real indication of the species' present-day occurrence.

The present article presents new data on the status of the marbled polecat in Yugoslavia collected by two of the authors (MM, MP). These data are briefly placed within the context of a broader assessment of the species' status within both Europe and the Palaearctic as a whole. This forms a component of ongoing work by the IUCN Small Carnivore Specialist Group's *Vormela* Group (see Robinson, 1998).

Distribution in Yugoslavia

The marbled polecat has been paid insufficient attention in Yugoslavia and both scientific and ethnozoological data on the species are scarce. The marbled polecat is known only in areas where it, according to local inhabitants, occurs quite frequently. According to our present knowledge, the western boundary of its European range extends along the west of Yugoslavia and no evidence exists to suggest the species' existence further west, although three extralimital records have been reported - two from "southern Dalmatia" by Atanassov (1966) and a single record from Maribor (formerly Marburg), Slovenia by Koller (1929): the last of these is certainly incorrect (B. Kryštufek, pers. comm.). A review of the data that served as the basis for the determination of the marbled polecat's distribution in former SFR Yugoslavia has been given by Mirić *et al.* (1983). However, further data have been collected since, and habitat requirements and degree of endangerment have been discussed by Savić *et al.* (1995).

New data have been gathered by conducting surveys, chiefly of hunters, foresters and country people. Where possible, physical evidence (specimens) have been obtained, and these are now kept in the collections of either the Institute for Biological Research "Siniša Stanković", Belgrade, or the Natural History Museum, Belgrade. In addition, a number of specimens are housed in the Natural History Collection of Priština Museum and the Institute for Nature Protection, Novi Sad Department, and some of the material discussed here is held in private collections.

So far, there have been no projects in Yugoslavia devoted solely to marbled polecat research. As a result, the number of records collected is rather disproportionate to the degree of research interest – largely because data have been gathered in the course of studies of other elements of Yugoslavia's mammal fauna. However, the colourful appearance of the marbled polecat attracts the attention of local people, and also renders misidentifications unlikely. Living close to village outskirts and having comparatively little fear of man, marbled polecats have had many encounters with people and these have resulted in a range of different outcomes.

This strikingly exotic species amongst the Eurasian mustelids inhabits a large part of Yugoslavia. Its range in Yugoslavia is discontinuous and comprises two main, comparatively discrete areas: eastern and western Serbia (Tables 1 & 2, Fig. 1). Of 38 new records of marbled polecats in Yugoslavia, only two (from the Morava river valley) suggest its presence in central Serbia. It is unlikely to occur widely in Vojvodina nowadays, despite credible testimony of a specimen killed in Bačka (Bačko Petrovo Selo village) and of a sighting in southeastern Banat (Kusić village).

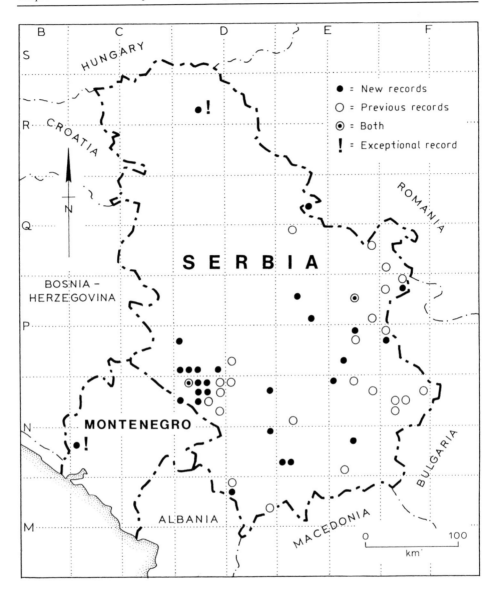

Fig. 1. Locations of new records of *Vormela peregusna* in Yugoslavia.

However, insufficient research rather than the absence of marbled polecats seems to be the reason for this scarcity of records in central Yugoslavia, and there are also no reliable records from either south and extreme south-east Serbia, or Montenegro. The first observation of the species in Montenegro (at Vilusi village amongst sub-mediterranean rocky shrubs), exceptional though it is, does show that our knowledge of the western boundary of the species' range is still inadequate.

Table 1. New records of *Vormela peregusna* in Yugoslavia. Collected = material held in state and private collections; observed = records not accompanied by voucher material; killed = animals killed (not shot).

No.	UTM	Locality	Date	Sex	Type of Data
1.	CN 03	Vilusi village, Nikšić	1986-spring	-	Observed
2.	DM 58	Šarković, Dobruna	-	-	Observed
3.	DN 07	Bare village, Giljeva Mt., Sjenica	1984-07-..	-	Observed
4.	DN 19	Sjenica town, outskirts	1986-summer	-	Observed (4 inds. killed by cars)
5.	DN 19	Ušak village, Sjenica	1986-07-..	-	Observed (6 juvs. killed)
6.	DN 19	Potkrš village, Sjenica	1987-04-..	-	Observed (killed)
7.	DN 27	Dolići village, Sjenica	1985-..-..	-	Observed (found dead)
8.	DN 28	Brnjica village, Sjenica	1983-..-..	?	Collected (skull)
9.	DN 28	Kneževac village, Sjenica	1984-..-..	-	Observed
			1986-..-..	-	Observed (skin only)
10.	DN 28	Dragojlovće village, Sjenica	1985-..-..	-	Observed
			1986-..-..	-	Observed
			1991-07-10	m	Collected (skeleton & taxidermy)
11.	DN 29	Vapa village, Sjenica	1986-..-..	-	Observed (frequent)
12.	DN 29	Štavalj village, Sjenica	1987-..-..	-	Observed (shot)
			1989-..-..	-	Collected (skin)
13.	DN 38	Duga Poljana village, Golija Mt.	1987-..-..	-	Collected (skin of shot animal)
14.	DN 38	Kamešnica village, Sjenica	1986-08-05	?	Collected (skull & skeleton)
15.	DN 38	Medjugora village, Pešter	1987-08-12	?	Collected (skull)
16.	DN 38	Draževiće village, Sjenica	1986-07-..	-	Observed (near burrow)
			1986-08-..		Observed (5 inds. "playing")
17.	DN 39	Stup village, Sjenica	1987-04-..	-	Observed
18.	DN 94	Kosovska Mitrovica, surroundings	1960-05-21	m	Collected (found killed)
19.	DN 98	Gornje Leviće village, Kopaonik Mt.	1950 - 1960	-	Observed many times
20.	DP 00	Akmačići village, Nova Varoš	1985-summer	-	Observed
			1988-03-14	m	Collected (skeleton & skull frag.)
			1990-09-..	-	Observed
21.	DP 00	Gujanića Mala, Akmačići, Nova Varoš	1986-summer	-	Observed (caught & killed)
22.	DP 03	Ljubiš-Čigota, Užice	1984-11-05	-	Collected (shot, taxidermy)
23.	DP 10	Komarani village, Nova Varoš	1986-08-..	m	Collected (caught, killed)
24.	DP 20	Ponorac village, Sjenica	1986-11-15	m	Collected (skull)
25.	DP 40	Gradac village, Sjenica	1986-summer	-	Observed (5 inds. killed)
		Fishpond in Gradac village, Sjenica	1990-..-..	-	Observed (a few found drowned)
26.	DR 26	Bačko Petrovo Selo village	1970-1980	-	Observed (killed)
27.	EN 01	Ugljare village, Priština	1955-06-10	m	Collected (caught alive)
28.	EN 11	Archaeological site of Ulpijana, near Gračanica village, Priština	1955-09-18	m	Collected (caught alive)
			1956-07-06	?	Collected (killed)
			1956-07-08	f	Collected (killed)
			1956-07-10	?	Collected (caught alive)

Table 1. Continued.

No.	UTM	Locality	Date	Sex	Type of Data
29.	EN 59	Krajkovac village, Prokuplje	1985 or 1986	-	Observed (live capture)
30.	EN 73	Kukavica Mt., Vranje	1985-..-..	-	Observed
31.	EP 27	Highway near Končarevo village, Jagodina	1995-07-27	m	Collected (killed by car)
32.	EP 35	Paraćin, town center	1997-summer	m	Collected (killed, taxidermy)
33.	EP 61	Draževac village, Aleksinac	1978-10-18	m	Collected (taxidermy)
34.	EP 74	Mt. Rtanj, southern slopes	1993-..-..	-	Observed
35.	EP 77	Zlot village, Bor	1993-..-..	-	Observed
36.	EQ 36	Kusić village, Bela Crkva	1980-..-..	-	Observed
37.	FP 03	Minicevo village, Knjaževac	1995-summer	-	Observed
38.	FP 28	Veljkovo village, Negotin	1985-..-..	-	Observed (shot)

Table 2. Previous records of marbled polecat (*Vormela peregusna*) in FR Yugoslavia from Mirič *et al.* (1983).

No.	UTM	Locality	Date	Data	Source
1.	DM 59	Djakovica, surroundings	-	Observed	Karaman (1931)
2.	DM 96	Prevalac Ridge, Šara Mt.	1980-07-05	Collected	Croatian NHM, Zagreb
3.	DN 19	Goračići, Zlatar Mt.	1970-..-..	Observed	Mirić *et al.* (1983)
4.	DN 37	Ninaja Mt.	1960-..-..	Observed	Mirić *et al.* (1983)
5.	DN 46	Žirče village, Tutin	1981-01-19	Collected	NHM, Belgrade
6.	DN 48	Ljudska reka valley	1960-..-..	Observed	Mirić *et al.* (1983)
7.	DN 49	Crna Reka village, Mt. Golija.	1958-..-..	Observed	Mirić *et al.* (1983)
8.	DN 59	Sebimilje village, Mt. Golija.	1960-..-..	Collected	NHM, Belgrade
9.	DP 51	Crepuljnik village, Studenica	1910-..-..	Collected	NHM, Belgrade
10.	EN 60	Ristovac village, Vranje	1907-09-19	Collected	NHM, Belgrade
11.	EN 79	Niš	1905-06-..	Collected	NHM, Belgrade
12.	EN 98	Niš-Suva planina Mt.	-	Observed	B.Petrov (pers. comm.)
13.	EP 73	Soko Banja	1978/79-..-..	Observed	Mirić *et al.* (1983)
14.	EP 95	Šljivar village, Zaječar	1979-spring	Collected	IBRSS, Belgrade
15.	FN 16	Suračevo village, Pirot	1981-..-..	Observed	Mirić *et al.* (1983)
16.	FN 17	Resnik village, Bela Palanka	1981/82-..-..	Observed	Mirić *et al.* (1983)
17.	FN 27	Pirot	1903-..-..	Collected	NHM, Belgrade
18.	FN 48	Dojkinci village, Pirot	1981-..-..	Observed	Mirić *et al.* (1983)
19.	FP 04	Mali Izvor village, Zaječar	1981-autumn 1982-06-..	Collected Collected	IBRSS, Belgrade
20.	FP 29	Negotin	-	Collected	NHM, Belgrade
21.	EP 77	Malinik, Zlot village	-	Observed	Papić (1950)
22.	FP 08	Salaš village, Negotin	1979-..-..	Observed	Mirić *et al.* (1983)
23.	FQ 00	Štubik village, Negotin	1982-..-..	Observed	Mirić *et al.* (1983)
24	EQ 92	Golubinje village, Donji Milanovac	1982-..-..	Observed	Mirić *et al.* (1983)
25.	EQ 14	Požarevac	-	Observed	B.Petrov (pers. comm.)
26.	EN 15	Podujevo	-	Observed	B.Petrov (pers. comm.)

The habitats of the marbled polecat in western Yugoslavia differ considerably from those in the east. In the west, marbled polecats occur in montane-steppic and woodland-steppic types of pastures, whilst cultivated, waste and fallow lands predominate in its eastern habitats, where it has been found from river terraces and low hills, through to mountainous meadows. In the western area it has been recorded at higher altitudes than in the east. The highest locality known is Prevalac ridge, Šarplanina Mountain – 1,500 m asl, and the lowest is Golubinje village - 60 m asl.

The limited use of intensive agricultural methods and agrochemicals, particularly in montane areas of Yugoslavia, seem not to cause a significant impact on the relative stability of marbled polecat populations. However, in Vojvodina and parts of central Serbia, agriculture is more intensive. As a result, in Vojvodina the greater part of the autochthonous steppes and woodland-steppes has been degraded to a cultured steppe habitat.

Particularly in western Serbia, it is not unusual for marbled polecats to inhabit the outskirts of settlements, into which they sometimes make forays - even occasionally taking smaller poultry and rabbits. According to the local people in western Serbia, *Vormela* will also steal the cheese and smoked meat that traditionally is kept in huts (*"mljekar"*) near houses! Synanthropic behaviour such as this obviously endangers the species far more than do either poaching or the effects of road traffic mortality. In certain periods the species' numbers have been noted to fluctuate in western Serbia, where almost no agrotechnical methods are practiced: this is believed to be a response to fluctuations in rodent numbers. Here rodent numbers vary from very low to relatively high and, as a result, the middle 1980s was a period of a high marbled polecat numbers in Serbia (see Table 1) as a consequence of high rodent abundances in the preceding period.

As in the rest of its European distribution, Yugoslavia has ranked the marbled polecat as a vulnerable (V) species (Savić *et al.* 1995) and it is included in the Preliminary Red List of Vertebrates of Yugoslavia (Vasić *et al.,* 1991). The Regulations concerning the Conservation of Serbia's Natural Rarities (Službeni glasnik 50/93), the Hunting Legislation of Serbia (Službeni glasnik 39, 44, 60/93) and the Closed Season Ordinance (Službeni glasnik 84/93) all permanently prescribe conservation of the marbled polecat, but Montenegro's legislation contains no reference to the species. Although the current state of marbled polecat populations in Yugoslavia may not point to an alarming degree of threat, the species' categorisation as vulnerable reflects the potential for drastic degradation in current ecological conditions, of the species' habitat, and/or changes in hunting management.

Conclusions

The marbled polecat occurs in the greater part of Yugoslavia. Its main distribution (characterised by areas with comparatively large numbers and stable populations) lies in eastern and western Serbia. The population in western Serbia currently represents the fringe population on the western boundary of *Vormela's* European range. We believe that range boundaries have largely been determined by natural factors, but the notable absence of the marbled polecat in northern and central (chiefly agrarian) parts of country may be a consequence of a negative anthropogenic influences, although this cannot be claimed with absolute certainty as there are no historical data from these areas. Furthermore, in Vojvodina where modern agriculture and agrochemical use have been most intense, and where ecosystem degradation is most conspicuous, an allied species known to be sensitive to habitat degradation (the steppe polecat, *Mustela eversmannii*) still occurs (see Mirić, 1976).

Current conservation measures, the fact that marbled polecat skins have no commercial value, and the relatively limited application of agrochemicals and intensive agricultural techniques have (so far) allowed species populations in FR Yugoslavia to remain at relatively stable levels. However, the ranking of the species as vulnerable and its complete legal protection both point to potential future threats to the species' survival.

The marbled polecat elsewhere

Although it is only the European subspecies that has IUCN Red List status (Groombridge, 1996) there has been increasing interest in the marbled polecat from a conservation point of view, and even discussion of the desirability of a captive breeding program (see Robinson, 1998). At the time of writing, measures such as this seem rather premature.

At present the data on *Vormela* within Europe are rather poor. Although there have been reviews of the status of the animal (e.g. Atanassov, 1966) these accounts usually restate old records (and often considerably more than 50 years old). Unfortunately, more recent attempts at mapping the species within Europe have had somewhat limited success (cf. Mitchell-Jones *et al.*, 1999). Although there are recent records available from Bulgaria through the work of Spassov (1997) and Yugoslavia (this article), contemporary data from Macedonia, Romania, Albania and Turkish Thrace are scant or lacking, and much (almost all?) of that from Greece is from before 1970. Despite this, records presented here, and recent work from Bulgaria (Spassov, 1997) and Israel (e.g. Ben-David, 1998) suggest that the plight of *Vormela* may not be a severe as previously thought.

The main indication of concern for *Vormela* has been apparent recent range recession. The evidence for this is limited, however, as it is now known that some of the more extreme European records cited by Spassov & Spiridonov (1993) are open to debate. As a result, the considerable historical reduction in the species' former range from central Europe and the north-western Balkans is probably an artefact of incorrect primary sources, e.g. Koller's (1929) record of *Vormela* from Slovenia (see also Abel & Griffiths, 1999). Furthermore, in all other parts of its range, *Vormela*'s distribution is poorly known indeed. Although a widespread southern Palaearctic distribution is suggested by authors such as Heptner *et al.* (1967), Abel's (1998) GIS analysis of published and museum specimen records suggests a more sporadic distribution. This situation was exacerbated by additional work in which records from before 1950 were removed (Abel & Griffiths, unpubl.). Certainly, this may reflect the overall rarity of *Vormela* throughout much of its range but, more likely, is simply an artefact of limited recording. Our real lack of knowledge of the species' occurrence is emphasised by the recent publication of records from China (Zhang Yongzu *et al.*, 1997) and a recent, incontrovertible report of *Vormela* from NE Saudi Arabia (Nader, 1991).

Robust ecological data on *Vormela* are limited. The species is generally considered to be one of steppic or semi-desert habitats, and is often regarded as a rodent predator (including suggestions of the existence of a specialist predator-prey relationship with colonial rodents such as hamsters and gerbils). Whereas *Vormela* certainly does prey on these species, other studies suggest that the marbled polecat is actually a more opportunistic predator. Ben-David (1988) reports feeding upon rodents, birds, insects and carrion, and that in summer mole crickets (Gryllotalpidae) were the dominant food item. Similarly, data presented here and reports collected by Spassov (1997) refer to occasional synanthropic behaviour and poultry raiding, whilst one Israeli naturalist reports an animal's stealing food put out for a domestic dog (Anon., 1986).

Whatever the true status of the marbled polecat it is clear that, in most areas of its range, data are presently insufficient to allow any form of conservation assessment. In Europe, where the dataset is more robust (although still leaving much to be desired) there is an almost complete lack of data on habitat selection, home range sizes, population densities or dynamics, or of reproductive or feeding ecology. As regards its status, much of the species' apparent range regression may be artefactual. Moreover, the marbled polecat is of no interest as a furbearer (although the pelts are sometimes sold as curiosities), and direct human effects upon the species probably stem primarily from road traffic mortality and occasional predator control exercises. Concerns over the degradation of steppic habitats and their associated rodent communities are probably legitimate, however. It is unfortunate, therefore, that there are almost no data on the fossil occurrence of *Vormela* other than from the Late Quaternary of Israel (see Dayan, 1994), and this makes investigation of the species' response to climatic and vegetational changes difficult to forecast.

References

Anon. (1986). Polecats all over. *Israel – Land and Nature*, **11** (3)**:** 148.

Atanassov, N. (1966). *Vormela peregusna* (Gueldenstaedt, 1770) in Bulgarien und auf der Balkanhalbinsel. *Zeitschrift für Säugetierkunde*, **31**: 454-464.

Abel, H.E. (1998). *Monitoring the status of* Vormela peregusna. BSc thesis. Kingston-upon-Hull; University of Hull (Dept. Geography).

Abel, H.E. & Griffiths, H.I. (1999). The current status of *Vormela peregusna* throughout its historical range. *Small Carnivore Conservation,* **21**: 16-28.

Ben-David, M. (1988). *Biology and ecology of the marbled polecat* (*Vormela peregusna syriaca*) *in Israel.* MSc thesis. Tel Aviv; University of Tel-Aviv.

Ben-David, M. (1998). Delayed implantation in the marbled polecat, *Vormela peregusna syriaca* (Carnivora, Mustelidae): evidence from mating, parturition, and post-natal growth. *Mammalia*, **62**: 269-283.

Chotolchu, N., Stubbe, M. & Samjaa, R. (1989). Verbreitung der Tigeriltis (Gueldenstaedt, 1770) in Eurasien und sein Status in der Mongolischen Volksrepublik. In: M. Stubbe (ed.), *Populationökologie marderartiger Säugetiere*: 585-596. Halle (Saale); Martin-Luther-Universität Halle-Wittenberg.

Dayan, T. (1994). Carnivore diversity in the Late Quaternary of Israel. *Quaternary Research*, **41**: 343-369.

Groombridge, B. (Ed.) (1996). *IUCN Red List of Threatened Animals.* Gland; International Union for the Conservation of Nature & Natural Resources.

Harrison, D.L. & Bates, P.J.J. (1991). *The Mammals of Arabia* (2nd ed.). Sevenoaks; Harrison Zoological Museum.

Heptner, V.G., Naumov, N.P., Urgenson P.B., Sludski, A.A., Chirkova, A.F. & Bannikov, A.G. (1967). [*The Mammals of the Soviet Union.* Vol. 2, part 1.] Moscow; Vysshaya Shkola (in Russian).

Koller, O. (1929): Über das Vorkommen des Tigeriltis (*Putorius sarmaticus*) bei Magdeburg (S.H.S.). *Zoologischer Anzeiger*, **83**: 70.

Mitchell-Jones, A.J., Amori, G., Bogdanovicz, W., Kryštufek, B., Reijnders, P.J.H., Spitzenberger, F., Stubbe, M., Thissen, J.B.M., Vohralík, V. & Zima, J. (1999). *The Atlas of European mammals.* London; T. & A.D. Poyser Ltd.

Mirić, Đ. (1976). Stepski tvor, *Mustela eversmannii* Lesson, 1827 (Mammalia, Carnivora) u jugo-istčnom delu panonskog basena. *Bulletin du Muséum d'Histoire Naturelle, Belgrade (Série B)*, **31**: 129-157 (in Serbo-Croat with German summary).

Mirić, Đ., Milenković, M. & Tvrtković, N. (1983). [Distribution of marbled polecat (*Vormela peregusna* Gueldenstaedt 1770, Mustelidae, Mammalia) in Yugoslavia.] *Drugi simpozijum o fauni SR Srbije Beograd*: 185-188 (in Serbian with English summary).

Nader, I.A. (1991). First record of the marbled polecat *Vormela peregusna* (Güldenstaedt, 1770) from Saudi Arabia (Mammalia: Carnivora, Mustelidae). *Fauna of Saudi Arabia*, **12**: 416-419.

Ognev, S.I. (1935). *Mammals of the USSR and Adjacent Countries. Vol. III Carnivora (Fissipedia and Pinnipedia)* (English Trans.1962). Jerusalem; Israel Program for Scientific Translations.

Qumsiyeh, M.B. (1996). *Mammals of the Holy Land.* Austin (Texas); Texas Technical University Press.

Robinson, P. (1998). *Vormela project report No. 1: 1998 (Unpublished report)*. Gland; IUCN Small Carnivore Specialist Group.

Savić, I.R., Paunović, M., Milenković, M. & Stamenković, S. (1995). [Diversity of mammalian fauna (Mammalia) of Yugoslavia, with a review of species of international importance.] In: V. Stevanović & V. Vasić (eds.), *Biodiverzitet Jugoslavije sa pregledom vrsta od međunarodnog značaja*: 517-554. Beograd; Biološki Fakultet & Ecolibri (in Serbian).

Službeni glasnik R Srbije (50/93). *Uredba o zaštiti prirodnih retkosti.*

Službeni glasnik R Srbije (39, 44, 60/93) *Zakon o lovstvu.*

Službeni glasnik R Srbije (84/93) *Naredba o lovostaju divljač.*

Spassov, N. (1997). *Study on the status of the marbled polecat (Vormela peregusna peregusna Güldenstaedt) in southern Dobrudja (Bulgaria) and elaboration of a plan for the management of its population in the country (Unpublished Report)*. Gland; IUCN & Bulgarian-Swiss Biodiversity Conservation Programme.

Spassov, N. & Spiridonov, G. (1993). *Vormela peregusna* (Güldenstaedt, 1770) - Tigeriltis. In: M. Stubbe & F. Krapp (Eds.), *Handbuch der Säugetiere Europas, Band 5: Raubsäuger - Carnivora (Fissipedia), Teil II: Mustelidae 2, Viverridae, Herpestidae, Felidae:* 816-854. Wiesbaden; AULA Verlag.

Vasić, V., Džukić, G., Janković, D., Simonov, N., Petrov, B. & Savić, I. (1991). [Preliminary List for Red Data Book of Vertebrate of Serbia.] *Zaštita prirode*, **43-44**: 121-132 (in Serbian with English summary).

Vereshchagin, N.K. (1959). [*Mlekopitayushchie Kavakaza: istoriya formirovaniya fauny.*]; Moscow and Leningrad Izdatelbstvo Akademii Nauk CCCP (in Russian).

Zhang Yongzu *et al.* (1997). *Distribution of mammalian species in China.* Beijing; China Forestry Publishing House.

CHAPTER 21

The status and conservation of Taiwan's mustelids

Liang-Kong Lin

Abstract

Taiwan lies at the junction of the Palaearctic and Oriental zoogeographical regions, and has a rich fauna and flora that incorporates elements from both. The mustelids of the island include two endemic subspecies, the Taiwan ferret badger and the Taiwanese yellow-throated marten, plus two other species and a new, as-yet undescribed *Mustela* sp. This paper discusses the status of these species and Taiwan's response to nature conservation concerns. The need for further research is also emphasised, particularly in the case of the Eurasian river otter, which now may be extinct on Taiwan.

Introduction

Taiwan is an island lying 130 km off the coast of mainland China. Approximately 35,960 km[2] in size, it has a tropical oceanic climate and mountainous topography. The island is approximately 390 km long and 144 km wide at its widest point, and the Tropic of Cancer passes through its centre. The Central Mountain Range covers two-thirds of the island's area and separates the island into eastern and western parts. The mountains of Taiwan are unusually steep and rugged. The highest peak, Jade Mountain, reaches an elevation of 3,950 m asl, and there are over 100 other peaks that exceed 3,000 m. While the western part of the island is characterised by lowlands, the eastern part has several coastal plains in the north but in the south it has a long rift valley that separates the Coastal Range (average elevation = 1,680 m asl) from the Central Range.

The altitudinal vegetation zones of Taiwan have been described by Liu (1972) and Su (1992). Nearly all of the lowland and most of the foothill areas have been converted from native vegetation to various types of agricultural croplands. Below 2,500 m the lower mountain slopes support dense hardwood forest with a thick understorey layer, the hardwood forest comprising 87% of Taiwan's natural vegetation. However, a vast area of virgin hardwood forest has been replaced by plantations of fast-growing conifers. As one moves upwards in elevation, natural conifers begin to appear, dominating the community above 3,500 m – this zone makes up about 13% of the island's natural vegetation. At the highest altitudes, repeated fires have led to the formation of extensive bamboo grasslands, which are quite persistent over time. An alpine area includes juniper scrub intermixed with grasses (mainly a low-growing form of bamboo) and a bare rocky summit. However, the area of this habitat type is quite small, comprising only about 0.5% of Taiwan's natural vegetation. Taiwan's tropical oceanic climate and mountainous topography make for wide variations in local ecological conditions. Because of the varied assortment of habitats and vegetation, the biota of Taiwan is exceptionally rich: at least seventy species of terrestrial mammal have been recorded (Cheng & Changchien, 1998).

Status and distribution of mustelids

Much of Taiwan's biogeographical interest stems from its position at the boundary of the Palaearctic Region and Oriental Region, and its fauna is a mixture of elements from the two. The five mustelids present include two species that occur also in the Chinese People's Republic (the Siberian weasel, *Mustela siberica*, and Eurasian otter, *Lutra lutra*), plus two species that are represented by endemic island subspecies (the Taiwan yellow-throated marten, *Martes flavigula chrysospila*, and Taiwanese ferret badger, *Melogale moschata subaurantiaca*). To this now can be added a newly-discovered, still-undescribed species (Lin, unpubl.). However, the record of Oriental short-clawed otter, *Amblonyx cinereus*, in Taiwan (Wilson & Reeder, 1993) is probably in error, and based on J.E. Gray's misprovenance of material collected by Swinhoe on Amoy in the 19th century (see Swinhoe, 1870: 625).

Before 1970, most of what was known about Taiwan's mustelids was based on data collected during the time of Japanese occupation (*i.e.* before 1945). These data were mainly taxonomic in nature, with very little emphasis on species distributions or ecologies even though, as early as 1932, there had been speculation on the status of Taiwan's mustelids. Horikawa (1932) mentions that the Siberian weasel was very rare in the mountain areas (*i.e.* in regions over 2,000 m) and that the more abundant yellow-throated marten was found more often in the southern part of the island than in the north. Horikawa also considered the otter to be common in rivers from sea level to 1,500 m, whilst the ferret badger was thought to be common in the mountains from sea level to 1,500 m. Subsequent to this there were few investigations of the Taiwanese mustelid fauna until comparatively recently.

Yen (1979) began a survey of the effects of aboriginal hunting on Taiwan's mammal populations, and concluded that the pressure of hunting upon mustelids was rather low. In a second survey of the effects of hunting, Wang (1986) interviewed hunters and visited "specimen shops" (at which can be bought pets and ingredients for Chinese traditional animal medicine). Wang concluded that while mustelid species certainly were hunted, they were not usually the focus of hunts, or consumed as game (primarily because of their strong odour). Furthermore, Wang suggests that hunting pressure was greater on otter and yellow-throated marten than on either Siberian weasel or ferret badger. The first field survey of the distribution and conservation status of Taiwan's larger mammals (McCullough, 1974) suggested that, although most mustelid populations seemed secure, the otter was rare. McCullough thought that otter rarity was due to human encroachment at low elevations and to the resultant habitat loss. In fact, between 1940 and 1980, Taiwan's larger mammal species (including otter and yellow-throated marten) shifted their distributions to higher elevations (Lin & Lin, 1983). This was probably a result of an overall decrease in land area and habitat availability, and may have led to increased stress upon species populations due to increased competition and to changes in climate and habitat.

In 1987 Taiwan passed its Wildlife Conservation Law. Two of Taiwan's mustelid species are considered to be threatened and so are protected by this law: the otter is listed as endangered (E), and the yellow-throated marten is listed as rare (R). Protection currently is mainly in the form of provision of national parks and nature reserve areas; these are mainly in Taiwan's Central Mountain Range and the remote eastern and southern parts of the island. However, very little of the plains and low-lands are protected, and it is on the plains where most human activity is concentrated and where the human population is densest.

The faunas of 18 of Taiwan's nature reserves (all managed by the Taiwan Forest Bureau) have been surveyed, and these are located in the Central Mountain Range. None of the surveys (see reviews by Lee & Lin, 1992; Lin, 1995) report the presence of otter, but yellow-throated marten was recorded from two nature reserves in southern Taiwan, whilst Siberian weasel and ferret badger were common in all the nature reserves.

Currently, the conservation status of otters seems to be the most worrying. The last published otter record is of a skull found in a specimen shop by Wang (1986), who also reports finding otter specimens in shops at the rate of one or two per year. From a questionnaire survey, Wang & In (1992) learned that while the otter was for-merly known from the Kenting area in the southern part of Taiwan, it had not been recorded within the past two decades. In the 1960s the United States Naval Medical Research Unit-2 (NAMRU-2) collected mammals from throughout Taiwan, but only caught two otters: one from the north-east region (Elan County) and one from the east coast (Hualien County) (Chen, pers. comm.); therefore otters were rare, even in 1970. As otters are associated with low elevation streams they are doubly threatened. These low altitude regions are those where human activity and encroachment are greatest and streams are correspondingly polluted. A 1976-1985 survey of the current pollution status of 19 major rivers and 32 streams in Taiwan (Tseng, 1989) concluded that all were either moderately or heavily polluted, espe-cially downstream – only the upstream regions were found to be relatively uncont-aminated. While there are several species of fish that are tolerant of these polluted conditions, the tolerance of otter is unknown and there may well be problems asso-ciated with the bioaccumulation of pollutants such as heavy metals, poly-chlorinat-ed biphenyls (PCBs) and organochlorine compounds. These low elevation streams are not in the protected national parks and have protection in only one or two wildlife areas. Indeed, Foster-Turley *et al.* (1990) list the Eurasian otter as being extinct in Taiwan, however, it may still be found on the island; if it exists still, it probably survives in the less-developed south-eastern part.

The Taiwanese yellow-throated marten is considered to be rare. It first was described from central Taiwan by Swinhoe (1866) but McCullough (1974) notes that the species, whilst rare, was not immediately threatened. More recently, Wang (1986) found specimens in shops at a rate of six or more per year, although only in shops in the southern part of the island. A survey of hunters (Wang, 1986) showed also that the yellow-throated marten is hard to catch. Aboriginal hunters claim that yellow-throated marten have some unique behaviours: they report seeing four or five individuals working together to hunt muntjac deer, *Muntiacus reevesi*, that they preyed upon animals trapped in snares, and that they also preferred to eat the internal organs of dead animals. In specimen shops Wang (1986) found that prices for yellow-throated marten varied widely: they were expensive in shops whose owners thought the species was rare, but comparatively cheap in shops whose owners were not thought to be knowledgeable about Taiwan's mammals. Primarily on the basis of his encounter rate in specimen shops, Wang (1986) concluded that yellow-throated martens were rare. More recently, most records are from the remote parts of the island, particularly the Central Mountain Range and the southern areas, but there are no recent records from the highly populated, industrialised north. Furthermore, of the 18 nature reserves in the Central Mountain Range, only two are known to harbour marten. Here the records of the species have been obtained by using camera traps, rather than by live trapping or from signs such as tracks or scats.

Taiwan's remote high mountains make it difficult for both hunters and scientists to trap or monitor wildlife. This is particularly emphasised when one considers that it was only in 1998 that a new species of *Mustela* was discovered in this area (Lin, unpubl.). The new species, currently known from two specimens and from two additional sightings, is found at 3,200 m in the central part of Taiwan. As this new species, a small mustelid similar to the stoat and weasels, has not been described, it has not yet been included in Taiwan's Wildlife Conservation Law.

At present, the Siberian weasel is considered to be the most abundant of the five Taiwanese mustelid species (Lee & Lin 1992). Even before 1987, when hunting was banned under the Wildlife Conservation Law, this mustelid was not seriously hunted; the general impression was that it was not desirable as food or for specimens because of its strong odour. Currently, the species remains common, probably either because of its omnivorous eating habits and generalised habitat requirements (Chuang & Lee, 1997), or because of weak synchronisation of female reproduction (Pei & Wang, 1995). Over the past few years, Siberian weasel are thought to be increasing their population size and expanding their distributional area. Half a century ago Horikawa (1932) considered this weasel to be rare in the mountainous regions, but now it is fairly common at all elevations. Its range expansion may be due to increased human activity and development in the mountain areas. Siberian weasel are fairly tolerant of human activity and are known to raid garbage dumps and campsites for food. In addition, Taiwan has 13 species of rodent, 11 species of insectivores, plus other small vertebrates, which are known to be exploited as food by the Siberian weasel.

Conclusion

In general, Taiwan's wildlife has become endangered because of a combination of hunting and habitat loss. In the case of mustelids, and especially otter and yellow-throated marten, habitat loss is the major factor, with hunting having had a negligible effect. In the future, management of the habitat of the two threatened species is of primary importance. Basic biological data for a third (undescribed) mustelid, *Mustela* sp., is still lacking. Its conservation status can only be deduced from its rarity and its recent discovery. Only two of Taiwan's mustelids can still be considered common, the endemic Taiwan ferret badger and the Taiwanese yellow throated marten, but the reasons for this remain unknown. Whilst their reproductive and feeding habits have been studied, their population dynamics have not and, to date, there have been no population studies of any Taiwanese carnivore. More specifically, however, in its provision of national parks and nature reserves, Taiwan has protected the habitat necessary for the protection of its terrestrial mustelids, but what is lacking is protected habitat for otter, and even the occurrence of the species on the island is debatable.

References

Cheng, S-C. & Changchien, L-W. (1998). [An introduction of terrestrial mammalian fauna in Taiwan.] *Nature Conservation Quarterly Issue*, **23**: 18-27 (in Chinese).

Chuang, S-A. & Lee, L-L. (1997). Food habits of three carnivore species (*Viverricula indica, Herpestes urva*, and *Melogale moschata*) in Fushan Forest, northern Taiwan. *Journal of Zoology*, **243**: 71-79.

Foster-Turley, P., Macdonald, S. & Mason, C. (1990). *Otters: an Action Plan for their conservation*. Gland; International Union for the Conservation of Nature & Natural Resources.

Horikawa, Y. (1932). [*Illustrated monograph of Taiwan mammals.*] Taipei; Natural History Society of Taiwan (in Japanese).

Lee, L-L. & Lin, L-K. (1992). [Status and research of mammals in Taiwan. In: C.-I. Peng (ed.), *The biological resources of Taiwan: a status report* (*Institute of Botany, Academia Sinica Monograph Series No. 11*)]: 245-267. Taipei; Academia Sinica (in Chinese).

Lin, J.-Y. & Lin, L-K. (1983). [A note on the zoogeography of the mammals in Taiwan]. *Annual of the Taiwan Museum*, **26**: 53-62 (in Chinese).

Lin, L.-K. (1995). [A description of the species-area relationship: a preliminary analysis for nature reserves in Taiwan national forests.] *Notes of Wildlifers and Newsletter of Wildlifers*, **3** (1): 3-7 (in Chinese).

Liu, T. (1972). [The forest vegetation of Taiwan.] *Quarterly Journal of Chinese Forestry*, **5**(4): 57-85 (in Chinese).

McCullough, D.R. (1974). *Status of larger mammals in Taiwan*. Taipei; Tourism Bureau Reports.

Pei, K. & Wang, Y. (1995). Some observations on the reproduction of the Taiwan ferret badger (*Melogale moschata subaurantiaca*) in southern Taiwan. *Zoological Studies*, **34** (2): 88-95.

Su, H.-J. (1994). [Species diversity of forest plants in Taiwan. In: C.-I. Peng & C.H. Chou (eds.), *Biodiversity and terrestrial ecosystems* (*Institute of Botany, Academia Sinica Monograph Series No. 14*)]: 87-98. Taipei; Academia Sinica (in Chinese).

Swinhoe, R. (1866). On a new species of beech-marten from Formosa. *Annals and Magazine of Natural History*, **18**: 286.

Swinhoe, R. (1870). Catalogue of the mammals of China (south of the River Yangtsze) and of the island of Formosa. *Proceedings of the Zoological Society of London*, **1870**: 615-653.

Tseng, S-K. (1989). Balancing economic growth and environmental protection – water pollution in Taiwan. In: C.-Y. Chang, P.-C. Chiang, Y.-P. Chu, H.-H. Hsiao & L.L. Severinghaus (eds.), *Taiwan 2000*: 138-155. Taipei; Academia Sinica (Institute of Ethnology).

Wang, Y. (1986). [*The study of the consumption of wildlife resources in commercial shops in Taiwan.*] Taipei; Council of Agriculture Reports (in Chinese).

Wang, Y. & In, L.-M. (1992). [*A survey on the status of some mammal species in the Kenting National Park.*] Pingtung; Kenting National Park Reports (in Chinese).

Wilson, D.E. & Reeder, D.M. (Eds.) (1993). *Mammal species of the world* (2nd ed.).Washington (DC); Smithsonian Institution Press.

Yen, C.-W. (1979). [*Effects of the aboriginal hunting activity on the status of wildlife in Taiwan.*] Taichung; Environmental Science Research Centre Reports (in Chinese).

INDEX TO SCIENTIFIC NAMES

SUBJECT INDEX